THE SOURCES OF SCIENCE

Number 18

THE SOURCES OF SCIENCE

Editor-in-Chief: HARRY WOOLF

WILLIS K. SHEPARD PROFESSOR OF THE HISTORY OF SCIENCE
THE JOHNS HOPKINS UNIVERSITY

1. WALLER: *Essayes of Natural Experiments*
   WITH A NEW INTRODUCTION BY A. RUPERT HALL

2. BOYLE: *Experiments and Considerations Touching Colours*
   WITH A NEW INTRODUCTION BY MARIE BOAS HALL

3. NEWTON: *The Mathematical Works of Isaac Newton,*
   2 vols.
   WITH A NEW INTRODUCTION BY DEREK T. WHITESIDE

4. LIEBIG: *Animal Chemistry*
   WITH A NEW INTRODUCTION BY FREDERIC L. HOLMES

5. KEPLER: *Kepler's Conversation with Galileo's Sidereal Messenger*
   TRANSLATED AND EDITED BY EDWARD ROSEN

7. TAYLOR: *Scientific Memoirs Selected from the Transactions of Foreign Academies of Science and Learned Societies, and from Foreign Journals,* 7 vols.
   WITH A NEW PREFACE BY HARRY WOOLF

10. *BULLETTINO DI BIBLIOGRAFIA E DI STORIA DELLE SCIENZE MATEMATICHE E FISICHE,* 20 vols.
    EDITED BY B. BONCOMPAGNI

11. GREW: *The Anatomy of Plants*
    WITH A NEW INTRODUCTION BY CONWAY ZIRKLE

13. *THE WORKS OF WILLIAM HARVEY, M.D.*
    TRANSLATED FROM THE LATIN WITH A LIFE OF THE AUTHOR BY ROBERT WILLIS, M.D.

The History and Present State of Electricity

The History and Present State

of Electricity

With Original Experiments

By JOSEPH PRIESTLEY

Volume 1

Reprinted from the Third Edition, London, 1755
With an Appendix containing two additional papers of
"Original Experiments" by the Author

And a new Introduction by Robert E. Schofield
DEPARTMENT OF HUMANITIES AND SOCIAL STUDIES
CASE INSTITUTE OF TECHNOLOGY
CLEVELAND, OHIO

The Sources of Science, No. 18

JOHNSON REPRINT CORPORATION
New York and London

1966

Introduction © 1966 *by*
JOHNSON REPRINT CORPORATION

Library of Congress Catalog Card Number: 66-19746

PRINTED IN THE UNITED STATES OF AMERICA

INTRODUCTION

For a book about to see the bicentenary of its first publication (London, 1767), Joseph Priestley's "History and Present State of Electricity" has retained both vitality and validity extraordinarily well. In language, historiography, and even in science, it shows its age less than most such works with a quarter its years. Now science books are notoriously ephemeral, while no one has yet shown that histories of science are to be excluded from the dictum that history must be rewritten every twenty-five years. Consequently, when one finds a book that thus defies its age, one may safely pronounce it a classic, select it for republication in yet another edition (its sixth in English), and still wonder at the combination of circumstances through which this first effort at science writing by a provincial dissenting clergyman and teacher was to achieve such distinction.

The first step toward understanding its continued appeal comes in the recognition that Priestley's "History" is neither history nor history of science as we would understand those terms. Though Priestley shared the "enlightened" faith in progress, and though he could not, had he wished, avoid the sense of internal development intrinsic to a treatment of science's history, his work does not attempt to trace an evolutionary growth toward present goals. Neither does it contain an analytic approach to his subject, that attempt to understand both discoveries and discoverers within the context of their periods demanded of history of science as a branch of intellectual history. That is to say, as a history of electricity, Priestley's work is deficient in qualities we would not hesitate to demand, quite rightly, from a similar work produced today.

Yet it is precisely in this that Priestley has escaped dating his work, for in tracing the evolution of his subject toward its contemporary state he must have selected the pertinent discoveries and ignored the seemingly irrelevant, while analysis must inevitably reveal the philosophy of science and of history accepted at the time. Priestley's "History" avoids these dangers by being not so much a history as a chronicle in which he presents, in order of time, accounts of all the notable electrical researches and discoveries, up to 1766, in a compressed paraphrase of the writers' own descriptions.

Here there is another element in the book's continued success, for as a chronicle it was singularly well timed. Priestley himself notes this in his preface, writing:

> I cannot help thinking myself to have been peculiarly fortunate, in undertaking the history of electricity, at the most proper time for writing it, when the materials were neither too few, nor too many to make a history; and when they were so scattered, as to make the undertaking highly desirable, and the work peculiarly useful to Englishmen. [viii] [1]

[1] All reference numbers in square brackets refer to page numbers in the printed text.

But this observation comprehends only a few of the elements that joined to make this an appropriate time for a work such as Priestley's. More than any other single period, the eighteenth century was the age of "experimental natural philosophy," and of all the subjects comprised in that description, electricity was surely the most popular, the most dramatic, and the most subject to change. When Francis Hauksbee began his work early in the century, the subject was little more than an elaboration of the amber-effect of the Greeks; by 1801 all the essential experimental phenomena of static electricity had been observed and noted, the instrumental armory of static "electricians" was substantially completed, and a beginning had been made toward the investigation of transient discharges and current electricity. Much of this change occurred within Priestley's lifetime and, except for the work of Galvani and Volta (subject of one of the last papers of his scientific career), the major developments occurred within the period covered by his "History."

Priestley was born in 1733, four years after Stephen Gray's discovery of electrical conductivity and the year of Charles DuFay's published account of vitreous and resinous electricity. The invention of the Leyden jar occurred in 1745, roughly five years before Priestley commenced his program of self-education in the sciences, while Franklin's first significant work in electricity was being published in the years spanning that self-education and Priestley's formal studies at Daventry Academy. There is more in these citations than a parade of near-coincidences. They illustrate the scientific atmosphere of Priestley's youth, showing in what direction and degree his scientific education was

to be influenced by electrical investigations. The publications in which the work that Priestley was later
to describe first appeared were not only available but,
whatever the formal language of their communication,
the scientific language was one that he could read
without the effort of cultural and temporal translation
required of (and seldom achieved by) later historians.
This was the scientific language in which he had
trained. We may note, for example, that the first
scientific work studied by Priestley, 'sGravesande's
"Elements of Natural Philosophy," was one of the
earliest works read by Benjamin Franklin in *his* preparation for a scientific career.[2]

Having chosen electricity as the first topic for his
scientific writing (science students being as prone to
popular fads as other men), Priestley's timing was
fortunate in yet another, and this time unique, way.
The precise circumstances attendant upon his commencing his "History" have been confused by minor
variations in Priestley's several accounts of its beginning and by apparent contradictions between all of
these and the facts relating to the earliest stages of
the work.[3] It seems probable, however, that he began
the writing of the work and then seized the opportunity of Franklin's presence in London to request
the patronage and assistance of that most famous of
contemporary electrical investigators. In any event, we
know that he journeyed to London in December,
1765, carrying a letter of introduction to John Canton,

[2] See Robert E. Schofield, "Scientific Background of Joseph
Priestley," *Annals of Science* 13, 150 (1957); and I. Bernard
Cohen, "Franklin and Newton," pp. 234–242. Philadelphia,
American Philosophical Society, Memoir 43, 1956.
[3] For an account of some of these difficulties, see Schofield,
"Scientific Background," pp. 154–155.

which also noted, in a postscript: "If Dr. Franklin be in Town, I believe Dr. Priestley would be glad to be made known to him."[4] Canton did introduce Priestley to Franklin and, during the same period, Priestley also met William Watson and Richard Price. These four—Canton, Franklin, Watson, and Price—agreed to assist Priestley in the writing of his history, and he took care that his readers should know of their help, with a statement in his preface:

> With gratitude I acknowledge my obligations to Dr. Watson, Dr. Franklin, and Mr. Canton for the books, and other materials with which they have supplied me, and for the readiness with which they have given me any information in their power to procure. In a more especial manner am I obliged to Mr. Canton, for those original communications of his, which will be found in this work, and which cannot fail to give a value to it, in the esteem of all the lovers of electricity. My grateful acknowledgements are also due to the Rev. Dr. Price, F.R.S. . . . for the attention . . . given to the work, and . . . the many important services . . . rendered me with respect to it. [ix, misprinted xi.]

Price alone, of the four, was not an acknowledged expert on electricity, and he was known as a teacher, expert in actuarial mathematics, and interested in all science, as well as keenly critical of fuzzy writing and thinking. The remaining three were the most famous British electricians of their age. Franklin, of course, is still celebrated for his research, but that of Canton and of Watson was only by comparison of less im-

[4] J. Seddon to John Canton, December 18, 1765, "Canton Papers," Vol. II ("Correspondence"), Archives of the Royal Society of London.

portance. Each of the three had received the Copley
Medal of the Royal Society and, together with
Priestley's own researches, their work on electricity
was the most important to be done in Britain between
that of Stephen Gray and Michael Faraday.[5] How
much help did these men actually give Priestley? He
fills in some of the details in his "Memoirs":

> During the course of my electrical experiments in
> this year [1766], I kept up a constant correspond-
> ence with Dr. Franklin, and the rest of my philo-
> sophical friends in London; and my letters circulated
> among them all, as also every part of my History as
> it was transcribed. This correspondence would have
> made a considerable volume, and it took up much
> time; but it was of great use with respect to the
> accuracy of my experiments, and the perfection of
> my work.[6]

The answers these correspondents wrote to Priestley's
letters seem to have been almost entirely destroyed
(apparently in the Birmingham Church-and-King
Riots of 1791), but a substantial selection of Priestley's letters to Franklin, Canton, and Price have been
preserved.[7] These confirm Priestley's suggestion that
the assistance he obtained was chiefly in the acquisi-
tion of source materials for his work and in advice
relating to his own electrical experiments. Nonethe-

---

[5] For the details of their research and its importance, see
I. Bernard Cohen, "Franklin and Newton," *passim.* Cavendish,
who might also have been included in this enumeration, failed
to publish his significant work, and was, therefore, of considerably less influence than the persons listed.

[6] "Memoirs of Dr. Joseph Priestley, to the Year 1795, written
by himself," p. 52. J. Johnson, London, 1806.

[7] Copies of these letters are included in the collection of
Priestley's scientific correspondence being edited for publication
by this writer.

less, to have obtained any advice on his book from any one of these was an achievement; to have all four act as editorial advisors was a coup that at once made his work the most authoritative statement on electricity available to contemporary Englishmen.

And so, also, does Priestley's "History" become, for subsequent generations of readers, the most authoritative statement on eighteenth-century British electrical research. Direct quotations from Canton and Franklin or paraphrased personal descriptions of the work of Watson, Franklin, or Canton—including one of the two best accounts of Franklin's kite experiment—make it a primary document relating to the research of Priestley's patrons. By implication, indeed, any part of the book specifically treating the work of any of them is a primary source, for one may reasonably assume that such passages had their prior approval. Moreover, any general interpretation of electrical research contained in the "History" can be regarded as the distillation, at least, of the views of the most significant molders of late eighteenth-century British electrical opinion. Contemporary readers, knowing this, accepted its interpretations and thus, by a process of self-fulfillment, the book is also a primary historical document relating to general scientific opinion of the time.

But Priestley's was not the only historical study of electricity to be published in the eighteenth century, nor the only one written by a discoverer and confidant of discoverers; nor, indeed, was it even the first such study to be written at length and in a popular style. Many scientists made an obeisance to Clio with a brief report of their "literature research" at the beginnings of a project; many writers of general treatises on electricity or natural philosophy included historical summaries. The contrast in type between such works and the ostensibly different "History" of Priestley is not as great as appears on the surface, but even accepting surface appearances, that "History" was preceded by at least one English, one German, and one French publication, formally offered as historical accounts of electricity. Granting minor differences of time and place, any one of these other "historical" studies had the same advantages of timing, many of them had equal access to direct information, yet none of them has lasted, in that combination of science and history of science, as has Priestley's "History."

To some degree, of course, such comparisons are unfair. The "Mémoires sur l'électricité" of Charles DuFay, for example, are still exciting reading as the primary account of his researches; if the history in his "Premier Mémoire" of 1733 is inadequate or wrong, who is to blame a busy scientist with more important things to do?[8] General treatises, such as the "Course of Natural Philosophy" (London, 1733–1744) of J. T. Desaguliers or the "Observations Physiques" (Paris, 1750) of J.-B. Secondat, were the century's equivalent of physics textbooks, and from them one can still learn much of the contemporary view of electricity but, though Desaguliers knew Gray, and Secondat knew Nollet, we would no more expect

[8] DuFay prided himself on the "rediscovery" of von Guericke's electrical researches and thus is primarily responsible for having introduced that error into histories of science (indirectly including Priestley's). Neither von Guericke nor his contemporaries seem to have thought of his research as electrical; it had little or no influence on the development of electricity, and only in the light of later investigations was it recognized as applicable to that subject—*vide*, N. H. de V. Heathcote, "Guericke's Sulphur Globe," and I. Bernard Cohen, "Guericke and DuFay," *Annals of Science* 6, 293–305 (1950) and 7, 207–209 (1951), respectively.

adequate history from them than we do of a modern science text.

There remain, however, the somewhat more comparable works. In 1745 there was a brief article (some five pages), "An historical account of the wonderful discoveries made in Germany, &c concerning electricity," printed in the *Gentleman's Magazine*. It was reprinted in Boston the same year, where Franklin may have seen it, but if Priestley ever saw it, he did not use it. Nor could he have, except perhaps for names to check elsewhere, for the anonymous author dwells too long, in his too few pages, on the wonders to have much time for the discoveries. The sketches of research would be confusing to anyone not himself an "electrician," and its only use has been as a demonstration that news of electrical discoveries was available through popular sources.[9] The "Geschichte der Electricitat" of Daniel Gralath is a different matter. Published in three parts in the 1747, 1754, and 1756 volumes of the *Versuche und Abhandlungen der Naturforschenden Gesellschaft in Danzig* by one of that group of German scientists who contributed so largely to electricity during the period between DuFay and Franklin, Gralath's "Geschichte" is still a valuable source for German research. Approximately 300 pages long and with an "Electrische Bibliothek" accompanying the last two parts, this work provided Priestley with most of the references that "corrected and enlarged" editions of his "History" after the first. But Priestley was unaware of its existence when writing his first edition, whereas later editions, having included Gralath's work, seem to have superseded it.

---

[9] *Gentleman's Magazine* **15**, 193–197 (1745), and Cohen, "Franklin and Newton," pp. 431–432 (from which I first learned of the article).

Historical bibliographies of electricity usually mention Gralath's "Geschichte" and occasional historical studies make use of it, but many more remain, like the early Priestley, ignorant of its existence. For whatever reasons, it cannot be said to have had the influence of Priestley's "History."[10] Finally, there is the "Histoire Générale et Particuliere de l'Électricité, ou, ce qu'en ont dit de curieux & amusant, d'utile & d'interessant, de réjouissant & de badin, quelques physiciens de l'Europe," published in three small volumes in Paris in 1752, probably by the Abbé N. de Mangin. Priestley had access to this work and used it in the earliest stages of his writing. It may, indeed, have been the spark that touched off his writing, but it can have been little more than a spark, and Priestley substituted other and more reliable references—notably Gralath—where possible in his revised editions. Without bibliography or footnotes, without even specific page references to book titles cited in the text, its explanations of experiments are cursory except for those of DuFay and Nollet and much of the book is devoted to polemic or to discussions of the medical uses of electricity. The "Histoire Générale" is known chiefly because of Priestley's use of it; it remains primarily a name in bibliographic listings and even its author is uncertain.[11]

These exemplify the eighteenth-century books with

---

[10] Even Edmund Hoppe's "Geschichte der Elektrizität" (Leipzig, 1884), the first significant German history of electricity after Gralath and one that both gives a biographical sketch of Gralath and mentions his history, makes far greater use of Priestley's work, including its references to German research.

[11] Scholarly opinion has tended to accept de Mangin as the author, though Michaud, "Biographie Universelle," Vol. 26, Art: Mangin, suggests a Jean-Antoine Guer as an alternative possibility. Neither Mangin nor Guer appear to have had qualifications for writing such a work.

which Priestley's "History" was, and has been, in competition. As a history, as a treatise on electricity, or as a primary source for important experimental discovery, it is the equal of any of them and better than most, but it is as a combination of all three that the "History" shows its clear superiority. Yet any one of these approaches might be thought beyond the talents of a young, unsophisticated tutor of languages. Where and how did Priestley become qualified to combine all three into a single classic study of eighteenth-century electricity? Most, perhaps all, of the answer to this question may lie in Priestley's biography when that has properly been told. As it is, we must rely on a partial answer, pieced from the bits gleaned from study of his "Memoirs" (the least introspective of autobiographies), from an analysis of the "History" itself, and from looking into the nature of his other writings. Nothing there tells us how he became able to attract and profit from the assistance of first-rate men, but we can find, in his career, some of the elements from which Priestley constructed his view of how the history of electricity should be written.

He was, for example, inclined throughout his life to approach intellectual problems in an historical manner, and though his "History and Present State of Discoveries relating to Vision, Light and Colours" (London, 1772) had by no means the success of that on electricity, his "History of the Corruptions of Christianity" (Birmingham, 1782), "History of Early Opinions concerning Jesus Christ" (Birmingham, 1786), and "General History of the Christian Church" (London, 1790; Northumberland, 1802–1803) have become minor classics, at least in Unitarian literature. No doubt prolonged use sharpened his facility with the tools of the historian's trade, but even before the "History of Electricity" was written he had demonstrated his knowledge of those tools and techniques. As a tutor of languages and belles-lettres at Warrington Academy, Priestley was one of the earliest teachers to advocate reform of the curriculum of English education to include substantial amounts of history. In connection with this recommendation, he introduced lectures on the history of England and on "History and General Policy," of which syllabuses were published with his "Essay on a Course of Liberal Education" (London, 1765), while the "Lectures on History and General Policy" were themselves published in 1788. These demonstrate that during the years he was writing on electricity, he was also deeply committed to an investigation of historiography, for Priestley's earliest approach to history was through concern for the methods and resources of historical research.

This is the concern which, in historical practice, is reflected in the exemplary citations, footnotes, and bibliography of the "History of Electricity." Very few of his contemporaries, and far too few of his successors, could write as Priestley does in his Preface:

> I have perused every original author, to which I could have recourse; and every quotation in the margin points to the authority that I myself consulted, and from which the account in the text was actually taken. Where I could not procure the original authors, I was obliged to take them at second hand, but the reference will always show where that has been done. [x]

There are some technical slips in his bibliography, which does not, in fact, include all of the works to which Priestley refers in his text, but between the footnote references and the citations in the bibliography, he has provided an extraordinarily complete listing of significant works (and many less significant ones) on electricity through 1766, when, except for his own research, the "History" stops. Most of the work depends upon the periodical journals of scientific societies, and on these Priestley had made himself something of an expert by the time the third edition (the one reprinted here) was published. On April 19, 1771, he wrote Franklin a letter listing some twenty such journals, with the prices booksellers were asking for complete sets; the majority of these Priestley owned, at an estimated cost of approximately £200.[12] Of the extent and detail of his "Catalogue of Books written on the Subject of Electricity, exclusive of Papers in Books of Philosophical Transactions and other Miscellaneous Works; distinguishing . . . those which the author had seen and made use of in compiling this work," little can be said that cannot better be seen directly, but few contemporary works could boast of a bibliography containing references to over seventy books, covering a period from 1600 to 1766, of which sixty percent were used in preparation of the text.

In still fewer books could there reasonably have been added the statement:

As the reader will see by the asterisms which books I have had the opportunity of perusing, he will see in what parts my history is most likely defective. And I shall think myself greatly obliged to any

[12] Priestley to Benjamin Franklin, April 19, 1771, Charles Roberts Autograph Collection, Haverford College Library, Haverford, Pennsylvania.

person, who will favour me with the use of any
treatise which contains a discovery of importance.
But I do not apprehend that any thing very material
can have escaped me. ["Catalogue," p. iv.]

How nearly Priestley made good his boast can be
seen by checking modern historical bibliographies of
electricity. Neither Mottelay's "Bibliographical History of Electricity" nor the "Wheeler Gift Catalogue"
cite any significant figure in electricity's history that
Priestley could have known and does not mention, at
least by the third edition of his history.[13] Only for
Nicolo Cabeo is Priestley's treatment seriously in
error. Knowing Cabeo only through Gralath's references, Priestley did not use the "Philosophia mag-
netica" of 1629 and was unaware of Cabeo's oblique
reference to electrical repulsion. Gralath also missed
this, and both he and DuFay ascribe the discovery of
electrical repulsion to von Guericke, as, therefore,
does Priestley.

A caveat ought, perhaps, to be entered here in
discussing the completeness of Priestley's historical
research. In the Preface to the first edition, Priestley
writes:

I think I have kept clear of any mean partiality
towards my own countrymen, and even my own
acquaintance. If English authors are oftener quoted
than foreign, it is because they were more easily
procured; and I have found a difficulty I could not

---

[13] Paul Fleury Mottelay, "Bibliographical History of Electricity
& Magnetism chronologically arranged" (London, 1922); Wil-
liam D. Weaver, ed., "Catalogue of the Wheeler Gift of Books,
Pamphlets, and Periodicals in the Library of the American
Institute of Electrical Engineers" (New York, 1909). Priestley
does, however, miss the references to the experiments of Swam-
merdam and of Sulzer which the later work of Galvani and
Volta was to show had electrical connotations.

have expected, in procuring foreign publications upon this subject. [xi]

The French translator, however, accused Priestley of "being, beyond all bounds, partial to my own countrymen, and particularly unjust to the French" [Preface to the Third Edition, xxxii] and, though Priestley writes that this was an accusation which "all other translators censure as in the highest degree illiberal," it was to some degree repeated in the German translation, and was again, in its more general form, repeated with more respectable authority by Edmund Hoppe in his "Geschichte der Elektrizitat." How much actual truth there is in the charge is difficult for anyone trained in an Anglo-American tradition of history of electricity to judge. To such a person Priestley's "History" seems free of parochialism, and the number of non-English references in the bibliography would confirm this supposition. It is, in any event, fairly easy to dispose of these particular accusations. The French translator was Mathurin Jacques Brisson, described by Franklin as "the last élève of Nollet." Brisson's real objection was Priestley's acceptance of Franklin's theory of electricity in preference to that of Nollet, which he criticizes. No work critical of Nollet could have been "fair" in Brisson's eyes. Johann Georg Krünitz, also a believer in Nollet's theory, carried over Brisson's notes in the German translation, which appears to be based on the French as well as on the first English edition. Krünitz's criticism has, therefore, the same weakness as Brisson's, except that German works *were* slighted in Priestley's first edition. Hoppe, unfortunately, seems to have used the German translation and accepted Krünitz's charge, rather than using the second or later English editions, for which Priestley had learned German and in which there are many more references to German researches, particularly based on the "geschichte" of Gralath.

Finally, in discussing Priestley's historical scholarship, we must dispose of a more serious charge that reflects also on his scholarly integrity. Mottelay has given that charge its most recent airing, with two statements in his "Bibliographical History of Electricity":

> Eeles' hypothesis, extracted from his "Philosophical Essays," (1771) . . . is treated of at length by George Adams in the fourth chapter of his "Essay on Electricity," wherein pertinent allusion is also made to the fact of Mr. Eeles having been purposely shut out of Priestley's "History and Present State of Electricity."

> In his treatment of Eeles' hypothesis Donovan gives some attention to the designed suppression by Priestley of Eeles' valuable papers from the *Philosophical Transactions*.[14]

These statements refer to some electrical researches and the two-fluid electrical theory of a Major Henry Eeles of Lismore, Ireland; but what the statements, particularly the second one, mean is hard to determine. Two of Eeles's papers were published in the *Philosophical Transactions*, neither is of any value, and Priestley refers to the second one in his "History" along with a reference to a paper which confutes Eeles's argument.[15] Priestley did not, therefore, "suppress" or "shut out" Eeles's *Philosophical Transactions*

[14] Mottelay, pp. 212 and 418, respectively.

[15] "A Letter from Mr. Henry Eeles . . . concerning the Cause of Thunder," *Philosophical Transactions* **47**, 524–529 (for 1751); "Letters of Henry Eeles, Esq.; concerning the Cause of the Ascent of Vapour and Exhalation, and those of Winds; and of the general Phenomena of the Weather and Barometer," *Philosophical Transactions* **49**, 124–154 (1755).

papers from his "History." If he is supposed to have prevented other papers by Eeles from being printed, this is ridiculous. Priestley never possessed the authority, within the Royal Society, to have done this were it possible, while Eeles's unpublished papers appear to have been submitted to the Society commencing in 1757, before Priestley had any connection with the Royal Society or any specific interest in electricity.

A reference back to M. Donovan's "Reflections on the Inadequacy of the principal Hypotheses to account for the Phaenomena of Electricity," removes the confusion from Mottelay's garbled paraphrase, but only by intensifying the charge. According to Donovan, quoting from Henry Eeles's "Philosophical essays, in several letters to the Royal Society" (London, 1771), Eeles's papers to the Royal Society, which "from some unknown causes . . . were never published" in its *Transactions,* contained a complete explanation of a two-fluid theory of electricity, supported by experiments strikingly similar to those performed by Robert Symmer and described two years later in Symmer's *Philosophical Transactions* paper of 1759.[16] Symmer's experiments are described in Priestley's "History," along with an elaboration of Symmer's two-fluid theory, doing it, in Priestley's words, ". . . more justice than has been done to it even by Mr. Symmer himself." This elaborated theory, according to Eeles, is precisely the same as his own and, though he accepts the possibility of Symmer's independency, the use of "my terms and expressions" shows that Priestley, as a Fellow of the Royal Society, had access to his unpublished letters and copied his theory from them.

[16] M. Donovan, "Reflections . . . &c.," *Philosophical Magazine* **44**, 401–403 (1814).

Neither of Eeles's published papers give any indication of a theory of electricity, though the second, beginning with obsequiousness, continuing to a criticism of Newton, and ending with abuse of the Society, rather explains why his further papers might not have been welcomed in the Society's publications. How Priestley, some eight to nine years later, might be expected to know of the existence of these further papers is not explained. Eeles's temper further misled him with regard to Priestley's fellowship in the Royal Society, for Priestley was not a Fellow when his "History" was being written; nor was he in London during the period of revision and printing before its publication.[17] It is possible that his correspondents, who were all Fellows, copied the relevant materials from the Society's archives for him, but that would compound the jeopardy of plagiarism; there is no sign of any such activity either in Priestley's correspondence or in the Society's records, and such behavior would mean that at least two persons, wholly unlikely to take ideas without giving credit for them, would have been involved rather than just one. Eeles's theory is couched in just those terms, derived from DuFay, Nollet, and other contemporary usage, that one would expect of an eighteenth-century theory of electricity. Why it would be impossible for Priestley, taking his cue from Symmer's work, to be equally independent with Symmer in the development of a two-fluid theory, Eeles does not explain.

Eeles's accusation was first made in a book printed in 1771, but Priestley seems never to have referred to

[17] Priestley was elected F.R.S. on June 12, 1766, before the "History" was published but not, according to his extant correspondence, before the writing was substantially completed. The correspondence also demonstrates that his contacts with London between his election and the publication was by letter.

it, not even in his "Philosophical Empiricism" (London, 1775), explicitly written in vigorous (and successful) defense against another plagiarism charge—this one with respect to his chemical experiments. Perhaps Priestley was saving his answer for that "Continuation" which he hoped someday to write, bringing his "History" past 1766; perhaps rather he was adopting the practice of his mentor, Franklin, who ignored such criticism, preferring that the facts speak for themselves. It is even possible that Priestley was unaware of the charge, for Eeles's work appears to have had but slight circulation, and the minor prominence later given the accusation appeared when Priestley might well have missed it. The "allusion" Mottelay cites from Adams's popular "Essay on Electricity" was not made by Adams but, in fact, appeared in the "corrections and additions" made by William Jones for the fifth edition of 1799, published five years after Priestley had been hounded from his country by political and religious reactionaries. Donovan's still more explicit repetition appeared ten years after Priestley's death. Mottelay's resurrection of the charge gives too little credit to the disproof afforded by Priestley's long and honorable career; it gives too much prominence to a theory hardly worth the trouble, and too much credence to a man demonstrably given to exaggeration and to abuse of others.

However deserving of our admiration, Priestley's historical scholarship was not directed to the uses of posterity; his motivation was pedagogic rather than bibliographic or historiographic. While writing the "History of Electricity," Priestley was employed as a teacher, and though he was by profession primarily a minister and, by avocation and the judgment of time, principally a scientist, throughout his life he was to be a teacher, by force of personality and conviction. Of his more than one hundred and fifty publications, the vast majority were polemic theology; the second largest category (exclusive of papers in scientific journals) was education, including "Lectures on Oratory and Criticism," "Lectures on the theory of Language," "Rudiments of English Grammar," "Familiar Introduction(s) to the Study of Electricity" and "of Perspective," and "Heads of Lectures on a Course of Experimental Philosophy." He was known as a teacher before he was known either as a scientist or theologian and, significantly, his educational works were reprinted more often than any of his other writings.

Priestley's earliest known association with electricity was educational, in connection with a small private school he started at Nantwich, Cheshire, in 1758. For use in his school he purchased some scientific apparatus, including an electrical machine, which he taught his students to use in performing lecture demonstrations.[18] When he left Nantwich for Warrington in 1761, he gave up the formal teaching of "natural philosophy"—Warrington already had, in John Holt, a science teacher—but not, obviously, his interest in science or science education. As late as 1765, with his "History" at least in the planning stages, Priestley wrote:

> Few are qualified to make new discoveries of importance; . . . but when discoveries have been made, and the principles of science have been ascertained, persons of inferior abilities . . . are sufficient to digest those principles into a convenient method.[19]

[18] Priestley, "Memoirs," p. 43.
[19] Priestley, "Description of a Chart of Biography," pp. 1–2. Warrington, 1765.

There can be little doubt that he was thinking of himself, and probably of his "History," when writing those lines.

Without false modesty, for nothing in his experience could have told him he could join the ranks of discoverers, Priestley planned his "History" as a teaching vehicle, a treatise on the subject of experimental electricity, digested and methodized in the historical form he was so often to adopt. This is clear throughout the text, but is perhaps best illustrated by his statement:

> One thing extremely useful to the progress of farther discoveries is to know what has really been done by others, and where the science stands at present. . . . But the sources . . . are too much scattered, and too distant for most persons to have access to them. This was the first motive of the present undertaking . . . that electricians, having a distinct idea of what the progress of electrical knowledge has been, may see more clearly what remains to be done, and what pursuits best promise to reward their labour. [Vol. 2, p. 57]

Nor would the historical form have seemed particularly unusual for such a purpose in Priestley's day, when history was regularly searched for guidance. When used in this sense, history has the broader meaning, still contained in the French "histoire," of Bacon's histories of the various crafts and trades. A Baconian history of how men had done electricity in the past would seem, to eighteenth-century scientists, for whom "Baconianism" was a term of high praise, reasonable instruction on how electricity might be done in the future.

A Baconian "history" would not, however, necessarily imply the chronological ordering of experimental discoveries, which is probably not the best way to methodize the principles proceeding from them. There were several writers, indeed, who tried a more rationalistic design, but for a teaching treatise there is much to be said for introducing new concepts and techniques as they arise in the course of time. When this is done in the exhaustive detail of Priestley's "History," provided the student has the patience and is not lost in a maze of fact, description, and explanation, he should end his reading at the state of knowledge possessed by the experimenters in the last stages covered by the history. Priestley avoided the dangers of excessive detail partly by the skill with which he compressed elaborate discussion into concise statement, but still more by the simplicity of his language and the clarity of his explanation. He consciously developed a plain and easy English style for use in the "History," declaring, "my object was not to acquire the character of a fine writer, but of an useful one."[20] Ultimately he adopted, as his model for science writing, the style of Benjamin Franklin. Since Franklin had earlier used Addison as his model, Priestley could hardly have chosen better for an English that could be simple, lucid, and graceful. That he might have chosen considerably worse may be seen by imagining Priestley's "History" written in the stately periods of those eighteenth-century stylists, Samuel Johnson or Edward Gibbon, or by comparing Priestley's writing with the tortured obscurity of a modern scientific monograph.

But clarity of explanation requires more than simplicity of language, particularly in a subject as prone

[20] Priestley, "Memoirs," p. 51.

to accident and confusion as static electricity. That electrical conductivity should first have been noted in two substances, wood and linen thread, now defined as nonconductors, is but one example of the genuine anomalies to be unraveled, while an age in which electricity might as reasonably seem the cause of earthquake and meteor as it was of lightning naturally produced more than a single experimenter who deluded his readers, or himself, or both, with discoveries no one since has been able to verify. Knowing that physics lecturers, in possession of complete explanations, can still find difficulty in reproducing the standard experiments of static electricity, one can easily understand the complications of establishing the explanations and standardizing the experiments— and the problems of explaining the material before either has been done. Priestley evaded some of these problems by describing anomalous experiments, without explanation or comment, nearly in the words of the experimenter. Though this leads to confusion with other materials, similarly presented because they needed neither explanation nor comment, it has the personal advantage of avoiding premature commitment and the educational one, common to Priestley's usual teaching technique, of requiring the student to achieve his own understanding from the presented facts.

A large number of experiments had, however, recently received explanation through a single unifying theory of electricity and, though Priestley tried to avoid theory in the historical part of his work and to treat competing theories equally in the more theoretical sections, Franklin's single-fluid theory, as modified by Æpinus, remains the means of providing understanding most consistently adopted throughout the book. Priestley's "History" was, in fact, the first significant popular treatise in English to focus on the synthesis of electrical phenomena achieved by this one-fluid theory. By his discussion of that theory, its origins and modifications, and the successes it had achieved in providing both explanation and direction to experimental research, Priestley made a substantial contribution to the establishment of what Thomas Kuhn has described as the first paradigm for electricity.[21]

Since this accepted pattern of scientific-electrical thought held sway throughout the eighteenth century, and even provided a viable alternative to the revived two-fluid theory of the nineteenth century, a student could find Priestley's "History" a useful text for over fifty years.[22] That students did not find it more useful, and that professional scientists soon ceased to read it was due to Priestley's failure to adopt some quantitative methods to summarize his prolix qualitative descriptions. Æpinus, for example, had developed an algebraic formulation to express the attraction and repulsion relationships of electric fluid and common matter. Priestley's failure to mention this in his discussion of Æpinus constitutes the major criticism John Robison was to make of the "History"—and Robison was, in a way, justified, though Æpinus's ignorance of the force law made his analysis a futile exercise in algebraic ingenuity.[23] Although Robison seems unaware of it, Priestley knew the inverse-

[21] Thomas S. Kuhn, "Structure of Scientific Revolutions," pp. 13–15; 17–18. Chicago, 1963.

[22] I. Bernard Cohen, "Franklin and Newton," pp. 548–560.

[23] For Robison's criticism, see his "System of Mechanical Philosophy" (David Brewster, ed.), Vol. 4, pp. 2 ff. Edinburgh, 1822.

square relationship of electrical force to distance; he could have provided the necessary base for extending Æpinus's calculations and failed to do so. Priestley could also have defined explicitly the relation between capacitance of condensors, the area of their coated plates, and the distance between them; he could have expressed quantitatively the relation between conductivity of wires, their lengths, and their cross sections; he could even have given some numerical values for comparative conductivities of metals. All these relationships are implicit in his discussion, but they were left for others to rediscover, enunciate, and sometimes win reputations on.

Priestley had no feeling for numbers; he was not a mathematician and his sole use for theory was as a guide to more experiments and as a clue to the discovery of new phenomena. It was as an experimenter that he was to achieve his scientific reputation, and it was as the writer of a history of experiments, a treatise on how these were to be performed and for what purpose, that he began his scientific career. Not surprisingly, therefore, a major merit of Priestley's "History" is the excellence of its descriptions of experiments. This depended, rather more than he was ever quite to understand, on the existence of a theory that defined and separated essentials from nonessentials, but it also depended on Priestley's facility in the laboratory. He acquired this in the course of writing, as he used the apparatus and repeated the experiments he was writing about. The results of this labor are manifest in the "History" and alone nearly justify its reading. From its directions and from the plates, the majority of which were drawn by Priestley, it is possible to construct the apparatus and make the experiments—indeed, with sufficient care, even to get the results—of the seventeenth and eighteenth centuries, whether they be those critical to electricity's history or simply those intended as "entertainment for young electricians."

Before long, repeating the experiments of others turned into performing experiments for himself, and the expositor was transformed into an explorer. Whether by his own choice or at the insistence of his patrons, he had hardly won their promises to assist him before he was experimenting for them, and his first letter to John Canton after returning to Warrington from London, described what Priestley thought were new discoveries.[24] He was mistaken in this belief, but soon he was, in fact, performing experiments that either extended previous information or led into entirely new paths. This work Priestley described in the "History of Electricity" and in five papers, first published in the *Philosophical Transactions of the Royal Society* and subsequently reprinted either in later editions of the "History" or in his volumes on chemistry. All of his experiments were, therefore, published at least five times, except those described in the last two *Philosophical Transactions* papers, which make their third appearance in the Appendix to this edition.[25]

[24] The earliest "original" experiments described in the "History" are dated "January 1766," less than a month after Priestley met his patrons. The first letter to Canton is dated February 14, 1766; see footnote 7.

[25] By including these papers in the Appendix, this edition of Priestley's "History" brings together for the first time all of his substantial work on electricity. The "Familiar Introduction to the Study of Electricity" (London, 1768; later editions: 1769; 1777; 1786) is but a shortened and simplified version of material from the "History," and his other experiments involving electricity were chemical experiments in origin, intent, and significance.

In spite of their repeated publication, and in spite of Benjamin Franklin's attempt to gain for Priestley the Copley Medal of the Royal Society for the earliest of them, Priestley's electrical experiments have consistently been neglected.[26] And this is not because of their insignificance, though some, of course, are less valuable than others. Many scientists have been proud to claim discoveries Priestley first described. He was, for example, the first to note the conductivity of carbon and the first to see the carbon arc; in his only extant letter to Humphry Davy, he had gently to correct Davy and reassert his claim.[27] Benjamin Wilson was probably the first distinctly to describe the phenomena known as the "electric wind," but it was Priestley's ingenious experiments that convinced doubters, including Benjamin Franklin, that a "current of *real* air proceeds from the Points of Bodies electrified"; later experimenters were again to deny this point and it had, independently, to be re-established.[28] Oliver Lodge, who was little sparing in his criticisms of Priestley's scientific instincts, was unaware of Priestley's work on the "lateral explosion" when he rediscovered the same phenomenon in 1888

[26] See Robert E. Schofield, "Electrical Researches of Joseph Priestley," *Archives Internationale d'Histoire des Sciences* **64**, 277–286 (1963), for the latest of the few papers to describe Priestley's original experimental investigations in electricity.

[27] Priestley to Humphry Davy, October 31, 1801; "Fragmentary Remains, Literary and Scientific, of Sir Humphry Davy" (John Davy, ed.), p. 51. London, 1858.

[28] See Myron Robinson, "A History of the Electric Wind," *American Journal of Physics* **30**, 366–372 (1962), though Robinson fails to appreciate Priestley's role in this discovery. Franklin's statement is contained in his "Brief Account of that Part of Doctor Priestley's Work on Electricity which related the new Experiments made by himself," Decade V, Vol. 41, "Record Book of the Royal Society," Archives of the Royal Society; see footnote 7.

and renamed it "side flash."[29] "Priestley's Rings"—the colored circles marked on metal plates that have received a spark discharge—are usually credited to him, but few people yet recognize that Priestley was the first person clearly to state, on substantial grounds, the inverse-square force-distance relationship for electrical charges. Reasoning from Franklin's experiments, which showed that pith balls were not electrified when hanging within a charged metal cup, Priestley wrote:

> May we not infer from this experiment, that the attraction of electricity is subject to the same laws with that of gravitation, and is therefore according to the squares of the distances, since it is easily demonstrated, that were the earth in the form of a shell, a body in the inside of it would not be attracted to one side more than the other. [Vol 2, p. 374]

This, unfortunately, seems to be his only flirtation with a quantitative statement of experimental results. Unfortunate, because his most extended sets of experiments, relating to conductivity, the nature of electric fluid, and the discharging of Leyden jars, might otherwise have been more noticed, to the earlier advancement of electricity. Starting from a supposed discovery of the conductivity of mephitic air (carbon dioxide) and the real discovery of that of

[29] Sir Philip Hartog, "Newer Views of Priestley and Lavoisier," *Annals of Science* **5**, 11 (1941), footnote 7; P. T. Riess seems, however, to have noted Priestley's work in his "Ueber die Seitenentladung der elektrischen Batterie," *Abhandl. K. Akad. Wiss. Berlin* **1849**, 1–34; see Hartog, "Joseph Priestley and his Place in the History of Science," an address at the weekly evening meeting of the Royal Institution of Great Britain, Friday, April 24, 1931, p. 33 (bibliography).

carbon, Priestley went on to an investigation of conductivity in general. He also added black lead and red-hot glass to the list of conductors and ultimately declared: "independent of moisture, there is probably a gradation in all substances, from the most perfect conductors to the most perfect non-conductors of electricity."[30] This belief led naturally to an investigation of comparative conductivities, particularly of various metals. For this purpose he devised three different methods, any one of which was capable of greater precision of results than any to be conducted for years—including the more famous experiments later made (and much later published) of Henry Cavendish.[31] It was from these experiments that Priestley determined that the conductivity of metal wire was a function inversely of length and directly of cross section. It was also as a result of these experiments that he was able to give a table of comparative conductivities: lead, tin, iron, brass, copper, silver, gold; which was not to be bettered until the elaborate experiments of William Snow Harris, in 1827, moved gold into its correct place between brass and copper.[32]

[30] "History," Vol. 2, p. 4; as Hartog has earlier noted ("Newer Views," p. 9), the "probably" was added to the more forceful statement of the first edition, p. 435.

[31] J. Clerk Maxwell, ed., "The Electrical Researches of the Honourable Henry Cavendish, F.R.S." Cambridge, 1879. Cavendish used his own physiological sensations as a measure of comparative conductivities of various solutions. Priestley's methods, though also involving circuit impedances, were capable of reproduction and even of expression in linear dimensions—see Schofield, "Electrical Researches."

[32] William Snow Harris, "On the Relative Powers of Various Metallic Substances as Conductors of Electricity," *Philosophical Transactions* 117, 18–24 (1827). Harris was apparently unaware of Priestley's earlier work, as were Davy (1821), Becquerel (1825), and Ohm (1826), all of whom made experiments with aims similar to and no better results than Priestley's—see Schofield, "Electrical Researches," for some of the details of this work.

Proceeding from this set of investigations to those on the nature of "electric fluid," Priestley came, apparently as a consequence of his failure to find a momentum for it, to question the existence of a fluid as such, and even to suggest (though this only in a private letter) that "electrification may be only some new modification of the matter of which the body consisted before electrification."[33] Finally, extending his investigation of lateral discharge, Priestley observed the oscillatory discharge of the Leyden jar and even indicated, confusedly and without understanding, something of the nature of the circuit necessary to produce such a discharge—nearly ninety years before the phenomenon was again noted, this time as a consequence of theoretical prediction.

All of these, and more—experiments, suggestions for experiments, and queries—are in Priestley's "History" to be read by anyone, scientist or amateur, who cared to look. And many did look, until the discovery of current electricity and the application of mathematics to electrical investigations made Priestley's qualitative work with static electricity seem quaint and unimportant, and closed his book for all but those interested in history. The contemporary reception of the "History," by readers of all kinds, must have pleased and perhaps surprised Priestley. Shortly after the publication of the first edition, it was reviewed at length in the widely circulated *Monthly Review*. The review, extending over issues of three months, was a thorough report of its contents, with extensive quotation, and essentially ended up with the declaration:

[33] Hartog, "Newer Views," p. 12, footnote 16.

The design and plan . . . are excellent; and the execution masterly. We cannot sufficiently commend the Author's care in collecting, and skill in arranging and digesting, with perspicuity, such an immense variety of facts and observations. . . . On the whole, we think we may justly characterize this work as the joint product of labour and genius.[34]

The "History" was widely circulated. Benjamin Franklin bought several copies for distribution to American colleges; Harvard got one, and Yale, which got another, actually had adopted it, by 1788, as a supplemental text to Enfield's "Institutes of Natural Philosophy." A second edition appeared in English in 1769, a third and fourth in 1775, and a fifth in 1794. A French translation was published in 1771 and a German one in 1772.

Priestley had asked that anyone with corrections or additions write to him, and even suggested that:

. . . if any person shall make discoveries in electricity, which he would chuse to see recorded in this history, he will oblige me by a communication of them; and if they be really original, a proper place shall certainly be assigned them in the next edition. [xvi–xvii]

Subsequent editions did contain corrections and additions suggested by correspondents, and though he never wrote the "Continuation" of his history that was to contain the discoveries, these too were sent to him from all over Britain and Europe. From letters, articles in journals, and references in books, it is

[34] Review of "The History and Present State of Electricity," *Monthly Review* **37**, 93–105; 241–254; 449–464 (1767). The review was written by William Bewley, a surgeon and apothecary of Great Massingham, Norfolk, who, not surprisingly, became a good friend of Priestley after the review appeared.

possible to learn of a few of the persons influenced by Priestley and his "History." A Mr. Ronayne of Ireland and William Henly of London sent him communications, which he passed on to the Royal Society. Alessandro Volta first wrote to him in connection with electrical studies, as did Torbern Bergman, the chemist of Sweden; both continued their correspondence on chemical subjects. John Winthrop and Andrew Oliver wrote from the American Colonies. Jan IngenHousz began an electrical correspondence from Vienna, which continued from Holland and London, on botanical and chemical experiments. And surely Priestley's later associations with John Michell, in connection with the "History of Optics," with Abraham Bennet, mentioned in Bennet's "New Experiments on Electricity" (Derby, 1789), and with Martinus von Marum, suggesting electrochemical experiments for the famous Marum electrical machine, were as much founded on a demonstrated mutual interest in electricity as on Priestley's reputation as a chemist.[35]

To these names can be added those of other experimenters who knew and used Priestley's work to their advantage, though there is no clear evidence of correspondence. Henry Cavendish, for example, refers to the "History" and to visits and private communications from Priestley in his papers, published and unpublished. It is not an unreasonable inference, from the nature of their work and its temporal relationships, that Priestley's investigations suggested many of the problems and techniques that Cavendish was to exploit so magnificently. William Herschel, best

[35] See earlier, footnote 7.

known for his astronomical work, made his "professional" debut as a scientist by reading papers on electrical subjects before the Bath Philosophical Society; the topics were suggested to him by the "Queries" published in Priestley's "History."[36] In fact, only Coulomb and Galvani, of the really significant electrical experimenters of Priestley's day, seem to have left no published evidence of having used the "History."[37]

It was inevitable that scientists, after some twenty-five years, would tend not to read Priestley's "History." Robison's reference, in his "System of Mechanical Philosophy" of 1822, was an anachronism appearing in the posthumous publication of an eighteenth-century natural philosopher; it was, in any event, concerned with the "History" as a text and was already critical of Priestley's quantitative deficiencies. Davy, Becquerel, Ohm, and William Snow Harris were even ignorant of Priestley's work in areas of their own electrical investigations. While there was not a universal ignoring of Priestley's electricity—Thomas Young calls particular attention to one of Priestley's articles in his "Course of Lectures on Natural Philosophy" of 1807, Alexander Dallas Bache is known to have read the "History" in 1840, and it was referred

[36] For Cavendish, see footnote 31, earlier, and Schofield, "Electrical Researches"; For Herschel, see J. L. E. Dreyer, ed., "The Scientific Papers of Sir William Herschel," Introduction. London, 1912.

[37] No reference to Priestley's name was found in a cursory examination of the writings of either man; the works of neither, however, give any detailed account of their authors' reading in electrical subjects. Hebbel E. Hoff, "Galvani and the Pre-Galvani Electrophysiologists," *Annals of Science* 1, 157–172 (1936), suggests that there is much doubt "whether he [Galvani] really had read very extensively in electrical or even electrophysiological literature."

to by Riess in 1849—on the whole, "Priestley on Electricity" was henceforth to be the concern primarily of historians.

Their continued use of it is not always evident, particularly during the first half of the nineteenth century when standards of historical scholarship fell lamentably from those set by Priestley himself. Historical sketches of science in general, and of electricity in particular, frequently reveal their debt to Priestley by no more than the repetition of certain felicitous phrases or the division of their work into those groupings used in the "History." By the end of the nineteenth century, however, except for those histories so dependent on undefined trains of secondary sources that the authors were unaware of their initial dependence on Priestley, "The History and Present State of Electricity" was avowedly recognized as the classic history and primary source that has been described above. Hoppe's criticism notwithstanding, many of his early footnote references, in the "Geschichte der Elektrizitat" are to the "History" (in its German edition), while the early chronological divisions are those of Priestley. Park Benjamin's "Age of Electricity" (London, 1886) refers to "Priestley's grand 'History of Electricity,'" and his "Intellectual Rise in Electricity" (New York, 1895), though limited to the period up to Benjamin Franklin, clearly shows its dependence on that "grand" work. Today, the "History" is a standard reference for any histories of science or electricity that cover the period, and such books as Edmund Whittaker's "History of the Theories of Aether and Electricity" show that scientist-historians are even reading Priestley's own experiments and recognizing the value that was in them.

The appearance of a modern edition of "The History and Present State of Electricity, with Original Experiments," one hundred and seventy years since it last was published, attests to the steadily increasing interest in the history of science for itself, as a part of intellectual history, and as a means of extending to nonscientists an understanding of scientific actions and values. More than ever before, the classics of science and of the history of science are in demand and new editions of many of these have already appeared. Priestley's "History," being both science and history of science, being (what is so rare for such a work) both easy and pleasant to read, inevitably had to join them. But the new edition, the collectors' scramble for old ones, and the continued use of any available edition by students and scholars, may also stand as a twentieth-century agreement with that eighteenth-century reviewer: "excellent . . . masterly . . . skill . . . perspicuity . . . the joint product of labour and genius."

Bibliographical Note

The present edition of Joseph Priestley's "History and Present State of Electricity, with Original Experiments" is reprinted from the third edition of 1775, with an appendix containing two additional papers of "original experiments" reprinted from their second publication in Volume 2 of Priestley's "Experiments and Observations on different Kinds of Air" pp. 241–262 (2nd edn., 1776), and Volume 2 of his

"Experiments and Observations relating to various Branches of Natural Philosophy," pp. 258–286 (1781). Unless there are exceptionally attractive features about other editions, reprints of this variety are usually taken from the first or the last edition to be published during the author's life—in this instance, the edition of 1767 or that of 1794. There are, however, serious doubts that Priestley had any connection with the publication of the 1794 edition, particularly as he left England in April, 1794, on his self-imposed exile to the United States. In any case, this fifth edition is substantially the same as the fourth edition of 1775, which in turn is merely the quarto version of the third (octavo) edition of the same year. So far as content is concerned, the choice is essentially between the 1767 edition and one of those stemming from the additions and corrections leading to the 1775 version.

Among the latter editions, the selection seems perfectly clear. The third edition is the only one of them to be printed in octavo and this, in spite of its two volumes, is easier to handle and read than the heavy and bulky quarto printings. Typographically the quarto versions may be slightly more attractive, but only because the greater page size adds to the space framing the words; the typeface is identical. The plates also are the same, in size and content, in all three editions. Given the equivalence of text, the greater ease in handling an octavo and its conformity with standard library size makes the third edition an obvious choice.

Selection of the third over the first edition seems equally obvious, though both sentiment and scholarship can present some counterarguments. Format considerations remain the same: octavo third compared to the quarto first (and second); identical typeface; plates printed from the same engravings, with minor changes in lettering and the addition of a "Fig. 9" to Plate I, to illustrate one of the new original experiments. Again the advantage is to the third edition. Textually, something can be said for either side. Both the second and third editions contain additions based on further reading and, though neither carries the general history beyond the dates covered in the first, both reprint additional "original experiments" from the *Philosophical Transactions*. The third is, however, the "final" version to leave Priestley's hands, with some slight additions beyond those of the second, and with the corrections of both first and second edition errors. For general history of science, textually and scientifically, the third edition is superior to the first and has, therefore, been chosen for this reprint.

Sentimentally and for scholarly investigation of Priestley's life and career, there remain the arguments for the first edition, and conceivably also for appendices reprinting first editions of all the separate papers of experiments. The wording has changed slightly between editions as greater knowledge brought caution and hindsight to temper the enthusiasms of first writing. Additional information has also varied some accounts of earlier work and might also have influenced Priestley's own experimental plans and procedures. For an edition such as this one, however, general considerations must outweigh special ones, particularly as the latter can, in the end, be satisfied only with an original first edition. A variorum edition, which would combine advantages of both approaches, is far too pretentious for a work such as this and would cost far more in time, space, and money than the results would warrant. The most obvious ways in which the third edition differs from the first can, however, be indicated so that this reprint of the third can, with caution, be used to judge the contents of the first.

The principal differences relate to new references, new experiments, and corrections and emendations rising out of criticism and maturity. All references to German language sources were added after the first edition. This notably means the "Geschichte" and the "Bibliothek" of Daniel Gralath, J. C. Wilcke's German edition of Franklin's "Experiments and Observations" with its notes and introduction, and the three works of J. F. Hartmann listed in Priestley's "Catalogue of Books." In consequence of these German references, the descriptions of German and Scandinavian research are more accurate and detailed, but the only changes of significance are: the addition of Nicolo Cabeo's name to the history; a substantial revision of the Leyden jar story, with the addition of von Kleist's experiments, and several new bibliographic references known only through Gralath. The other major reference additions are: Waller's translation of the "Essayes" of the Accademia del Cimento ("The Sources of Science," No. 1, Johnson Reprint Corporation, New York and London, 1964); the "new edition with additions" of Franklin's "Experiments and Observations" of 1769; a new (1767) volume of Nollet's "Lettres sur l'électricité"; and the change of the "Secondat's history of electricity" to the more correct "Secondat's histoire d'electricité in his Observations Physiques."

In the third edition, the heading for Part VIII has

been changed from "New Experiments in Electricity,
made in the Year 1766" to cover the addition of three
new sections, XIII, XIV, and XV, for which the
former XIII was renumbered XVI, etc. These sections
are essentially reprints of the following papers: "An
Account of Rings consisting of all the Prismatic
Colours, made by Electrical Explosions on the Surface
of Pieces of Metal," *Philosophical Transactions* **58**,
68–74 (1768); "Experiments on the lateral Force of
Electrical Explosions," and "Various Experiments on
the Force of Electrical Explosions," *Philosophical
Transactions* **59**, 57–62; 63–70 (1769). The papers
we have added in the Appendix similarly appeared
first as: "Experiments and Observations on Charcoal"
and "An investigation of the lateral Explosion, and of
the Electricity communicated to the electrical Circuit,
in a Discharge," *Philosophical Transactions* **60**, 211–
227; 192–210 (1770). Any changes in wording from
the original versions are chiefly accounted for by the
change in format of their new publication. It is probable that they were set in type from the *Philosophical
Transactions,* with minor corrections to improve the
phrasing and occasionally to reduce what, in retro-
spect, seemed the overassertiveness of some passages
in the originals.

How many changes of this variety, to adjust to
criticism or temper the positiveness of some hypothesis, there are between the first and third editions
would be impossible to determine without a line-by-
line comparison of both. Most of these also are of
relatively small importance, though in some instances
—as in the change regarding the range of conductivity, previously noted—the result is to weaken the
value of Priestley's speculations. Some of the critical

comments about French experiments and conclusions have been softened (p. 126, Vol. 1, III, compared with p. 98, I; or pp. 128–129, Vol. 1, III, compared with pp. 100–101, I, for example) in obvious consequence of Brisson's complaints of unfairness, and the addition of a list of metals in order of melting (Vol. 2, p. 371) is also a result of the French translation. The *Monthly Review* article had the result of adding a paragraph (Vol. 1, p. 496) on the electrical power of the *Gymnotus* or electric fish and some additional "Queries" to Section II, Part IV. Greater experience with electrical apparatus modified some of Priestley's statements in Part V, particularly in the regular substitution of glass for the "baked wood" that had been named as an insulator in the first edition. In the same part, IngenHousz's name has been added to that of Ramsden (cited in the errata of the first edition) as inventor of a circular-plate electrical machine—probably because of a complaint from IngenHousz. Finally, a class of changes seems to reflect Priestley's increased knowledge of chemistry—for example, "Phlogiston of Frobenius" changed to "ethereal spirit of Frobenius" (p. 76, I; 97, Vol. 1, III), elimination of "no substance in a state of fluidity is electric except air" (p. 77, I; 98, Vol. 1, III), the rewriting of Section III, Part VIII, substituting "fixed air" for "mephitic air," and the recasting to summarize in an uninteresting paragraph what had been an interesting four-page description of a set of erroneously interpreted experiments and their resolution.

Clearly one cannot substitute the third edition for the first, nor this brief résumé for an examination of the changes from first through second to third editions, in an investigation of the process by which

Joseph Priestley became a scientist. Yet it should be equally clear that the third edition represents the "History of Electricity" in its most useful form, as that classic in the history of science which has justified this reprint.

Robert E. Schofield

THE

HISTORY

AND

PRESENT STATE

OF

ELECTRICITY,

WITH

ORIGINAL EXPERIMENTS,

By JOSEPH PRIESTLEY, LL.D. F.R.S.

THE THIRD EDITION,
CORRECTED AND ENLARGED.

Caufa latet, vis eft notiffima.   OVID.

VOL. I.

LONDON,

Printed for C. BATHURST, and T. LOWNDES, in Fleet-Street;
J. RIVINGTON, and J. JOHNSON, in St. Paul's Church-Yard;
S. CROWDER, G. ROBINSON, and R. BALDWIN, in Pater-
noster Row; T. BECKET, and T. CADELL, in the Strand.

MDCCLXXV.

T O

THE RIGHT HONOURABLE

JAMES Earl of Morton,

President of the Royal Society,

This H I S T O R Y, &c.

I S,

WITH THE GREATEST RESPECT

INSCRIBED

By his LORDSHIP's

Most Obedient,

And Most Humble

SERVANT,

JOSEPH PRIESTLEY.

THE
PREFACE
TO THE
FIRST EDITION.

IN writing the *Hiſtory and Preſent State of Electricity*, I flatter myſelf that I ſhall give pleaſure, as well to perſons who have a taſte for Natural Philoſophy in general, as to electricians in particular; and I hope the work will be of ſome advantage to the ſcience itſelf. Both theſe ends would certainly be anſwered in a conſiderable degree, were the execution at all anſwerable to the deſign.

THE Hiſtory of Electricity is a field full of pleaſing objects, according to all the genuine and univerſal principles of taſte, deduced from a knowledge of human nature. Scenes like theſe, in which we ſee a gradual riſe and progreſs in things, always exhibit a pleaſing ſpectacle to the human mind. Nature, in all her delightful walks, abounds with ſuch views, and they are in a more eſpecial manner connected with every thing that relates to human life and happineſs; things, in their own nature, the moſt intereſting to us. Hence it is, that the power of aſſociation has annexed crouds of pleaſing ſenſations to the contemplation of every object, in which this property is apparent.

THIS pleafure, likewife, bears a confiderable refemblance to that of the fublime, which is one of the moft exquifite of all thofe that affect the human imagination. For an object in which we fee a perpetual progrefs and improvement is, as it were, continually rifing in its magnitude; and moreover, when we fee an actual increafe, in a long period of time paft, we cannot help forming an idea of an unlimited increafe in futurity; which is a profpect really boundlefs, and fublime.

THE pleafures arifing from views exhibited in *civil*, *natural*, and *philofophical* hiftory, are, in certain refpects, different from one another. Each has its advantages, and each its defects: and both their advantages and defects contribute to adapt them to different claffes of readers.

CIVIL hiftory prefents us with views of the ftrongeft paffions and fentiments of the human mind, into which every man can eafily and perfectly enter, and with fuch incidents, refpecting happinefs and mifery, as we cannot help feeling, would alarm and affect us in a very fenfible manner; and therefore, we are at prefent alarmed and affected by them to a confiderable degree. Hence the pleafure we receive from civil hiftory arifes, chiefly from the exercife it affords our paffions. The imagination is only entertained with fcenes which occafionally ftart up, like interludes, or epifodes, in the great drama, to which we are principally attentive. We are prefented, indeed, with the profpect of

gradual

gradual improvement during the rife of great empires; but, as we read on, we are obliged to contemplate the difagreeable reverfe. And the hiftory of moft ftates prefents nothing but a tedious uniformity, without any ftriking events, to diverfify and embellifh the profpect. Befides, if a man have any fentiment of virtue and benevolence, he cannot help being fhocked with a view of the vices and miferies of mankind; which, though they be not all, are certainly the moft glaring and ftriking objects in the hiftory of human affairs. An attention, indeed, to the conduct of divine Providence, which is ever bringing good out of evil, and gradually conducting things to a more perfect and glorious ftate, tends to throw a more agreeable light on the more gloomy parts of hiftory; but it requires great ftrength of mind to comprehend thofe views; and, after all, the feelings of the heart too often overpower the conclufions of the head.

NATURAL hiftory exhibits a boundlefs variety of fcenes, and yet infinitely analogous to one another. A naturalift has, confequently, all the pleafure which the contemplation of uniformity and variety can give the mind; and this is one of the moft copious fources of our intellectual pleafures. He is likewife entertained with a profpect of gradual improvement, while he fees every object in nature rifing by due degrees to its maturity and perfection. And while new plants, new animals, and new foffils are per-

petually

petually pouring in upon him, the moſt pleaſing views of the unbounded power, wiſdom,
and goodneſs of God are conſtantly preſent
to his mind.   But he has no direct view of
human ſentiments and human actions; which,
by means of their endleſs aſſociations, greatly heighten and improve all the pleaſures of
taſte.

THE hiſtory of philoſophy enjoys, in ſome
meaſure, the advantages both of civil and
natural hiſtory, whereby it is relieved from
what is moſt tedious and diſguſting in both.
Philoſophy exhibits the powers of nature, diſcovered and directed by human art. It has,
therefore, in ſome meaſure, the boundleſs
variety with the amazing uniformity of the
one, and likewiſe every thing that is pleaſing
and intereſting in the other.   And the idea
of continual riſe and improvement is conſpi-
cuous in the whole ſtudy, whether we be attentive to the part which nature, or that which
men are acting in the great ſcene.

IT is here that we ſee the human underſtanding to its greateſt advantage, graſping
at the nobleſt objects, and increaſing its own
powers, by acquiring to itſelf the powers of
nature, and directing them to the accom-
pliſhment of its own views; whereby the ſe-
curity, and happineſs of mankind are daily
improved.   Human abilities are chiefly con-
ſpicuous in adapting means to ends, and in
deducing one thing from another by the method of analogy; and where ſhall we find
inſtances of greater ſagacity, than in philoſophers

fophers diverfifying the fituations of things, in order to give them an opportunity of fhowing their mutual relations, affections, and influences; deducing one truth and one difcovery from another, and applying them all to the ufeful purpofes of human life.

IF the exertion of human abilities, which cannot but form a delightful fpectacle for the human imagination, give us pleafure, we enjoy it here in a higher degree than while we are contemplating the fchemes of warriors, and the ftratagems of their bloody art. Befides, the object of philofophical purfuits throws a pleafing idea upon the fcenes they exhibit; whereas a reflection upon the real objects and views of moft ftatefmen and conquerors cannot but take from the pleafure, which the idea of their fagacity, forefight, and comprehenfion would otherwife give to the virtuous and benevolent mind. Laftly, the inveftigation of the powers of nature, like the ftudy of Natural Hiftory, is perpetually fuggefting to us views of the divine perfections and providence, which are both pleafing to the imagination, and improving to the heart.

BUT though other kinds of hiftory may, in fome refpects, vie with that of philofophy, nothing that comes under the denomination of hiftory can exhibit inftances of fo fine a rife and improvement in things, as we fee in the progrefs of the human mind, in philofophical inveftigations. To whatever height we have arrived in natural fcience, our be-

ginnings

ginnings were very low, and our advances
have been exceedingly gradual. And to look
down from the eminence, and to fee, and
compare all thofe gradual advances in the
afcent, cannot but give the greateft pleafure
to thofe who are feated on the eminence, and
who feel all the advantages of their elevated
fituation. And confidering that we ourfelves
are, by no means, at the top of human
fcience; that the mountain ftill afcends beyond our fight, and that we are, in fact, not
much above the foot of it, a view of the
manner in which the afcent has been made,
cannot but animate us in our attempts to advance ftill higher, and fuggeft methods
and expedients to affift us in our farther
progrefs.

GREAT conquerors, we read, have been
both animated, and alfo, in a great meafure,
formed by reading the exploits of former
conquerors. Why may not the fame effect
be expected from the hiftory of philofophy
to philofophers? May not even more be expected in this cafe? The wars of many of
thofe conquerors, who received this advantage from hiftory, had no proper connection
with former wars: they were only analogous
to them. Whereas the whole bufinefs of
philofophy, diverfified as it is, is but one;
it being one and the fame great fcheme, that
all philofophers, of all ages and nations,
have been conducting, from the beginning of
the world; fo that the work being the fame, the
labours of one are not only analogous to thofe
of

of another, but in an immediate manner fubfervient to them; and one philofopher fucceeds another in the fame field; as one Ro-
man proconful fucceeded another in carrying on the fame war, and purfuing the fame
conquefts, in the fame country. In this cafe,
an intimate knowledge of what has been done
before us cannot but greatly facilitate our future progrefs, if it be not abfolutely neceffary
to it.

THESE hiftories are evidently much more
neceffary in an advanced ftate of fcience, than
in the infancy of it. At prefent philofophical difcoveries are fo many, and the accounts
of them are fo difperfed, that it is not in the
power of any man to come at the knowledge
of all that has been done, as a foundation for
his own inquiries. And this circumftance appears to me to have very much retarded the
progrefs of difcoveries.

NOT that I think philofophical difcoveries
are now at a ftand. On the other hand, as
quick advances feem to have been made of
late years, as in any equal period of time
paft whatever. Nay, it appears to me, that
the progrefs is really accelerated. But the
increafe of knowledge is like the increafe of
a city. The building of fome of the firft
ftreets makes a great figure, is much talked
of, and known to every body; whereas the
addition of, perhaps, twice as much building, after it has been fwelled to a confiderable fize, is not fo much as taken notice of,

and

and may be really unknown to many of the inhabitants. If the additions which have been made to the buildings of the city of London, in any fingle year of late, had been made two or three centuries ago, it could not have efcaped the obfervation of hiftorians; whereas, now, they are fo fcattered, and the proportion they bear to the whole city is fo fmall, that they are hardly noticed. For the fame reafon, the improvements that boys make at fchool, or that young gentlemen make at an academy, or the univerfity, are more taken notice of than all the knowledge they acquire afterwards, though they continue their ftudies with the fame affiduity and fuccefs.

THE hiftory of experimental philofophy, in the manner in which it ought to be written, to be of much ufe, would be an immenfe work; but it were much to be wifhed, that perfons who have leifure, and fufficient abilities, would undertake it in feparate parts. I have executed it, in the beft manner I have been able, for that branch which has been my own favourite amufement; and I fhall think myfelf happy, if the attempt excite other perfons to do the like for theirs.

I CANNOT help thinking myfelf to have been peculiarly fortunate, in undertaking the hiftory of electricity, at the moft proper time for writing it, when the materials were neither too few, nor too many to make a hiftory; and when they were fo fcattered, as

to

to make the undertaking highly defirable, and the work peculiarly ufeful to Englifh-men.

I LIKEWISE think myfelf exceedingly happy in my fubject itfelf. Few branches of Natural Philofophy would, I think, make fo good a fubject for a hiftory. Few can boaft fuch a number of difcoveries, difpofed in fo fine a feries, all comprifed in fo fhort a fpace of time, and all fo recent, the principal actors in the fcene being ftill living.

WITH feveral of thefe principal actors it has been my fingular honour and happinefs to be acquainted; and it was their approbation of my plan, and their generous encouragement that induced me to undertake the work. With gratitude I acknowledge my obligations to Dr. Watfon, Dr. Franklin, and Mr. Canton, for the books, and other mate-rials with which they have fupplied me, and for the readinefs with which they have given me any information in their power to pro-cure. In a more efpecial manner am I oblig-ed to Mr. Canton, for thofe original commu-nications of his, which will be found in this work, and which cannot fail to give a value to it, in the efteem of all the lovers of electri-city. My grateful acknowledgements are al-fo due to the Rev. Dr. Price, F R. S. and to the Rev. Mr. Holt, our profeffor of Natural Philofophy at Warrington, for the attention they have given to the work, and for the many important fervices they have rendered me with refpect to it.

To

To the gentlemen above mentioned the public is, likewife, indebted for whatever they may think of value in the *original experiments* which I have related of my own. It was from converfing with them that I was firft led to entertain the thought of attempting any thing new in this way, and it was their example, and favourable attention to my experiments, that animated me in the purfuit of them. In fhort, without them, neither my experiments, nor this work would have had any exiftence.

THE hiftorical part of this work, the reader, I hope will find to be full and circumftantial, and at the fame fuccinct. Every new fact, or important circumftance I have noted as it arofe ; but I have abridged all long details, and have carefully avoided all digreffions and repetitions. For this purpofe, I have perufed every original author, to which I could have recourfe ; and every quotation in the margin points to the authority that I myfelf confulted, and from which the account in the text was actually taken. Where I could not procure the original authors, I was obliged to quote them at fecond hand, but the reference will always fhow where that has been done. That I might not mifreprefent any writer, I have generally given the reader his own words, or the plaineft tranflation I could make of them ; and this I have done, not only in direct quotations, but where, by a change of perfon, I have made the language my own.

I MADE

I MADE it a rule to myfelf, and I think I have conftantly adhered to it, to take no notice of the miftakes, mifapprehenfions, and altercations of electricians; except fo far as, I apprehended, a knowledge of them might be ufeful to their fucceffors. All the difputes which have no way contributed to the difcovery of truth, I would gladly confign to eternal oblivion. Did it depend upon me, it fhould never be known to pofterity, that there had ever been any fuch thing as envy, jealoufy, or cavilling among the admirers of my favourite ftudy. I have, as far as my beft judgment could direct me, been juft to the merits of all perfons concerned. If any have made unjuft claims, by arrogating to themfelves the difcoveries of others, I have filently reftored them to the right owner, and generally without fo much as giving a hint that any injuftice had ever been committed. If I have, in any cafe, given a hint, I hope it will be thought, by the offending parties themfelves, to be a very gentle one; and that it will be a *memento*, which will not be without its ufe.

I THINK I have kept clear of any mean partiality towards my own countrymen, and even my own acquaintance. If Englifh authors are oftener quoted than foreign, it is becaufe they were more eafily procured; and I have found a difficulty I could not have expected, in procuring foreign publications upon this fubject.

I FIND

I FIND it impoffible to write a preface to this work, without difcovering a little of the enthufiafm which I have contracted from an attention to it, by expreffing my wifhes, that more perfons, of a ftudious and retired life, would admit this part of experimental philofophy into their ftudies. They would find it agreeably to diverfify a courfe of ftudy, by mixing fomething of action with fpeculation, and giving fome employment to the hands and arms, as well as to the head. Electrical experiments are, of all others, the cleaneft, and the moft elegant, that the compafs of philofophy exhibits. They are performed with the leaft trouble, there is an amazing variety in them, they furnifh the moft pleafing and furprifing appearances for the entertainment of one's friends, and the expence of inftruments may well be fupplied, by a proportionable deduction from the purchafe of books, which are generally read and laid afide, without yielding half the entertainment.

THE inftruction we are able to get from books is, comparatively, foon exhaufted; but philofophical inftruments are an endlefs fund of knowledge. By philofophical inftruments, however, I do not here mean the globes, the orrery, and others, which are only the means which ingenious men have hit upon, to explain their own conceptions of things to others; and which, therefore, like books, have no ufes more extenfive than the

views

views of human ingenuity; but such as the air-pump, condensing engine, pyrometer, &c. (with which electrical machines are to be ranked) and which exhibit the operations of nature, that is of the God of nature himself, which are infinitely various. By the help of these machines, we are able to put an endless variety of things into an endless variety of situations, while nature herself is the agent that shows the result. Hereby the laws of her action are observed, and the most important discoveries may be made; such as those who first contrived the instrument could have no idea of.

In electricity, in particular, there is the greatest room to make new discoveries. It is a field but just opened, and requires no great stock of particular preparatory knowledge: so that any person who is tolerably well versed in experimental philosophy, may presently be upon a level with the most experienced electricians. Nay, this history shows, that several raw adventurers have made themselves as considerable, as some who have been, in other respects, the greatest philosophers. I need not tell my reader of how great weight this consideration is, to induce him to provide himself with an electrical apparatus. The pleasure arising from the most trifling discoveries of one's own, far exceeds what we receive from understanding the much more important discoveries of others; and a mere reader has no chance of finding new truths, in comparison of him who now and then

amuses

amuſes himſelf with philoſophical experiments.

Human happineſs depends chiefly upon having ſome object to purſue, and upon the vigour with which our faculties are exerted in the purſuit. And, certainly, we muſt be much more intereſted in purſuits wholly our own, than when we are merely following the track of others. Beſides, this pleaſure has re-inforcements from a variety of ſources, which I ſhall not here undertake to trace; but which contribute to heighten the ſenſation, far beyond any thing elſe of this kind that can be experienced by a perſon of a ſpeculative turn of mind.

It is a great recommendation of the ſtudy of electricity, that it now appears to be, by no means, a ſmall object. The electric fluid is no local, or occaſional agent in the theatre of the world. Late diſcoveries ſhow that its preſence and effects are every where, and that it acts a principal part in the grandeſt and moſt intereſting ſcenes of nature. It is not, like magnetiſm, confined to one kind of bodies, but every thing we know is a conductor or non-conductor of electricity. Theſe are properties as eſſential and important as any they are poſſeſſed of, and can hardly fail to ſhow themſelves wherever the bodies are concerned.

Hitherto philoſophy has been chiefly converſant about the more ſenſible properties of bodies ; electricity, together with chymiſtry, and the doctrine of light and colours,

ſeems

feems to be giving us an inlet into their internal ftructure, on which all their fenfible properties depend. By purfuing this new light, therefore, the bounds of natural fcience may poffibly be extended, beyond what we can now form an idea of. New worlds may open to our view, and the glory of the great Sir Ifaac Newton himfelf, and all his contemporaries, be eclipfed, by a new fet of philofophers, in quite a new field of fpeculation. Could that great man revifit the earth, and view the experiments of the prefent race of electricians, he would be no lefs amazed than Roger Bacon, or Sir Francis, would have been at his. The electric fhock itfelf, if it be confidered attentively, will appear almoft as furprifing as any difcovery that he made; and the man who could have made that difcovery, by any reafoning *a priori*, would have been reckoned a moft extraordinary genius : but electrical difcoveries have been made fo much by accident, that it is more the powers of nature, than of human genius, that excite our wonder with refpect to them. But if the fimple electric fhock would have appeared fo extraordinary to Sir Ifaac Newton, what would he have faid upon feeing the effects of a modern electrical battery, and an apparatus for drawing lightning from the clouds ! What inexpreffible pleafure would it give a modern electrician, were the thing poffible, to entertain fuch a man as Sir Ifaac for a few hours with his principal experiments !

To

To return from this excurfion to the bufinefs of a preface: befides relating the hiftory
of electrical difcoveries, in the order in which
they were made, I thought it neceffary, in
order to make the work more ufeful, efpecially to young electricians, to fubjoin a me-
thodical treatife on the fubject, containing the
fubftance of the hiftory in another form, with
obfervations and inftructions of my own. The
particular ufes of thefe parts of the work are
expreffed at large in the introductions to
them.   And, in the laft place, I have given
an account of fuch original experiments as
I have been fo fortunate as to hit upon
myfelf.

I INTITLE the work the *Hiftory and Prefent State of Electricity* ; and whether there be
any more additions of the whole work or not,
care will be taken to preferve the propriety of
the title, by occafionally printing ADDI-
TIONS, in the fame fize, as new difcoveries
are made; which will always be fold at
a reafonable price to the purchafers of the
book; or given *gratis*, if the bulk be inconfiderable.

CONSIDERING what refpectable perfons
have already honoured this work with their
valuable communications, I hope it will not
be deemed arrogance in me, if I here ad-
vertife, that if any perfon fhall make difcoveries in electricity, which he would chufe to
fee recorded in this hiftory, he will oblige
me by a communication of them; and if
they be really original, a proper place fhall
cer-

certainly be affigned to them in the next edition, or paper of additions. And I hope that, if electricians in general would fall into this method, and make either a periodical, or occafional, but joint communication of their difcoveries to the public, the greateft advantage would thence accrue to the fcience.

THE bufinefs of philofophy is fo multiplied, that all the books of general philofophical tranfactions cannot be purchafed by many perfons, or read by any perfon. It is high time to *fubdivide* the bufinefs, that every man may have an opportunity of feeing every thing that relates to his own favourite purfuit; and all the various branches of philofophy would find their account in this amicable feparation. Thus the numerous branches of a large overgrown family, in the patriarchal ages, found it neceffary to feparate; and the convenience of the whole, and the ftrength, and increafe of each branch were promoted by the feparation. Let the youngeft daughter of the fcience fet the example to the reft, and fhow that fhe thinks herfelf confiderable enough to make her appearance in the world without the company of her fifters.

BUT before this general feparation, let each collect together every thing that belongs to her, and march off with her whole ftock. To drop the allufion: let hiftories be written of all that has been done in every particular branch of fcience, and let the whole be feen

at one view. And when once the entire progrefs, and prefent ftate of every fcience fhall
be fully and fairly exhibited, I doubt not but
we fhall fee a new and capital *æra* commence
in the hiftory of all the fciences. Such an
eafy, full, and comprehenfive view of what
has been done hitherto could not fail to give
new life to philofophical inquiries. It would
fuggeft an infinity of new experiments, and
would undoubtedly greatly accelerate the progrefs of knowledge; which is at prefent retarded, as it were, by its own weight, and
the mutal entanglement of its feveral parts.

I WILL juft throw out a farther hint, of
what, I think, might be favourable to the
increafe of philofophical knowledge. At prefent there are, in different countries in Europe, large incorporate focieties, with funds
for promoting philofophical knowledge in
general. Let philofophers now begin to fubdivide themfelves, and enter into fmaller com-
binations. Let the feveral companies make
fmall funds, and appoint a director of experiments. Let every member have a right to
appoint the trial of experiments in fome proportion to the fum he fubfcribes, and let a periodical account be publifhed of the refult of
them all, fuccefsful or unfuccefsful. In this
manner, the powers of all the members
would be united and increafed. Nothing
would be left untried, which could be com-
paffed at a moderate expence, and it being
one perfon's bufinefs to attend to thefe experiments, they would be made, and reported
without

without lofs of time. Moreover, as all in-
corporations in thefe fmaller focieties fhould
be avoided, they would be encouraged only
in proportion as they were found to be ufeful;
and fuccefs in fmaller things would excite
them to attempt greater.

I by no means difapprove of large, general
and incorporated focieties. They have their
peculiar ufes too; but we fee by experience,
that they are apt to grow too large and their
forms are too flow for the difpatch of the *mi-
nutiæ* of bufinefs, in the prefent multifarious
ftate of philofophy. Let recourfe be had to
rich incorporated focieties, to defray the expence of experiments, to which the funds of
fmaller focieties fhall be unequal. Let their
tranfactions contain a fummary of the more
important difcoveries, collected from the
fmaller periodical publications. Let them, by
rewards, and other methods, encourage thofe
who diftinguifh themfelves in the inferior focieties; and thus give a general attention to
the whole bufinefs of philofophy.

I wish all the incorporated philofophical
focieties in Europe would join their funds (and
I wifh they were fufficient for the purpofe) to
fit out fhips for the complete difcovery of the
face of the earth, and for many capital experiments which can only be made in fuch extenfive voyages.

Princes will never do this great bufinefs
to any purpofe. The fpirit of adventure feems
to be totally extinct in the prefent race of
merchants. This difcovery is a grand defide-

b 2 ratum

ratum in fcience; and where may this pure and noble enthufiafm for fuch difcoveries be expected but among philofophers, men uninfluenced by motives either of policy or gain? Let us think ourfelves happy if princes give no obftruction to fuch defigns. Let them fight for the countries when they are difcovered, and let merchants fcramble for the advantage that may be made of them. It will be an acquifition to philofophers if the feat of war be removed fo far from the feat of fcience; and frefh room will be given to the exertion of genius in trade, when the old beaten track is deferted, when the old fyftem of traffic is unhinged, and when new and more extenfive plans of commerce take place. I congratulate the prefent race of philofophers on. what is doing by the Englifh court in this way *; for with whatever view expeditions into the South Seas are made, they cannot but be favourable to philofophy.

NATURAL PHILOSOPHY is a fcience which more efpecially requires the aid of wealth. Many others require nothing but what a man's own reflection may furnifh him with. They who cultivate them find within themfelves every thing they want. But experimental philofophy is not fo independent. Nature will not be put out of her way, and fuffer her materials to be thrown into all that variety of fituations which philofophy requires, in order to difcover her wonderful powers, with-

* Written in the year 1756.

out

out trouble and expence. Hence the patronage of the great is effential to the flourifhing ftate of this fcience. Others may project great improvements, but they only have the power of carrying them into execution.

BESIDES, they are the higher claffes of men which are moft interefted in the extenfion of all kinds of natural knowledge; as they are moft able to avail themfelves of any difcoveries, which lead to the felicity and embellifhment of human life. Almoft all the elegancies of life are the produce of thofe polite arts, which could have had no exiftence without natural fcience, and which receive daily improvements from the fame fource. From the great and the opulent, therefore, thefe fciences have a natural claim for protection; and it is evidently their intereft not to fuffer promifing inquiries to be fufpended for want of the means of profecuting them.

BUT other motives, befides this felfifh one, may reafonably be fuppofed to attach perfons in the higher ranks of life to the fciences; motives more exalted, and flowing from the moft extenfive benevolence. From Natural Philofophy have flowed all thofe great inventions, by means of which mankind in general are able to fubfift with more eafe, and in greater numbers upon the face of the earth. Hence arife the capital advantages of men above brutes, and of civilization above barbarity. And by thefe fciences alfo it is, that the views of the human mind itfelf are enlarged, and our common nature improved and ennobled. It is for the honour of the

fpecies,

species, therefore, that these sciences should be cultivated with the utmost attention.

AND of whom may these enlarged views, comprehensive of such great objects, be expected, but of those whom divine providence has raised above the rest of mankind. Being free from most of the cares peculiar to individuals, they may embrace the interests of the whole species, feel for the wants of mankind, and be concerned to support the dignity of human nature.

GLADLY would I indulge the hope, that we shall soon see these motives operating in a more extensive manner than they have hitherto done; that by the illustrious example of a few, a taste for natural science will be excited in many, in whom it will operate the most effectually to the advantage of science and of the world; and that all kinds of philosophical inquiries will, henceforward, be conducted with more spirit, and with more success than ever.

WERE I to pursue this subject, it would carry me far beyond the reasonable bounds of a preface. I shall therefore conclude with mentioning that sentiment, which ought to be uppermost in the mind of every philosopher, whatever be the immediate object of his pursuit; that speculation is only of use as it leads to *practice*, that the immediate use of natural science is the power it gives us over nature, by means of the knowledge we acquire of its laws; whereby human life is, in its present state, made more comfortable and happy; but that the greatest, and noblest

use

use of philosophical speculation is the discipline of the heart, and the opportunity it affords of inculcating benevolent and pious sentiments upon the mind.

A 'PHILOSOPHER ought to be something greater, and better than another man. The contemplation of the works of God should give a sublimity to his virtue, should expand his benevolence, extinguish every thing mean, base, and selfish in his nature, give a dignity to all his sentiments, and teach him to aspire to the moral perfections of the great author of all things. What great and exalted beings would philosophers be, would they but let the objects about which they are conversant have their proper moral effect upon their minds! A life spent in the contemplation of the productions of divine power, wisdom, and goodness, would be a life of devotion. The more we see of the wonderful structure of the world, and of the laws of nature, the more clearly do we comprehend their admirable uses, to make all the percipent creation happy: a sentiment, which cannot but fill the heart with unbounded love, gratitude, and joy.

EVEN every thing painful and disagreeable in the world appears to a philosopher, upon a more attentive examination, to be excellently provided, as a remedy of some greater inconvenience, or a necessary means of a much greater happiness; so that, from this elevated point of view, he sees all temporary evils and inconveniences to vanish, in the glorious prospect of the greater good to which they are subservient. Hence he is able to venerate and

rejoice

rejoice in God, not only in the bright fun-
fhine, but alfo in the darkeft fhades of nature,
whereas vulgar minds are apt to be difcon-
certed with the appearance of evil.

Nor is the cultivation of piety ufeful to us
only as *men,* it is even ufeful to us as *philofophers:* and as true philofophy tends to promote piety, fo a generous and manly piety is
reciprocally, fubfervient to the purpofes of philofophy; and this both in a direct and indirect
manner. While we keep in view the great
final caufe of all the parts and the laws of nature, we have fome clue, by which to trace the
efficient caufe. This is moft of all obvious in
that part of philofophy which refpects the animal creation. As the great and excellent Dr.
Hartley obferves. " Since this world is a
" fyftem of benevolence, and confequently its
" author the object of unbounded love and a-
" doration, benevolence and piety are our on-
" ly true guides in our inquiries into it; the
" only keys which will unlock the myfteries
" of nature, and clues which lead through her
" labyrinths. Of this all branches of natural
" hiftory, and natural philofophy afford abun-
" dant inftances. In all thefe inquiries, let the
" inquirer take it for granted previoufly, that
" every thing is right, and the beft that can be
" *ceteris manentibus*; that is, let him, with
" a pious confidence, feek for benevolent
" purpofes, and he will be always directed to
" the right road; and after a due continuance
" in it, attain to fome new and valuable truth;
" whereas every other principle and motive of
" examination, being foreign to the great plan
" on

" on which the univerfe is conftructed, muft lead
" into endlefs mazes, errors, and perplexities*."

WITH refpect to the indirect ufe of piety, it
muft be obferved, that the tranquility, and
chearfulnefs of mind, which refults from devotion forms an excellent temper for conducting philofophical inquiries; tending to make
them both more pleafant, and more fuccefsful.
The fentiments of religion and piety tend to
cure the mind of envy, jealoufy, conceit, and
every other mean paffion, which both difgrace
the lovers of fcience, and retard the progrefs of
it, by laying an undue bias upon the mind,
and diverting it from the calm purfuit of truth.

LASTLY, let it be remembered, that a tafte
for fcience, pleafing, and even honourable as
it is, is not one of the higheft paffions of our
nature, that the pleafures it furnifhes are even
but one degree above thofe of fenfe, and therefore that temperance is requifite in all fcienti-
fical purfuits. Befides the duties of every man's
proper ftation in life, which ought ever to be
held facred and inviolate, the calls of piety,
common friendfhip, and many other avoca-
tions ought generally to be heard before that
of ftudy. It is, therefore, only a fmall fhare of
their leifure, that moft men can be juftified in
giving to the purfuit of fcience; though this
fhare is more or lefs, in proportion to a man's
fituation in life, his natural abilities, and the opportunity he has for conducting his inquiries.

I SHALL conclude with another paffage from
Dr. Hartley to this purpofe. " Though the pur-

* Hartley's Obfervations on Man, Vol. ii. p. 245.

fuit

" suit of truth be an entertainment and em-
" ployment suitable to our rational natures, and
" a duty to him who is the fountain of all
" knowledge and truth, yet we muſt make fre-
" quent intervals and interruptions ; elſe the
" ſtudy of ſcience, without a view to God and
" our duty, and from a vain deſire of applauſe,
" will get poſſeſſion of our hearts, engroſs
" them wholly, and by taking deeper root
" than the purſuit of vain amuſements, be-
" come, in the end, a much more dangerous,
" and obſtinate evil than that. Nothing can
" eaſily exceed the vain-glory, ſelf-conceit,
" arrogance, emulation, and envy, that are
" found in the eminent profeſſors of theſciences,
" Mathematics, Natural Philoſophy, and even
" Divinity itſelf. Temperance in theſe ſtudies
" is, therefore, evidently required, both in or-
" der to check the riſe of ſuch ill paſſions, and
" to give room for the cultivation of other eſ-
" ſential parts of our natures. It is with theſe
" pleaſures as with the ſenſible ones ; our ap-
" petites muſt not be made the meaſure of
" our indulgence, but we ought to refer all
" to a higher rule.

" But when the purſuit of truth is directed
" by this higher rule, and entered upon with a
" view to the glory of God, and the good of
" mankind, there is no employment more
" worthy of our natures, or more conducive to
" their purification and perfection *."

* Hartley's Obſervations on Man, Vol. ii. p. 255, &c.

Warrington,
    March 1767.

                                    P R E-

PREFACE

SECOND EDITION.

THE method I took to diftinguifh the books I had feen from thofe I had not feen, in the catalogue of electric authors, fub-joined to the firft edition of this work, has been attended with the advantage I promifed myfelf from it; feveral perfons, who were in poffeffion of the books I had not feen, having communicated them to me; and I have care-fully perufed them, and digefted their con-tents into this fecond edition. Far the greater part of thefe new authors, the reader will per-ceive by the catalogue, were German, and wrote in high Dutch, a language with which, I believe, the literati of this country are but little acquainted, which might be the reafon why neither myfelf nor my friends had ever heard of them before. Though the new ma-terials they have fupplied cannot be faid to be of the firft importance, many of the articles are very curious, and I hope the reader, as well as myfelf, will think that they have well repaid me for my trouble in learning the language.

IT is certainly much to be regretted that philofophers have not one common language; but neither the theory of language in general, nor the nature and analogies of things to be ex-

preffed

preſſed by it are yet ſufficiently underſtood, to enable us to contrive a new and philoſophical one, which might be eaſily learnt, and would be completely adequate to all the purpoſes of ſcience; and Latin is a language which perſons of a philoſophical turn of mind have ſeldom leiſure to make themſelves ſo much maſters of, as to write in it with that elegance which the taſte of the age requires. Beſides, books written in Latin are but little read, at leaſt, in England; and therefore could have no ſale with us. Theſe circumſtances make it the more neceſſary, that there ſhould be, in every country, perſons poſſeſſed of a competent knowledge of foreign languages, who ſhould be attentive to the progreſs of ſcience abroad, and communicate to their countrymen all uſeful diſcoveries as they are made.

BESIDES the improvements in the hiſtory, and other parts of this work, the reader will find, in this edition, an addition of three intire ſections of original experiments. All that are of the leaſt conſequence are printed, and ſold ſeparately, for the benefit of thoſe who purchaſed the firſt edition.

LEEDS, Jan. 1769.

ADVER-

PREFACE

THIRD EDITION.

TO the fecond edition of this work I made confiderable additions, by an account of fuch difcoveries as had been made in the interval between that and the firft edition; and thefe *additions* I publifhed feparately for the ufe of thofe who had purchafed the firft edition. But in this edition I have inferted no account of any thing that was done after the publication of the fecond, becaufe I referve an account of them for a *Continuation of the Hiftory*, which, if God fpare my life, I propofe to write fome years hence, when I hope there will be a greater ftock of materials for it.

I HAVE, however, confiderably improved this edition, by a fuller account of difcoveries made by feveral foreigners, in confequence of becoming poffeffed of the original publications, whereas before I was obliged to content myfelf with quoting them at fecond hand. The reader will therefore find a much larger account of what was done by the Academicians del Cimento, by Mr. Du Fay, and fome others. The alterations of the references, or the additions to them, will generally fhow where I have done this *.

* In the account of the experiments of Mr. Monnier, thinking proper to change the place of one of the articles, I neglect-

ed

To the account I have given of the reception of Dr. Franklin's fyftem in France, I would add what I have fince been informed of, viz. that Mr. Le Roi, fecretary to the Royal Academy of Sciences, who has diftinguifhed himfelf by his attention to various branches of philofophy, was the firft who adopted this theory in that country, and became an open and ftrenuous advocate for it. He alfo demonftrated the principles of it by original experiments ; an account of which is contained in two valuable Memoirs publifhed among thofe of the Royal Academy. In the former of thefe he proves, that there is an invariable diftinction between the appearance of electric light at the points of metalic bodies as *connected with*, or *prefented to* the prime conductor, or infulated rubber ; fo that what is called the *pencil*, is uniformly the appearance when the pointed wire is electrified pofitively, and the *ftar* when it is negative. See Ac. Par. 1753. In another memoir for the year 1755, he fhews, by ufing a globe of fulphur, that the refinous electricity of Mr. Du Fay is the very fame thing with the negative power of Dr. Franklin. Though the fame things had been demonftrated by others, and efpecially Father Beccaria, thefe philofophers made the difcovery independent of each other, and therefore have equal merit.

ed to cancel the former account, which the reader will pleafe to overlook, or expunge, from p. 145. The fuller account, from the original, is at p. 155. I mention this chiefly, that if any foreigner fhould tranflate from this edition, he may be admonifhed to omit the former paragraph.

WITH-

WITHOUT entering into particulars, I shall take the liberty to acquaint the reader, that, in the sixtieth volume of the Philosophical Transactions, there are two papers of mine on electrical subjects, one on what I have called the *lateral explosion*, and the other on the *conducting power of charcoal*.

IN the former I shew that, in certain circumstances, an electric spark detaches itself from the circuit of an explosion to bodies placed near it, and returns to it again at the same instant. Through the air I have made this spark three-fourths of an inch in length, and in vacuo more than twelve inches.

IN the other paper I shew, among other properties of charcoal, that its conducting power depends entirely on the degree of *heat* with which it is made. Some pieces do not conduct electricity at all, others as perfectly as silver or gold, and pieces of the former quality are always convertible into those of the latter, by the application of more heat.

ALSO, in my *observations on different kinds of air*, the reader will find, that I have demonstrated that the electric matter is, or contains phlogiston; by shewing that it affects all kinds of air as phlogiston does; particularly diminishing common air one fourth, and making it noxious, so as to make no effervescence with nitrous air.

IT may not be amiss to inform the reader, that the first translation of this work was into French, by a person who seems to have done it with no other view than to have an

oppor-

opportunity of expreſſing his diſlike of Dr. Franklin's ſyſtem, and of myſelf as the abettor of it, and of defending that of Mr. Nollet. In the *notes*, which all other tranſlators cenſure as in the higheſt degree illiberal, he repreſents me as being, beyond all bounds, partial to my own countrymen, and particularly unjuſt to the French; a charge from which I thought myſelf intirely exempt. I confeſs, however, that, inadvertently, I did give ſome handle to this cenſure in one paſſage, which I have therefore correcected in this edition. I have the pleaſure to be informed that a new tranſlation of this work, from this laſt edition, is undertaken by the excellent tranſlator of Dr. Franklin's Philoſophical writings, lately publiſhed. This gentleman will, I doubt not, do ample juſtice both to myſelf and to the ſubjecect.

CALNE, March 1775.

To the BINDER,

Place Plate I. *at the end of* Vol. I.
—— Plate II. *&c. at the end of* Vol. II.

THE
CONTENTS.

PART I.

THE HISTORY OF ELECTRICITY.

VOL. I.   c   PE-

PERIOD VIII.

PERIOD IX.

PERIOD X.

SEC.

SEC.

THE

THE
HISTORY
AND PRESENT STATE OF
ELECTRICITY.

PART I.

THE HISTORY OF ELECTRICITY.

PERIOD I.

EXPERIMENTS AND DISCOVERIES IN ELEC-
TRICITY PRIOR TO THOSE OF MR.
HAUKSBEE.

THE hiſtory of philoſophy contains
nothing earlier than the obſervation,
that yellow amber, when rubbed, has
the power of attracting light bodies. Thales
of Miletus, the father of the Ionic philoſophy, who flouriſhed about ſix hundred years
before Chriſt, was ſo much ſtruck with this
property of amber, that he imagined it was
animated. But the firſt writer, who expreſsly
mentions this ſubſtance, is Theophraſtus, who
flouriſhed about the year 300 before Chriſt.
He ſays, in his book concerning precious
ſtones, ſect. 53, that amber (which he ſuppoſes
to be a native foſſil) has the ſame property
of attracting light bodies with the lyncurium;
which, he obſerves, attracts not only ſtraws,
and ſmall pieces of ſticks, but even thin pieces

B   of

of copper and iron. What he fays farther of
the lyncurium will be related under the article
of the *tourmalin*, which Dr. Watfon has, in
a manner, proved to be the fame fubftance.

FROM ηλεκτρον, the Greek name for amber,
is derived the term ELECTRICITY, which is
now extended to fignify not only the power
of attracting light bodies inherent in amber,
but other powers connected with it, in whatever bodies they are fuppofed to refide, or to
whatever bodies they may be communicated.

THE attractive nature of amber is occafionally mentioned by Pliny, and other later naturalifts ; particularly by Gaffendus, Kenelm
Digby, and Sir Thomas Brown ; but excepting the electricity of the fubftance called *jet* *,
the difcovery of which was very late (though I
have not been able to find its author) no advances were made in electricity till the fubject
was undertaken by William Gilbert, a native
of Colchefter, and a phyfician at London ;
who, in his excellent Latin treatife *de magnete*,
publifhed in the year 1600, relates a great
variety of electrical experiments. Confidering the time in which this author wrote, and
how little was known of the fubject before
him, his difcoveries may be juftly deemed
confiderable, though they appear trifling when
compared with thofe which have been made
fince his time.

To him we owe a great augmentation of

* Mr. Bofe is faid to have fhown, that the *agate* was very
early known to have electric powers. Dantzick Memoirs,
Vol. I. p. 179.

the

the lift of electric bodies, as alfo of the bodies on which electrics can act; and he has carefully noted feveral capital circumftances relating to the manner of their action, though his theory of electricity was very imperfect, as might be expected.

AMBER and jet were, as I obferved before, the only fubftances which, before the time of Gilbert, were known to have the property of attracting light bodies when rubbed; but he found the fame property in the *diamond, fapphire, carbuncle, iris, amethyft, opal, vincentina, Briftol ftone, beryl,* and *cryftal.* He alfo obferves that *glafs,* efpecially that which is clear and tranfparent, has the fame property; likewife all *factitious gems,* made of glafs or cryftal; *glafs of antimony,* moft *fparry fubftances,* and *belemnites.* Laftly, he concludes his catalogue of electric fubftances with *fulphur, maftic, fealing wax* made of gum lac tinged with various colours, *hard rofin, fal gem, talc,* and *roche alum.* Rofin, he faid, poffeffed this property but in a fmall degree, and the three laft mentioned fubftances, only when the air was clear and free from moifture.

ALL thefe fubftances, he obferves, attracted not only ftraws, but all metals, all kinds of wood, ftones, earth, water, oil; in fhort, whatever is folid, and the object of our fenfes. But he imagined that air, flame, bodies ignited, and all matter which was extremely rare was not fubject to this attraction. Grofs fmoke, he found, was attracted very fenfibly, but that which was attenuated very little.

FRICTION,

FRICTION, he fays, is, in general, neceffary to excite the virtue of thefe fubftances; though he had one large and fmooth piece of amber which would act without friction. But with refpect to this he probably deceived himfelf. The moft effectual friction, he obferved to be that which was light and quick ; and he found that electrical appearances were ftrongeft when the air was dry, and the wind north or eaft, at which time electric fubftances would act ten minutes after excitation. But he fays, that a moift air, or a foutherly wind almoft annihilates the electric virtue. The fame effect he alfo obferved from the interpofition of moifture of any kind, as from the breath, and many other fubftances, but not always from the interpofition of farfnet. He fays that light and pure oil, fprinkled upon electrics, after excitation, did not obftruct their virtue ; but that brandy, or fpirit of wine, did. He alfo fays, that cryftal, talc, glafs, and all other electrics loft their virtue after being burnt or roafted. But this was, in fome meafure, a miftake. The heat of the fun, collected by a burning glafs, he fays, is fo far from exciting amber, and other electrics, that it impairs the virtue of them all; though, when electrics have been excited, they will retain their virtue longer in the fun-fhine than in the fhade.

MOST of the experiments of this author were made with long thin pieces of metal, and other fubftances, fufpended freely on their centers, to the extremities of which he prefented the electrics he had excited. His experiments

periments on water were made by prefenting a round drop of it upon a dry fubftance to the excited electric; and it is remarkable, that he obferved the fame conical figure of the electrified drops which Mr. Grey afterwards difcovered, and which will be related more at large in its proper place. Gilbert concluded, that air was not affected by electrical attraction, becaufe the flame of a candle was not: for the flame, he fays, would be difturbed if the air had the leaft motion given to it.

GILBERT imagined that electrical attraction was performed in the fame manner as the attraction of cohefion. Two drops of water, he obferved, rufh together when they are brought into contact; and electrics, he fays, are virtually brought into contact with the bodies they act upon, by means of their effluvia, excited by friction.

AMONG other differences between electric and magnetic attraction, fome of which are very juft, and others whimfical enough, he fays, that magnetic bodies rufh together mutually; whereas in electrical attraction it is only the electric that exerts any power. He obferves alfo particularly, that in magnetifm there is both attraction and repulfion, but in electricity only the former, and never the latter *.

SUCH were the difcoveries of our countryman Gilbert, who may juftly be called the father of modern electricity, though it be

* Gilbert de magnete, Lib. 2. Cap. 2.

true

true that he left his child in its very infancy.

LORD BACON, in his Phyfiological Remains, gives a catalogue of bodies attractive
and not attractive; but it differs in nothing
worth mentioning from that of Gilbert, and
he does not feem to have made any obfervations of his own relating to the fubject.

ABOUT 30 years after Gilbert, NICOLAUS
CABÆUS, a Jefuit at Ferrara, repeated his experiments; and found that *white wax*, almoft
all the *gums*, and *crude gypfum* were to be
ranked among electric bodies *.

THESE remarkable phenomena relating to
amber, and other electric fubftances, did not
efcape the attention of the inquifitive and fagacious Mr. Boyle, who flourifhed about the
year 1670. He made fome addition to the
catalogue of electric fubftances, and attended
to fome circumftances relating to electrical
attraction, which had efcaped the obfervation
of philofophers who lived before him.

HE found that the hard cake which remains
after evaporating good turpentine was electrical, as alfo the hard mafs which remains
after diftilling petroleum and fpirit of nitre,
glafs of lead, the caput mortuum of amber,
and the cornelian; but he could not find that
property in the emerald, and he thought that
glafs poffeffed it but in a very low degree.

HE found, that the electricity of all bodies
capable of having it excited in them was in-

---

* Dantzick Memoirs, Vol. 1. p. 180.

creafed by wiping, and warming them, previous to their being rubbed. By this means
he made an electric body, no bigger than
a pea, move a fteel needle, which was freely
poifed, three minutes after he had left off rubbing it. He alfo found, that it was ufeful to
have the furfaces of electric bodies made very
fmooth, except in the cafe of one diamond,
on which he tried fome experiments ; which,
though it was rough, was, he fays, poffeffed
of a ftronger electric virtue than any polifhed
one he had ever met with.

HE obferved that excited electrics would
attract all kinds of bodies promifcuoufly,
whether electric or not; that excited amber,
for inftance, would attract both powder of
amber, and fmall pieces of it; differing, as
he takes notice, from the property of the
load-ftone, which acts only on one kind of
matter. He found, that his electrics would
attract fmoke very eafily, and takes fome
pains to account for their not fenfibly attracting flame, which Gilbert excepted from
the bodies attracted by electricity.

THESE attractions, he found, did not depend upon the air : for he obferved that they
took place in vacuo. He fufpended a piece
of excited amber over a light body in a glafs
receiver, and faw, that when a vacuum was
made, and the amber let down near the light
body, it was attracted, as if it had been in
the open air *. But S. Beccaria afferts, that

---

* Hiftoire de l'ectricité.

there

there is no electrical attraction in a perfect vacuum.

Mr. Boyle made an experiment to try whether an excited electric was acted upon by other bodies, as ftrongly as it acted upon them, and it fucceeded : for, fufpending his excited electric, he faw that it was fenfibly moved by the approach of any other body. We fhould now be furprifed that any perfon fhould not have concluded *a priori*, that if an electric body attracted other bodies, it muft, in return, be attracted by them, action and reaction being univerfally equal to one another. But it muft be confidered, that this axiom was not fo well underftood in Mr. Boyle's time, nor till it was afterwards explained in its full latitude by Sir Ifaac Newton *

Mr. Boyle got a glimpfe, as we may fay, of the electric light: for he found that a curious diamond, which Mr. Clayton brought from Italy, gave light in the dark, when it was rubbed againft any kind of ftuff; and he found that, by the fame treatment, it became electrical. He alfo obferved the fame property in feveral other diamonds †.

These experiments of Mr. Boyle's, we fee, relate only to a few circumftances attending the fimple property of electrical attraction. The neareft approach that he made to the difcovery of electrical repulfion was his obferving, that light bodies, as feathers, &c. would

* Boyle's Mechanical production of electricity.
† Secondat's hiftory of electricity, p. 141.

cling

cling to his fingers, and other fubftances, after they had been attracted by his electrics. He had feen but little of the electric light, and little imagined what aftonifhing effects would be afterwards produced by the fame wonderful power, and how. large a field he was opening for philofophical fpeculation in future times.

Mr. Boyle's theory of electrical attraction was, that the electric emitted a glutinous effluvium, which laid hold of fmall bodies in its way, and, in its return to the body which emitted it, carried them back with it. One James Hartman, whofe account of amber is publifhed in the Philofophical Tranfactions *, pretends to prove by experiment, that electrical attraction was really owing to the emiffion of glutinous particles. He took two electric fubftances, viz. pieces of colophonia, and from one of them made a diftillation of a black balfam, and thereby deprived it of its attractive power. He fays, that the electric, which was not diftilled, retained its fatty fubftance, whereas the other was, by diftillation, reduced to a mere *caput mortuum*, and retained no degree of its bituminous fat. In confequence of this hypothefis, he gives it as his opinion, that amber attracts light bodies more powerfully than other fubftances, becaufe it emits oily and tenacious effluvia more copioufly than they do.

Contemporary with Mr. Boyle was Otto

Guericke,

Guericke, Burgomafter of Magdebourg, and
the celebrated inventor of the air-pump, who
is likewife intitled to a diftinguifhed place a-
mong the firft improvers of electricity.

THIS philofopher made his experiments
with a globe of fulphur, made by melting
that fubftance in a hollow globe of glafs, and
afterwards breaking the glafs from off it. He
little imagined that the glafs globe itfelf, with
or without the fulphur, would have anfwered
his purpofe as well. This globe of fulphur
he mounted upon an axis, and whirled it in a
wooden frame, rubbing it at the fame time
with his hand; and by this means he performed all the electrical experiments which
were known before his time.

HIS was the difcovery, that a body once
attracted by an excited electric was repelled
by it, and not attracted again till it had been
touched by fome other body. In this manner
he kept a feather a long time fufpended in
the air above his fulphur globe; but he obferved, that if he drove it near a linen thread,
or the flame of a candle, it inftantly retreated
to the globe, without having been in contact
with any fenfible body.

NEITHER the found, nor the light produced
by the excitation of his globe, efcaped the notice of this accurate philofopher, though he
feems not to have obferved them in a very
great degree: for he was obliged to hold his
ear near the globe to perceive the hiffing
found of the electric fire; and he compares the
light which it gave in the fame circumftances

to

to that which is feen when fugar is pounded in the dark.

But the moft remarkable experiments of this philofopher were two, which depend upon a property of the electric fluid that has not been illuftrated till within thefe late years; viz. that bodies immerged in electric atmof-pheres are themfelves electrified, and with an electricity oppofite to that of the atmofphere. Threads fufpended within a fmall diftance of his excited globe, he obferved to be often re-pelled by his finger brought near them, and that a feather repelled by the globe always turned the fame face towards it, like the moon with refpect to the earth. This laft experiment feems to have been wholly over-looked by later electricians, though it is a very curious one, and may be made with fo much eafe *.

To the members of the Academy *Del Ci-mento*, whofe labours contributed very con-fiderably to the advancement of various branches of natural knowledge, we are in-debted for feveral obfervations on the fubject of electricity.

They rank the electric bodies which they examined in the following order, according to the ftrength of their attractive power, *yel-low amber*, *fealing wax*, the *rofe diamond*, and of the fame ftrength with this the *white fapphire*, *emerald*, *white topaz*, *fpinelle*, and *ruby balleis*. After thefe they ranked all *tranf-*

* Experimenta Magdeburgica, Lib 4. Cap. 15.

parent

parent gems, and next to the precious ſtones
they placed *glaſs*, *cryſtal*, with *white and black
amber*, the power of all which they ſay is very
weak.

YELLOW amber appearing to them to have
the greateſt power of all electric ſubſtances,
they made all their experiments with it.
Among other things, they found that it attracted *ſmoke*, but not *flame*; and upon this occaſion they obſerved the curious phenomenon
of a *viſible electric atmoſphere*, which was afterwards re-diſcovered, and exhibited to more
advantage by Dr. Franklin. For they ſay,
that that part of the ſmoke which is attracted
by the amber remains, and unites itſelf to it,
like a ſmall cloud, and as the amber cools, it
riſes in ſmoke again, and vaniſhes. At the
ſame time they alſo obſerved a pretty curious
effect of electrical repulſion ; for they ſay
that part of the ſmoke was thrown off from
the amber, as from a looking-glaſs.

FLAME, they obſerved, was ſo far from being attracted by the amber, that, upon being
preſented to it, it preſently deprived it of all
its attractive power ; for if, after it had taken
up any thing, it was held to the flame, it would
immediately let it go again.

THEY found that all *fluid ſubſtances* were
ſenſible to the attractive power of amber, and
among the reſt even *mercury* ; and that when
the excited amber was preſented to a large
ſuperficies of any liquor, it roſe towards it in
a ſmall pointed eminence; an effect which,
they ſay, is beſt obſerved in *oil* or *balſam*. This
obſerva-

obfervation, we fhall find, was afterwards
made again, and more particularly attended
to by Mr. Grey *.

THESE gentlemen took a great deal of pains
to try whether amber would attract in *vacuo*,
but to no purpofe, not being able to exclude
the air, fo as to rub the amber in vacuo, and
apply it to the light body they had provided,
with any effect; but neither could they make
the amber act in the fame confined fituation
even when the air was not at all excluded †.

THEY alfo found, with Mr. Boyle, that a
piece of excited amber, fufpended by a thread,
was attracted by other bodies prefented to it,
juft like a magnetical needle ‡.

LASTLY, thefe gentlemen found that when
the excited amber was dipped in fome liquors,
it immediately loft its power, but not after
being dipped in others. In this laft clafs they
enumerate feveral kinds of *oil*, *tallow*, *fat*,
and *butter*, and it is now found that the conducting power of thefe fubftances is fo fmall,
that they are more properly claffed among the
non-conductors §.

I SHALL in the next place obferve, that Mr.
Boyle, Otto Guericke, and thefe gentlemen,
made their experiments about the fame time,
and feemed to have derived no advantage
whatever from each other's labours.

* Effays on Natural Experiments, tranflated by Walker, p.
128, &c.
† Ib. p. 43.
‡ Ib. p. 129.
§ Effays on Natural Experiments, tranflated by Walker, p.
131.

A

A MUCH finer appearance of electric light than that which Otto Guericke's sulphur globe exhibited was observed by Dr. Wall. The account of it is published in the Philosophical Transactions *.

MAKING experiments upon artificial phosphorus, which he took to be an animal oil coagulated with a mineral acid, he was led to conjecture that amber, which he supposed to be a mineral oil coagulated with a mineral volatile acid, might be a natural phosphorus; and with this view he began to make experiments upon it, the result of which, being very curious and surprising, it will be most agreeable to my readers to see in the very words of the observer himself.

" I FOUND," says he, " by gently rub-
" bing a well polished piece of amber with
" my hand, in the dark, that it produced a
" light: whereupon I got a pretty large piece
" of amber, which I caused to be made long
" and taper, and drawing it gently through my
" hand, being very dry, it afforded a consider-
" able light.

" I THEN used many kinds of soft animal
" substances, and found that none did so well
" as wool. And now new phenomena of-
" fered themselves: for, upon drawing the
" piece of amber swiftly through the woollen
" cloth, and squeezing it pretty hard with
" my hand, a prodigious number of little
" cracklings were heard, and every one of these

* Phil. Transf. abridged, Vol. 4. p. 275.

" produced

" produced a little flash of light; but when
" the amber was drawn gently and slightly
" through the cloth, it produced only a light
" but no crackling; but by holding one's
" fingers at a little distance from the amber,
" a large crackling is produced, with a great
" flash of light succeeding it. And, what to
" me is very surprising, upon its eruption, it
" strikes the finger very sensibly, wheresoever
" applied, with a push or a puff, like wind.
" The crackling is full as loud as charcoal on
" fire, and five or six cracklings, or more,
" according to the quickness of placing the
" finger, have been produced from one single
" friction, light always succeeding each of
" them.

" Now I make no question, but upon
" using a longer and larger piece of amber,
" both the cracklings and light would be
" much greater, because I never yet found
" any crackling from the head of my cane,
" though it is a pretty large one. This light
" and crackling seems, in some degree, to re-
" present thunder and lightning.'

AFTER reciting this experiment, he gives
it as his opinion, that all, or most bodies,
which have electricity, give light, and that it
is the light which is the cause of their being
electrical. He found that light could also be
produced by rubbing jet, red sealing wax,
made with gum lac and cinnabar, and the diamond. He even imagined he could distinguish true from false diamonds by this test.

NOTWITHSTANDING Dr. Wall made this
beautiful

beautiful difcovery, as he imagined (for he feems not to have feen what Otto Guericke had written) of light proceeding from amber and other electric bodies, we fee that he laboured under a great deal of confufion and mifapprehenfion with refpect to it. He fays, that one thing appeared ftrange to him in the courfe of thefe experiments, which was, that though, upon friction with wool in the day time, the cracklings feemed to be full as many and as large, yet that, by all the trials which he made, very little light appeared, though in the darkeft room. He fays that the beft time for making thefe experiments is when the fun is 18° below the horizon, and that when the fun was fo low, though the moon fhone ever fo bright, the light was the fame as in the darkeft room, which made him chufe to call it a noctiluca.

It is remarkable that Dr. Wall compares the light and the crackling of his amber to thunder and lightning: fo early was a fimilarity between the effects of electricity and lightning obferved. But little was it imagined that the refemblance between them extended any farther than to appearances and effects. That the caufe was the fame in both, was a difcovery referved for Dr. Franklin, in a much later period.

The great Sir Ifaac Newton, though he by no means makes a principal figure in the hiftory of electricity, yet made fome electrical obfervations which engaged the attention of his philofophical friends; and which,
independent

independent of their being made by him, do
well deferve to be tranfmitted to pofterity.
They feem to fhew, that he was the firft who
obferved, that excited glafs attracted light
bodies on the fide oppofite to that on which
it was rubbed.

HAVING laid upon the table a round piece
of glafs, about two inches broad, in a brafs
ring, fo that the glafs might be one eighth of
an inch from the table, and there rubbing
the glafs brifkly, little fragments of paper laid
on the table, under the glafs, began to be attracted, and move nimbly to and fro. After
he had done rubbing the glafs, the papers
would continue a confiderable time in various
motions; fometimes leaping up to the glafs,
and refting there a while, then leaping down
and refting there, and then leaping up and
down again ; and this fometimes in lines
feemingly perpendicular to the table, fometimes in oblique ones; fometimes alfo leaping up in one arch, and leaping down in another, divers times together, without fenfibly
refting between; fometimes fkipping in a bow
from one part of the glafs to another, without
touching the table, and fometimes hanging by
a corner, and turning often very nimbly, as
if they had been carried about in the midft of
a whirlwind, and being otherwife varioufly
moved, every paper with a different motion.
Upon his fliding his finger on the upper fide
of the glafs, though neither the glafs, nor the
inclofed air below, were moved, yet he obferved, that the papers, as they hung under
C   the

the glafs, would receive fome new motion, inclining this way or that, according as he moved his finger.

SOME of the motions, as that of hanging
by a corner and twirling about, and that of
leaping from one part of the glafs to another
without touching the table happened but feldom ; but, he fays, it made him take the more
notice of them *.

AN account of this experiment Sir Ifaac fent
to the members of the R. Society in the year
1675, defiring it might be tried by them;
and after fome ineffectual attempts, and receiving further inftructions how to make it,
they at length fucceeded, and the thanks of
the fociety were formally returned to him †.

UPON repeating the experiment with fome
variety of circumftances, Sir Ifaac obferves,
that rubbing varioufly, or with various things,
altered the cafe. At one time he rubbed a
glafs four inches broad, and one fourth thick,
with a napkin, twice as much as he ufed to
do with his gown, and nothing would ftir,
and yet prefently after, rubbing with fomething elfe, the motion foon began. After
the glafs had been much rubbed, he thought
the motions were not fo lafting, and the day
following he found the motions fainter, and
more difficult to be excited than at firft ‡.

SIR ISAAC alfo mentions electricity in two
queries annexed to his treatife on Optics, from

* Birch's Hift. of the R. Society, Vol. 3. p. 260, &c.
† Ib. 271.   ‡ Ib. p. 270.

which

which we learn, that he imagined electric bodies when excited emitted an elastic fluid, which freely penetrated glass, and that the emission was performed by the vibratory motions of the parts of the excited bodies *.

PERIOD II.

THE EXPERIMENTS AND DISCOVERIES OF MR. HAUKSBEE.

AFTER Gilbert, Mr. Boyle, and Otto Guericke, Mr. Hauksbee, who wrote in the year 709, diſtinguiſhed himſelf by experiments and diſcoveries in electricity. He firſt obſerved the great electric power of glaſs, the light proceeding from it, and the noiſe occaſioned by it, together with a variety of phenomena relating to electrical attraction and repulſion. He was indefatigable in making experiments, and there are few perſons to whom we are more indebted for a real advancement of this branch of knowledge. This will appear from the following ſuccinct account of his experiments, related not exactly in the order in which he has publiſhed them, but according to their connection. This method I have choſen, as beſt adapted to give the moſt diſtinct view of the whole.

I SHALL firſt relate the experiments he made concerning *electrical attraction and re-*

* Newton's Optics, octavo, p. 314, and 327.

pulſion,

pulfion, in many of which we fhall fee reafon
to admire his ingenious contrivances, and
fhall fee that little was added to his obfervations, till the capital difcovery of a *plus* and
minus electricity by Dr. Watfon and Dr.
Franklin, and the farther illuftration of that
doctrine by Mr. Canton.

THE moft curious of his experiments concerning electrical attraction and repulfion are
thofe which fhew the direction in which thofe
powers are exerted.

HAVING tied threads round a wire hoop,
and brought it near to an excited globe or cylinder, he obferved, that the threads kept a
conftant direction towards the center of the
globe, or towards fome point in the axis of
the cylinder, in every pofition of the hoop;
that this effect would continue for about four
minutes after the whirling of the globe ceafed,
and that the effect was the fame whether the
wire was held above or under the glafs; or
whether the glafs was placed with its axis
parallel, or perpendicular to the horizon.

HE obferved, that the threads pointing towards the center of the globe were attracted
and repelled by a finger prefented to them;
that if the finger, or any other body, was
brought very near the threads, they would
be attracted; but that if it were brought to
the diftance of about an inch, they would be
repelled, the reafon of which difference he
did not feem to underftand *.

* Phyfico-Mechanical Experiments, p. 75.

HE

HE tied threads to the axis of a globe and cylinder, and found that they diverged every way in ftraight lines from the place where they were tied, when the globe was whirled and rubbed. In both cafes, he fays, the threads would be repelled by the finger held on the oppofite fide of the glafs, even without touching the glafs; though they would fometimes fuddenly jump towards it *. He obferved farther, that by blowing with his mouth towards the glafs, at three or four feet diftance, the threads would have a very confiderable motion given to them.

HE found that threads, hanging freely in an unexcited globe, at reft, would be moved by the approach of any excited electric at a confiderable diftance, except in moift weather; which failure he accounts for, by fuppofing the moifture on the furface of the glafs prevented the free paffage of the electric effluvia through it †.

THE varieties he obferved on the appearances and properties of the *electric light*, are even more curious and furprifing than his difcoveries concerning electric attraction and repulfion; and it is fomething remarkable that Mr. Haukfbee's tranfition to electric light was like that of Dr. Wall, viz. from the light of phofphorus.

MR. HAUKSBEE firft produced a confiderable quantity of light by fhaking quick-

* Phyfico-Mechanical Experiments, p. 78.
† Ib. p. 100.

filver

filver in a glafs veffel, out of which the air was exhaufted. Sometimes what he calls ftrange flafhes of pale light were feen darting in a variety of directions, when the mercury was put in motion within an exhaufted receiver *. But the difcovery was probably accidental, and he did not feem, at that time, to know the reafon of the appearance. He called this light the *mercurial phofphorus*, and did not confider the glafs as any way concerned in producing it.

He alfo found, that this appearance of electric light (which he ftill calls the mercurial phofphorus) did not require a very perfect vacuum, nor even a near approach to it †. Nay he fometimes produced that appearance of light by fhaking mercury in a veffel, in which the air was of the fame denfity with the external atmofphere; but ftill he had no idea of the glafs contributing to the phenomenon ‡.

He obferved a ftrong light in vacuo, and a fmall one in the open air, from rubbing amber upon woollen, but feems to have confidered it as any hard body rubbing againft a foft one ‖. He alfo obferved a vivid purple, and afterwards a pale light produced by rubbing glafs upon woollen in vacuo §. He fays that every frefh glafs firft gave a purple, and then a pale light, and that woollen tinctured

---

* Phyfico Mechanical Experiments, p. 12.
† Ib. p. 14.　　　　　　‡ Ib. p. 18.
‖ Ib. p. 26.　　　　　　§ Ib. p. 32.

with

with falt or fpirits produced a new, ftrong, and fulgurating light *.

In the following experiments we find his ideas of electric light much more diftinct, and the appearances the fame that are ufually exhibited by our prefent electrical machines, the ftructure of which, we fhall find to be nearly the fame with thofe which he ufed.

He provided himfelf with a machine in which he could whirl a glafs globe; and he obferved, when the air was extracted out of it, that, upon applying his hand to the globe, a ftrong light appeared on the infide, and, upon letting in the air, he obferved the light on the outfide alfo; but with fome very confiderable differences in its appearances, ftriking upon his fingers, and other bodies held near the globe. He alfo obferved, upon this occafion, that one fourth of an atmofphere in the globe did very little diminifh the light within. It is pleafing to obferve, that the fimilar appearance in this experiment, and that with mercury in vacuo before-mentioned, made him fufpect, though only fufpect, that the light produced in the former cafe proceeded not from the mercury, but from the glafs.

The next experiment is of a very delicate and curious nature. It is not to be wondered at, that Mr. Haukfbee did not underftand the circumftances which contributed to it, as

* Phyfico-Mechanical Experiments, p. 34.

the

the explication of it depends upon principles which were not difcovered till a much later period by Mr. Canton.

HOLDING an exhaufted globe within the effluvia of an excited one, he obferved a light in the exhaufted globe, which prefently died away, if it was kept at reft; but which was revived, and continued very ftrong, if the exhaufted globe was kept in motion. Prefenting an exhaufted tube to the effluvia of an excited globe, it produced what he calls an interrupted flafhing light. He imagined that the exhaufted globe was excited by the attraction of the effluvia from the other globe, fo little did he underftand the true caufe of this curious experiment *. When he fays that light is producible by the effluvia of one glafs falling upon another, he adds; that electric (by which he means attractive) matter, is not to be brought forth by any fuch feeble ftrokes. He had before obferved that, upon rubbing an exhaufted tube, it difcovered no attractive power, nor gave any light outwards, but only inwards.

HE found that when the friction was performed in vacuo, no electricity (that is attraction) could be produced †; but that though the *attractive quality* required the prefence both of the external and internal air, in order to its fhewing itfelf, yet the *light* requires the prefence of only one of them in order to its appearance; for that either a glafs globe full

* Phyfico-Mechanical Experiments, p. 82.
† Ib. 242.

of

of air rubbed *in vacuo*, or with its air exhausted and rubbed *in pleno*, would produce a very
confiderable light *.

He fays alfo, that thofe lights are lefs fenfibly affected by the return of air, which are
produced by the attrition of exhaufted glafs
in pleno, than thofe which are produced by
the attrition of giafs full of air in vacuo; for
that, in the former cafe, no great alteration
was found in the light or colour, until a certain quantity of air was let into the infide of
the exhaufted glafs; but that, in the latter
cafe, both light and colour were fenfibly
changed, upon every admiffion of air to the
outfide of the full glafs †.

THE greateft electric light Mr. Haukfbee
produced, was when he enclofed one exhaufted cylinder within another not exhaufted,
and excited the outermoft of them, putting
them both in motion. Whether their motions
confpired or not, he obferved, made no difference. When the outer cylinder only was
in motion, he fays, the light was very confiderable, and fpread itfelf over the furface
of the inner glafs. What furprifed him moft
was, that after both glaffes had been in motion fome time, during which his hand had
been applied to the furface of the outer glafs,
the motion of both ceafing, and no light at
all appearing; if he did but bring his hand
again near the furface of the outer glafs,

---

* Phyfico-Mechanical Experiments, p. 248.
† Ib. p. 248.

there would be flashes of light, like lightning, produced in the inner glass; as if, he
says, the effluvia from the outer glass had
been pushed with more force upon it by means
of the approaching hand *. This experiment
was similar to those which he made with the
excited and exhausted globe, and with the exhausted tube; and his reasoning upon it shews,
that he was still far from being fully apprized
of all the circumstances attending this fact.

THE next experiments which I shall relate
of Mr. Haukſbee's, are those which shew
the great copiousness, and extreme subtilty of
electric light. They are really amazing, and
have not yet been pursued in the manner
they deserve.

HE lined more than half of the inside of
a glass globe with sealing wax, and having
exhausted the globe, he put it in motion;
when, applying his hand to excite it, he saw
the shape and figure of all the parts of his
hand distinctly and perfectly, on the concave
superficies of the wax within. It was as if
there had only been pure glass, and no wax
interposed between his eye and his hand. The
lining of wax, where it was spread the thin-
nest, would but just allow the sight of a candle
through it in the dark; but in some places
the wax was, at least, one eighth of an inch
thick; yet even in those places, the light and
the figure of his hand were as distinguish-
able through it, as any where else. Nay

† Physico-Mechanical Experiments, p. 87.

though,

though, in fome places, the fealing wax did not adhere fo clofely to the glafs as in others, yet the light on thefe appeared juft as on the reft *.

THESE experiments fucceeded equally with pitch inftead of fealing wax. And he obferved, that when the air was let into the glafs, every part of it, the lined part and the unlined, feemed to attract with equal vigour †. Melted flowers of fulphur had no fuch effect, but common fulphur anfwered as well as fealing wax, or pitch. In both thefe laft experiments the fulphur was found to have been feparated from the glafs ‡.

USING a large quantity of common fulphur in the fame manner, the light in the infide was four times as great, but the figure of his fingers was not fo diftinguifhable as in the former cafes. He likewife obferved, that on the part near the axis, where the fubftance of the fulphur was the greateft, no light was produced; which he attributed, chiefly, to the flownefs of the motion in that place §.

UPON the admiffion of a fmall quantity of air into the globe, thus partially lined with fealing wax, the light wholly difappeared on the part covered with the wax, but not on the other.

HE alfo obferved, that when all the air was let in, and the hoop of threads before-

* Phyfico-Mechanical Experiments, p. 168.
† Ib. 269.   ‡ Ib. 274.   § Ib. 275.

mentioned

mentioned held over the glafs, the threads
were attracted at greater diftances by the part
which was coated with the wax than by the
other : when all the air was exhaufted, he
fays, the wax would attract bodies placed
near the out-fide of the glafs; that even in
this cafe, the threads preferved their central
direction, though not fo vigoroufly as when
the air was let in; but that they would not
be attracted at all, when there was no wax
on the infide of the exhaufted globe.

MR. HAUKSBEE was not unattentive to
the *found* made by the emiffion of the electric
effluvia, or to the manner in which it affected the fenfe of *feeling*. He obferved, that
when an excited tube of glafs attracted various bodies, and threw light upon them, as
they were held near it, a noife, which he
calls a *fnapping*, was likewife heard. He
alfo fays, that the rubbed tube, held near the
face, gave a feeling, as if fine hairs had been
drawn over it; and when he repeated the experiment of whirling and rubbing the glafs
globe, he obferved the light to proceed from
it with fome noife, and to make a kind of
preffure upon the finger, when it was held
within half an inch of it *.

NOR was Mr. Haukefbee's attention confined to the electric power of *glafs*.   He made
experiments with a globe of *fealing wax*, in
the center of which was a globe of wood ;
from which he concluded, that the electricity

* Phyfico-Mechanical Experiments, p. 65.

of

of fealing wax was, in general the fame with
that of glafs, but different from it in degree.
He could not make any light adhere to his
finger when prefented to the excited fealing
wax, any more than when it was prefented
to an exhaufted and excited globe of glafs.

He provided himfelf, in like manner, with
a globe of fulphur, and another of rofin with
a mixture of brick duft, but the fulphur could
hardly be excited at all; whereas the rofin acted more powerfully than the fealing wax had
done. This he afcribed to its being ufed while
it was warm: for, in the fame warm ftate,
it attracted leaf brafs without any attrition at
all *.

He fays, that the excited rofin gave no
light in the dark, and the fulphur but little †.

With refpect to the power of electricity in
general, he obferved, that a flight friction was
fufficient to excite it, and that a greater preffure, or a more violent motion did not confiderably increafe it ‡. He fays, that all the
phenomena of electricity were improved by
warmth; and diminifhed by moifture; which
he attributed to the refiftance that the aque-
ous particles gave to the effluvia; and, like
Mr. Boyle, and others before him, he was confirmed in this hypothefis, by finding, that
the interpofition of linen cloth prevented any
effects from being obferved beyond it.

---

* Phyfico-Mechanical Experiments, p. 154.
† Ib. p. 156.   ‡ Ib. p. 54.

HE also obferved, that when the tube was filled with other matter than air, as with dry writing fand (which he actually tried) the attractive power of the effluvia was confiderably abated; but he did not know what kind of bodies would produce that effect. He himfelf obferves, that he found the electric virtue of a folid cylinder of glafs to be, not indeed quite fo ftrong as that of a hollow tube, but more permanent *.

THAT Mr. Haukfbee, after all, had no clear idea of the diftinction of bodies into electrics and non-electrics, appears from fome of his laft experiments, in which he attempted to produce electric appearances from metals, and from the reafons he gives for his want of fuccefs in thofe attempt . " From " thefe experiments," he fays, " I may fafe- " ly conclude, that if there be any fuch " quality as light to be excited from a brafs " body, under the forementioned circum- " ftances," viz. of whirling and rubbing, " all the attrition of the feveral bodies I have " ufed for that purpofe, have been too weak " to force it from it. And indeed, con- " fidering the clofenefs of the parts of metals, " and with what firmnefs they adhere, en- " tangle, and attract one another, a fmall " degree of attrition is not fufficient to put " their parts into fuch a motion as to pro- " duce an electrical quality, which quality, " under the forementioned circumftances, I

* Phyfico-Mechanical Experiments, p. 64.

" take

" take to be the appearance of light in such a
" medium."

CONSIDERING what great fuccefs Mr.
Haukfbee had with his globe of glafs, and
his machine to give motion to it, it is furprifing that the ufe of it fhould have been fo long
difcontinued after his death. To this circumftance we may perhaps, in a great meafure,
afcribe the flow progrefs that was afterwards
made in electrical difcoveries. Mr. Haukfbee's
fucceffors confined themfelves to the ufe of
tubes. I fuppofe becaufe they were lighter,
more portable, and more eafily managed in
the experiments which they chiefly attended
to : but the ufe of the globe would certainly
have put them much fooner in the way of
making the capital difcoveries, which were
afterwards made in electricity.

PERIOD

PERIOD III.

THE EXPERIMENTS AND DISCOVERIES OF
MR. STEPHEN GREY, WHICH WERE
MADE PRIOR TO THOSE OF MONSIEUR DU
FAY, AND WHICH BRING THE HISTORY
OF ELECTRICITY TO THE YEAR 1733.

NOTWITHSTANDING the important difcoveries of Mr. Haukſbee, and the pro-
miſing appearance they made, as an opening
to farther difcoveries, we find, after him, a
great chafm in the hiſtory of electricity, an
interruption of difcoveries, and, as far as we
can learn, of experiments too, for the fpace
of near twenty years; and at a time when philofophical knowledge of every other kind was
making the moſt rapid progreſs, under the
aufpices of the great Sir Iſaac Newton.   But
the attention of this great man happened to be
engaged by other fubjects, and this very circumftance might be the reafon why the attention of other philofophers were alſo diverted
from electricity.

AFTER this long interval, commences a new
æra in the hiſtory of electricity; in which we
ſhall have the works of another labourer in
this new field of philofophy to contemplate,
viz. Mr. Stephen Grey, a penfioner at the
Charter Houfe.   No perfon who ever applied
to this ſtudy was more affiduous in making
experiments, or had his heart more intirely
in

in the work. This will appear by the prodigious number of experiments he made, and
some confiderable difcoveries with which his
perfeverance was crowned; as well as by the
felf-deceptions, to which his paffionate fond-
nefs for new difcoveries expofed him.

BEFORE the year 1728, Mr. Stephen **Grey**
had often obferved, in electrical experiments
made with a glafs tube, and a down feather
tied to the end of a fmall ftick, that, after its
fibres had been drawn towards the tube, they
would, upon the tube's being withdrawn, cling
to the ftick, as if it had been an electric body, or as if there had been fome electricity
communicated to the ftick, or to the feather.
This put him upon thinking, whether, if the
feather were drawn through his fingers, it
might not produce the fame effect, by acquiring fome degree of electricity. This experiment fucceeded accordingly, upon his firft
trial; the fmall downy fibres of the feather
being attracted by his finger, when held near
it; and fometimes the upper part of the feather
with its ftem would be attracted alfo.

IT will be obvious to every electrician, that
the fuccefs of this experiment depended upon
other principles, than thofe to which he had
a view in making it. Proceeding, however,
in the fame manner, he found the following
fubftances to be all electric; *hair, filk, linen,
woollen, paper, leather, wood, parchment,* and
ox gut in which leaf gold had been beaten.
He made all thefe fubftances very warm, and
fome of them quite hot before he rubbed them.

D   He

He found light emitted in the dark by the
filk and the linen, but more efpecially by a
piece of white *preffing paper*, which is of the
fame nature with card paper. Not only did
this fubftance, when made as hot as his fingers
could bear, yield a light; but, when his fingers
were held near it, a light iffued from them
alfo, attended with a crackling noife, like that
produced by a glafs tube, though not at fo
great a diftance from the fingers *.

THE preceding experiments bring us to the
eve of a very confiderable difcovery in electricity, viz. the communication of that power
from native electrics, to bodies, in which it is
not capable of being excited; and alfo to a
more accurate diftinction of electrics from
non-electrics. I fhall relate the manner in
which thefe important difcoveries were made
pretty fully, but, at the fame time, as fuc-
cinctly as poffible.

IN the month of February, 1729, Mr. Grey,
after fome fruitlefs attempts to make metals
attractive, by heating, rubbing, and ham-
mering, recollected a fufpicion which he had
fome years entertained; that, as a tube communicated its light to various bodies when
it was rubbed in the dark, it might poffibly,
at the fame time, communicate an electricity
to them, by which had hitherto been underftood only the power of attracting light bodies. For this purpofe he provided himfelf
with a tube three feet five inches long, and

---

* Philofophical Tranfactions abridged, Vol. viii. p. 9.

near one inch and two tenths in diameter; and to each end was fitted a cork, to keep the duft out when the tube was not in ufe.

THE firft experiments he made upon this occafion were intended to try, if he could find any difference in its attraction when the tube was ftopped at both ends by the corks, and when left entirely open ; but he could perceive no fenfible difference. It was, however, in the courfe of this experiment that, holding a down feather over againft the upper end of the tube, he found that it would fly to the cork, being attracted and repelled by it, as well as by the tube itfelf. He then held the feather over againft the flat end of the cork, and obferved, that it was attracted and repelled many times together; at which, he fays, he was much furprifed, and concluded, that there was certainly an attractive virtue communicated to the cork by the excited tube.

HE then fixed an ivory ball upon a ftick of fir, about four inches long; when, thrufting the other end into the cork, he found, that the ball attracted and repelled the feather, even with more vigour than the cork had done, repeating its attractions and repulfions many times fucceffively. He afterwards fixed the ball upon long fticks, and upon pieces of brafs and iron wire, with the fame fuccefs; but he obferved, that the feather was never fo ftrongly attracted by the wire, though it were held very near the tube, as by the ball at the end of it.

WHEN

WHEN a wire of any confiderable length was ufed, its vibrations, caufed by the action of rubbing the tube, made it troublefome to manage. This put Mr Grey upon thinking whether, if the ball were hung to a pack-thread, and fufpended by a loop on the tube, the electricity would not be carried down the line to the ball; and he found it to fucceed according to his expectation. In this manner he fufpended various bodies to his tube, and found all of them to be capable of receiving electricity in the fame manner.

AFTER trying thefe experiments with the longeft light canes and reeds that he could conveniently ufe, he afcended a balcony twenty-fix feet high; and, faftening a ftring to his tube, he found, that the ball at the end of it would attract light bodies in the court below.

He then afcended to greater heights, and by putting his long canes in the end of his tube, and faftening a long ftring to the end of the canes, he contrived to convey the electricity to much greater diftances than he had done before; till, being able to carry it no farther perpendicularly, he next attempted to carry it horizontally; and from thefe attempts arofe a difcovery, of which he was not in the leaft aware when he began them.

IN his firft trial he made a loop at each end of a packthread, by means of which he fufpended it, at one end, on a nail driven in-to a beam, the other end hanging downwards. Through the loop which hung down, he put the

the line to which his ivory ball was faſtened,
fixing the other end of it by a loop on his
tube; ſo that one part of the line, along
which the electricity was to be conveyed, viz.
that to which the ball was faſtened, hung
perpendicular, the reſt of the line lay horizontal. After this preparation, he put the
leaf braſs under the ivory ball, and rubbed
the tube, but not the leaſt ſign of attraction
was perceived. Upon this he concluded, that
when the electric virtue came to the loop
of the packthread, which was ſuſpended on
the beam, it went up the ſame to the beam;
ſo that none, or very little, of it went down
to the ball; and he could not, at that time,
think of any method to prevent it.

On June the 30th, 1729, Mr. Grey paid a
viſit to Mr. Wheeler, to give him a ſpecimen
of his experiments; when, after having made
them from the greateſt heights which the
houſe would admit, Mr. Wheeler was deſirous
of trying whether they could not carry the
electric virtue to a greater diſtance horizontally. Mr. Grey then told him of the fruitleſs
attempt he had made to convey it in that direction: upon which Mr. Wheeler propoſed
to ſuſpend the line to be electrified by another
of *ſilk*, inſtead of *packthread*; and Mr. Grey
told him, it might do better, on account of
its ſmallneſs; as leſs of the virtue would probably paſs off by it than had done by the thick
hempen line, which he had uſed before. With
this expedient, they ſucceeded far beyond
their expectations.

D 3   THE

THE firſt experiment they made after this expedient occurred to them, was in a matted gallery at Mr. Wheeler's houſe, July 2d, 1729, about ten o'clock in the morning, as Mr. Grey, after his uſual manner, has minutely recorded it. About four feet from the end of the gallery, they faſtened a line acroſs the place. The middle part of this line was ſilk, the reſt pack thread. They then laid the line to which the ivory ball was hung, by which the electric virtue was to be conveyed to it from the tube, and which was eighty feet and a half in length, acroſs this ſilken line, ſo that the ball hung about nine feet below it. The other end of the line was, by a loop, faſtened to the tube, which they excited at the other end of the room. After this preparation, they put the leaf braſs under the ivory ball, and, upon rubbing the tube, it was attracted, and kept ſuſpended for ſome time.

THE gallery not permitting them to go any greater lengths with a ſingle line of communication, they contrived to return the line, making the whole length of it almoſt twice that of the gallery, or about one hundred and forty-ſeven feet, which anſwered very well. But, ſuſpecting that the attraction would be ſtronger without doubling or returning the line, they made uſe of a line one hundred and twenty-four feet long, running in one direction in the barn ; and, as they expected, they found the attraction ſtronger than
when

when the line had been returned in the gallery.

JULY the 3d, proceeding to make more returns of the line, the filk which fupported it happened to break, not being able to bear the weight of it, when fhaken with the motion that was given to it by rubbing the tube. Upon this they endeavoured to fupport it by a fmall iron wire, inftead of the filken ftring; but this alfo breaking, they made ufe of a brafs wire a little thicker. But this brafs wire, though it fupported the line of communication very well, did not anfwer the purpofe of thefe young electricians: for, upon rubbing the tube, no electricity was perceived at the end of the line. It had all gone off by the brafs wire which fupported it. They had recourfe to brafs wires, as being ftronger than their filken lines, and no thicker; for the fame reafon that they had before ufed filken lines in preference to hempen ftrings; becaufe they could have them ftronger, and at the fame time fmaller. But the refult of this experiment convinced them, that the fuccefs of it depended upon their fupporting lines being *filk*, and not, as they had imagined, upon their being *fmall*. For the electric virtue went off as effectually by the fmall brafs wire, as it had done by the thick hempen cord.

BEING obliged, therefore, to return to their filken lines, they contrived them to fupport very great lengths of the hempen line of communication; and actually conveyed the electric virtue feven hundred and fixty-five feet,

nor

nor did they perceive that the effect was fenfibly diminifhed by the diftance *.

In the fame manner in which *filk* was found
to be a non-conductor, it is probable that,
about the fame time, *hair*, *rofin*, *glafs*, and
perhaps fome other electric fubftances, were
found to have the fame property, though the
difcovery be no where particularly mentioned : for we fhall prefently find Mr. Grey
making ufe of them, to infulate the bodies
which he electrified.

AFTER this, Mr. Grey and his friend amufed themfelves with trying how *large* furfaces
might be impregnated with the electric effluvia; electrifying a large map, table cloth, &c.
They alfo carried the electric virtue feveral
ways at the fame time, and to a confiderable
diftance each way.

THE magnetic effluvia, they found, did not
in the leaft interfere with the electric ; for
when they had electrified the load ftone, with
a key hanging to it, they both attracted leaf
brafs like other fubftances.

SOME time after this, Mr. Wheeler, in
the abfence of Mr. Grey, electrified a red-
hot poker, and found the attraction to be the
fame as when it was cold. He alfo fufpended a live chicken upon the tube by the legs,
and found the breaft of it ftrongly electrical †.

---

* Phil. Tranf. abridged, Vol. vii. p. 15.
† Ib. p. 16.

In August, 1729, Mr. Grey advanced one step farther in his electrical operations. He found that he could convey the electric virtue from the tube to the line of communication without touching it, and that holding the excited tube near it was sufficient. Repeating his former experiments with this variation, in conjunction with Mr. Wheeler, and among others, carrying the electric virtue several ways at the same time without touching the line, they always observed, that the attraction was strongest at the place which was most remote from the tube; a fact which they might have observed, if they had attended to it, in their former experiments *.

Some time in the same month, Mr. Wheeler and Mr. Grey in conjunction made some experiments, in order to try whether the electric attraction was in proportion to the quantity of matter in bodies; and with this view they electrified a solid cube of oak, and another of the same dimensions which was hollow; but they could not perceive any difference in their attractive power; though it was Mr. Grey's opinion, that the electric effluvia passed through all the parts of the solid cube †.

On the 13th of August in the same year, Mr. Grey made another improvement in his electrical apparatus, by finding that he could electrify a *rod*, as well as a *thread*, without

* Phil. Transf. abridged, Vol. vii. p. 17.
† Ib. p. 17.

inferting any part of it into his excited tube. He took a large pole twenty-feven feet long, two inches and one half in diameter at one end, and one inch and one half at the other. It was a fort of wood which is called horfe-beach, and had its rind on. This pole he fufpended horizontally by hair lines, and at the fmall end of the pole he hung a cork, by means of a packthread about one foot long, and put a fmall leaden ball upon the cork, to keep the packthread extended. Then the leaf brafs being put under the cork, the tube rubbed, and held near the larger end of the pole, the cork ball at the oppofite end attracted the leaf brafs ftrongly, to the height of an inch or more. Mr. Grey alfo obferved, that though the leaf brafs was attracted by any part of the pole, it was not near fo ftrongly as by the cork *.

ABOUT the beginning of September, Mr. Grey made experiments, to fhew that the electric effluvia might be carried in a circle, as well as along lines, and be communicated from one circle to another; and alfo that it might be done whether the circles were verti-cal, or horizontal.

ABOUT the latter end of autumn, or the beginning of winter 1729, Mr. Grey refum-ed his inquiries after other electrical bodies, and found many more to have the fame pro-perty, but he mentions only the dry leaves of feveral trees; from whence he concluded, that

* Phil. Tranf. abridged, Vol. vii. p. 18.

the

the leaves of all vegetables had that attractive
virtue *.

WE are now advanced to a new scene of
Mr. Grey's electrical experiments, viz. upon
fluids, and upon *animal bodies*. Having no other
method of trying whether any substances
could have the electric virtue communicated to them, but by making them raise light
bodies placed upon a stand under them, it
may easily be imagined, that he could not
well contrive to put a fluid body into that situation. The only thing that Mr. Grey could
do in this way, was to make use of a bubble,
in which form a fluid is capable of being held
in a state of suspension. Accordingly on
March 23d and 25th, 1730, he dissolved soap
in Thames water, and suspending a tobacco
pipe, he blew a bubble at the head of it; and,
bringing the excited tube near the small end,
he found the bubble to attract leaf brass to
the height of two, and of four inches †.

APRIL the 8th, 1730, Mr. Grey suspended
a boy on hair lines in a horizontal position,
just as all electricians had, before, been used
to suspend their hempen lines of communication, and their wooden rods; then, bringing
the excited tube near his feet, he found that
the leaf brass was attracted by his head with
much vigour, so as to rise to the height of
eight, and sometimes of ten inches. When
the leaf brass was put under his feet, and the

---

* Phil. Transf. abridged, Vol. vii. p. 19.
† Ibid.

tube

tube brought near his head, the attraction was
fmall; and when the leaf brafs was brought
under his head, and the tube held over it,
there was no attraction at all. Mr. Grey does
not attempt to affign any reafon for thefe appearances. It was not till many years after
this time, that the influence of *points* in receiving and emitting the electric effluvia was
obferved. While the boy was fufpended, Mr.
Grey amufed himfelf with making the electricity operate in feveral parts of his body, at
the fame time; and at the end of long rods,
which he made him hold in his hands, and
in diverfifying the experiment feveral other
ways *.

It is curious to obferve the inference which
Mr. Grey makes from thefe experiments. By
them, fays he, we fee, that animals receive
a greater quantity of electric fluid than other
bodies; and that it may be conveyed from
them feveral ways at the fame time, to confiderable diftances. He had no idea that the
bodies of animals receive electricity only by
means of the moifture that is in them, and
that this hempen line of communication,
and his wooden rods could not have been
electrified at all, if they had been perfectly
dry.

In all thefe experiments Mr. Grey obferved, that the leaf brafs was attracted to a much
greater height from the top of a narrow ftand
than from the table; and, at leaft, three times

* Phil. Tranf. abridged, Vol. vii. p. 20.

higher

higher than when it was laid on the floor of the room.

ABOUT this time Mr. Grey communicated to the Royal Society his suspicion, that bodies attracted more or less according to their *colour*, though the substance was the same, and the weight and size equal. He says, he found red, orange, and yellow attracted at least three or four times stronger than green, blue, or purple; but he forbore communicating a more particular account of them, till he had tried a more accurate method which, he says he had thought of, to make the experiments. The communication, however, was never made. The thing itself was only a deception, as will be shewn in some subsequent experiments made by Monsieur du Fay *.

MR. GREY, having found that he could communicate electricity to a bubble of soap and water, was encouraged to attempt communicating it to water itself. In order to this, he electrified a wooden dish full of water, placed on a cake of rosin, or a pane of glass, and observed, that if a small piece of thread, a narrow slip of thin paper, or a piece of sheet glass was held over the water, in an horizontal position, at the distance of an inch or something more, they would be attracted to the surface of the water and then repelled; but he imagined that these attractions and repulsions were not repeated so often as they would have been, if the body had been solid.

* Phil. Transf. abridged, Vol. vii. p. 22.

BUT

BUT he afterwards contrived to fhew the effect of electricity upon water in another and more effectual manner. As this experiment was very curious and exhibited an appearance which was quite new to the electricians of thofe times, I fhall relate the particulars of it very fully, and generally in Mr. Grey's own words *.

HE filled a fmall cup with water higher than the brim, and when he had held an excited tube over it, at the diftance of about an inch or more, he fays, that if it were a large tube, there would firft arife a little mountain of water from the top of it, of a conical form; from the vertex of which there proceded a light, very vifible when the experiment was performed in a dark room, and a fnapping noife, almoft like that which was made when the finger was held near the tube, but not quite fo loud, and of a more flat found. Upon this, fays he, immediately the mountain, if I may fo call it, falls into the reft of the water, and puts it into a tremulous and waving motion.

WHEN he repeated this experiment in the fun fhine, he perceived that very fmall particles of water were thrown from the top of the mountain; and that, fometimes, there would arife a fine ftream of water from the vertex of the cone, in the manner of a fountain, from which there iffued a fine fteam or vapour, whofe particles were fo fmall as not

* Phil. Tranf. abridged, Vol. vii. p. 23.

to be feen; yet, he fays, he was certain it muft be fo; fince the under fide of the tube was wet, as he found when he came to rub it afterwards. He adds, that he had fince found, that though there does not always arife that cylinder of water, yet that there is always a ftream of invifible particles thrown on the tube, and fometimes to that degree as to be vifible on it.

When fome of the larger cups were ufed (his fizes were from three fourths to one tenth of an inch in diameter) which, he fays were to be filled as high as could be done without running over; the middle part of the furface, which was flat, would be depreffed, upon the approach of the tube, into a concave, and the parts towards the edge be raifed; and that when the tube was held over againft the fide of the water, little conical protuberances of water iffued out from it horizontally; and, after the crackling noife, returned to the reft of the water; and that fometimes fmall particles would be thrown off from it, as from the fmall portions of it above mentioned.

This laft experiment he repeated with hot water, and found that it was attracted much more ftrongly, and at a much greater diftance than before. The fteam arifing from the vertex was in this cafe vifible, and the tube was fprinkled with large drops of water.

He tried thefe experiments, in the fame manner, with quickfilver, which was likewife raifed up, but, by reafon of its gravity, not to fo great a height as the water: but, he fays, that

that the fnapping noife was louder, and lafted much longer than it did with the water *.

IT is not eafy to know what to make of the next fet of experiments which engaged the attention of Mr. Grey, or how far he deceived himfelf in the refults of them. He fancied that he had difcovered a *perpetual attractive power* in all electric bodies which did not require heating, rubbing, or any kind of attrition to be excited. The following experiments, he imagined proved the difcovery.

HE took nineteen different fubftances, which were either rofin, gum lac, fhell lac, bees wax, fulphur, pitch, or two or three of thefe differently compounded. Thefe he melted in a fpherical iron ladle, except the fulphur, which was beft done in a glafs veffel. When thefe were taken out of the ladle, and their fpherical furfaces hardened, he fays, they would not attract till the heat was abated, or till they came to a certain degree of warmth; that then there was a fmall attraction, which increafed till the fubftance was cold, when it was very confiderable †.

THE manner in which he preferved thefe fubftances in a ftate of attraction, was by wrapping them in any thing which would keep them from the external air. At firft, for the fmaller bodies, he ufed white paper, and for the larger ones, white flannel; but he afterwards found that black worfted ftockings

* Phil. Tranf. abridged, Vol. vii p. 24.
† Ibid.

would

would do as well. Being thus cloathed, he put them into a large firm box; where they remained, till he had occafion to make ufe of them.

He obferved thefe bodies for thirty days, and found that they continued to act as vigoroufly as on the firft or fecond day; and that they retained their power till the time of his writing, when fome of them had been prepared above four months.

He makes the moft particular mention of a large cone of ftone fulphur, covered with a drinking glafs in which it was made; and fays, that whenever the glafs was taken off, it would attract as ftrongly as the fulphur, which was kept covered in the box. In fair weather, the glafs would attract alfo, but not fo ftrongly as the fulphur, which never failed to attract, let the wind or the weather be ever fo variable; as would all the other bodies, only in wet weather, the attraction was not fo great as in fair weather.

He alfo mentions a cake of melted fulphur, which he kept without any cover, in the fame place with the body abovementioned, and where the fun did not fhine upon them; and fays, that it continued to attract till the time of his writing; but that its attraction was not one tenth part of that of the cone of fulphur which was covered.

These attractions he tried by a fine thread hanging from the end of a ftick. He held the electric body in one hand, and the ftick in the other; and could perceive the attraction at as great a diftance as he could hold them.

AT the time of his writing, he was upon the fubject of permanent electricity in glafs, but had not then completed his experiments *.

GREAT light will be thrown upon thefe experiments of Mr. Grey by fome that will be hereafter related of Mr. Wilcke. It is probable that the glafs veffel in thefe experiments was poffeffed of one electricity, and the fulphur, &c. of the other. But the two electricities were not difcovered till afterwards.

WE are now come to a different fet of electrical experiments, made by Mr. Grey and Mr. Wheeler in conjunction, fimilar to fome of Mr. Haukfbee's.

IN the firft place, Mr. Grey made fome experiments, which, probably unknown to him, had been made before by Mr. Boyle, on excited glafs, and feveral other bodies *in vacuo*, and found that they would attract at very near the fame diftance as *in pleno*. To determine this, he fufpended the excited fubftance in a receiver of an air-pump, and when it was exhaufted, he let the electric down to a proper diftance from fome light bodies, placed on a ftand below. The event was, as near as could be judged, the fame in vacuo as in the open air, if the experiment was made in the fame receiver, and if the electric was brought to the light bodies at the fame diftance of time from the act of excitation †.

---

* Phil. Tranf. abridged, Vol. vi. p. 27.   † Ibid.

ABOUT the latter end of Auguſt 1732, Mr.
Grey and Mr. Wheeler ſuſpended, from the
top of a receiver, a white thread, which hung
down to the middle of it. Then exhauſting
the receiver, and rubbing it, the thread was
attracted vigorouſly. When it was at reſt,
and hung perpendicularly, the excited tube
attracted it; and when the tube was taken
away ſlowly, the thread returned to its perpendicular ſituation; but the tube being removed haſtily, the thread jumped to the oppoſite ſide of the receiver. This laſt effect followed, if the hand was haſtily removed from
the receiver; and at firſt it appeared, in both
caſes, unaccountable to them; but upon farther conſideration, they concluded, that it
proceeded from the motion of the air, made
by the tube, or the hand, which ſhook off the
attraction on that ſide, and not on the other *.
They alſo found, that an excited tube would
attract the thread through another receiver,
which was put over that in which it was ſuſpended. And, ſometime after, Mr. Wheeler
found that the thread was attracted through
five receivers put one over another, and all
exhauſted: he even thought that, in this caſe,
the attraction was rather ſtronger than when
a ſingle receiver was uſed   N. B. The more
effectually to keep any thing of moiſture out
of the receivers, which would have been of
bad conſequence in this experiment, inſtead
of wet leather, he made uſe of a cement made

* Phil. Tranſ. abridged, Vol. vii. p. 56.   † Ibid. p. 97.

of wax and turpentine, which Mr. Boyle ufed
in his experiments *.

Thefe two gentlemen, about the fame time,
made a curious experiment which, they fay,
fhewed that attraction is communicated thro'
opaque, as well as tranfparent bodies, not in
vacuo But a little knowledge of metal, as a
conductor of electricity, would have faved
them the trouble they gave themfelves. They
took a large hand-bell, and taking out the
clapper, they fufpended a cork, befmeared
with honey, from the top of it; and fet it on
a piece of glafs, on which they had put fome
leaf brafs. The excited tube was then brought
near feveral parts of the bell; and, upon taking it up, feveral pieces of leaf brafs were
found fticking to the cork, and others were
removed from the places in which they had
been left, having, probably, been attracted
by the bell †.

We fee by how fmall fteps advances were
made in the fcience of electricity, by fome experiments made by Mr. Grey, 16th June 1731,
and which he has thought worth recording;
though they contain hardly any thing which
we fhould think new, notwithftanding the
difcoveries appeared pretty confiderable to
him.

HE electrified a boy ftanding on cakes of
rofin, as ftrongly as he had before electrified
him when fufpended on hair lines. He afterwards electrified a boy fufpended on hair lines,

* Phil. Tranf, abridged, Vol. vii. p. 97.   † Ibid. 96.

by means of a line of communication from
another boy who was electrified, at some feet
distance from him. He varied this experiment with rods and boys several ways; and
concluded from it, that the electric virtue might
not only be carried from the tube, by a rod,
or line, to distant bodies, but that the same
rod, or line, would communicate that virtue
to another rod, or line, at a distance from it;
and that, by this other rod, or line, the attractive force might be carried to still more
distant bodies. This experiment shews that
Mr. Grey had not properly considered the line
of communication, and the body electrified by
it, as one and the same thing, in an electrical
view, differing only in form, as they were
both alike conductors of electricity.

In December following, Mr Grey carried
this experiment something farther, by con-
veying electricity to bodies which did not
touch the line of communication, making it
pass through the center of hoops standing on
glass. One of his hoops was twenty, another
forty inches in diamer *.

* Phil. Tranf. abridged, Vol. vii. p. 100.

PERIOD IV.

THE EXPERIMENTS AND DISCOVERIES OF MR. DU FAY.

HITHERTO the fpirit of electricity feems to have been confined to England; but, about this time, we find that it had paffed the feas, and that ingenious foreigners were ambitious of diftinguifhing themfelves, and acquiring reputation in this new field of glory. Mr. Du Fay, intendant of the French king's gardens, and member of the academy of fciences at Paris, affiduoufly repeated the experiments above-mentioned of Mr. Grey, and likewife added to the common ftock many new ones of his own. To him we are alfo indebted for the obfervation of feveral general properties of electricity, or rules concerning the method of its action, which had not been taken notice of before, and which reduced to fewer propofitions what had been difcovered concerning it. Thefe experiments were comprifed in eight memoirs, inferted in the Hiftory of the Academy of Sciences for the years 1733, 1734 and 1737; and an account of fome of them alfo makes an article in the Philofophical Tranfactions, dated December 27, 1733. The firft of his memoirs contain a hiftory of electricity, brought down to the year 1732 *.

* Dantzick Memoirs, Vol. i. p. 195.

H3

HE found that all bodies, except metallic, soft, and fluid ones, might be made electric, by first heating them, more or less, and then rubbing them on any sort of cloth. He also excepts those substances which grow soft by heat, as gum; or which dissolve in water, as glue. He also remarked, that the hardest stone and marble required more chafing and heating than other bodies, and that the same rule obtains with regard to woods; so that box, lignum vitæ, and other kinds of very hard wood must be chafed almost to a degree of burning; whereas fir, lime-tree, and cork require but a moderate heat *. Among the more perfect electrics he enumerates all *vitrifications*, the Venetian and Muscovite *talc*, the *phosphorus of Berne, gypsum, transparent selenites*, and in general all *transparent stones*, of whatsoever kind †. Of *salts* he tried only *alum*, and *sugar candy*, both of which he found to be electrical, after warming and rubbing; and he supposed that all the rest would be found to have the same properties, if due precautions were observed in making the experiments. He also observed the electricity of all kinds of *hair, silk, wool*, and *cotton*, and especially, what appeared to him very extraordinary, the powerful electricity of the *back of a dog*, and still more that of a *cat* ‡.

HE found that not only damp air, but also great heat was prejudicial to electricity, and

---

* Phil. Tranf. abridged, Vol. viii. p. 393.
† Ac. Par. 1733. M. p. 105.   ‡ Ib. p. 107.

that his experiments often failed in the warm-
eft hours of a moderately hot day *.   Alſo
when he heated feveral bodies, in order to excite their electric power, he found that in ſome
the hotteſt, and in others the cooleſt parts only were electrical †.

HE ſays, that, purſuing Mr. Grey's experiments, to make water receive electricity, he
found, that all bodies, without exception,
whether ſolid or fluid, were capable of it,
when they were placed on glaſs, or ſealing-
wax ſlightly warmed, or only dried, and the
excited tube was brought near them.   He particularly mentions his having made the experiments with ice, lighted wood, red hot iron ‡,
coal, and every thing that happened to be at
hand at the time; and to his great ſurprize, remarked, that ſuch bodies as were of themſelves the leaſt electric, had the greateſt degree of electricity communicated to them by
the approach of the excited tube §.

To determine whether the tranſparency of
glaſs was the cauſe of the tranſmiſſion of the
electric effluvia through that ſubſtance (for no
one at that time ſuſpected that bodies could be
affected by electricity through glaſs in conſequence of its being actually permeable to the
electric matter) he uſed ſealing wax, and found
that light bodies were affected through that

* Dantzick Memoirs, Vol. i. p. 211.
† Ac. Par. 1733, M. p. 109.
‡ Nollet's Recherches, p. 212
§ Ac. Par. 1733. M. p. 115.

opaque

opaque fubftance, as much as through glafs *.

He refutes Mr. Grey's affertion concerning the different electricity of differently colour-ed bodies, and fhews that it proceeded not from the colour as a *colour*, but from the fub-ftance which was employed in dying it †.

In order to determine whether fimple *colour* had any influence in electricity, he introduced a beam of the fun's light into a darkened room, and made his experiments on bodies illumi-nated with the different primitive colours; and he found that, in no refpect whatever, did the different colours make any difference in the power of receiving, communicating, or deftroying electricity ‡.

Having communicated the electricity of the tube, by means of a packthread, after Mr. Grey's manner, he obferved, that the experiment fucceeded better for wetting the line; and though he made the experiment at the diftance of one thoufand two hundred and fifty-fix feet, when the wind was high, the line making eight returns, and paffing through two different walks of a garden, that the elec-tric virtue was ftill communicated §. He alfo made ufe of glafs tubes, fometimes lined with fealing wax, and found that it anfwered as well as filk lines, and was often more con-veniently applied ‖.

Our ingenious electrician varied this ex-periment by fufpending two cords with their

* Ac. Par. 1737, M. p. 338.   † Ibid. 1733. M. p. 337.
‡ Ib. p. 334.   § Phil. Tranf. abridged, Vol. viii. p. 395.
‖ Ac. Par. 1733. M. p. 345.

ends oppofite to one another, and found that
when they were placed at no greater diftance
than an inch, the electricity was communicated without any fenfible diminution from
the one to the other; but at the diftance of a
foot it was hardly fenfible.   When the cords
were placed at the diftance of three inches, he
found that a lighted candle held between them
did not prevent the tranfmiffion of electricity,
nor did the blaft of a pair of bellows *. Bringing wood and other conducting fubftances, fufpended by filk, to this electrified cord, he
found, as he had concluded *a priori*, that it
loft only part of its electricity; the whole
quantity being equally diftributed between
them †.

The electric fpark from a living body, which
makes a principal part of the diverfion of
gentlemen and ladies, who come to fee experiments in electricity, was firft obferved by
Mr. du Fay, accompanied at that time, as in
moft of his experiments, by the Abbé Nollet,
who, afterwards, we fhall find, did himfelf
obtain a diftinguifhed name among electricians.

MR. DU FAY, having got himfelf fufpended on filk lines, as Mr. Grey had done the
child mentioned above, obferved, that, as foon
as he was electrified, if another perfon approached him, and brought his hand within
an inch, or thereabouts, of his face, legs,
hands, or cloaths, there immediately iffued

* Ac. Par. 1733. M. p. 350.   † Ibid. p. 352.

from

from his body one or more pricking shoots,
attended with a crackling noise. He says this
experiment occasioned to the person who
brought his hand near him, as well as to himself, a little pain, resembling that of the sudden prick of a pin, or the burning from a spark
of fire; and that it was felt as sensibly through
his cloaths, as on his bare face, or hands. He
also observes, that, in the dark, those snappings were so many sparks of fire *

THE Abbé Nollet says he shall never for-
get the surprize, which the first electrical spark
which was ever drawn from the human body
excited, both in Mr. du Fay, and in him-
sef ‡.

HE says that those snappings and sparks
were not excited, if a bit of wood, of cloth,
or of any other substance than a living human
body, was brought near him; except metal,
which produced very nearly the same effect
as the human body. He was not aware, that
it was owing to points, or partial dryness, in
the substances which he mentions, that they
did not take a full and strong spark. He seems
also to have been under some deception, when
he imagined that the flesh of dead animals
gave only an uniform light, without any snap-
ping, or sparks §.

FROM this circumstance, however, he, at
that time concluded, that the bodies of liv-

* Phil. Transf. Vol. viii. p. 395. Ac. Par. 1733. M.
p. 353.
‡ Leçons de Physique, Vol. vi. p. 408.
§ Phil. Transf. abridged, Vol. viii, p. 395. Ac. Par. 1734.
M. 714.

ing animals, (and alſo metals) were ſurround-
ed with an atmoſphere of vapour, which was
actually ſet on fire by electric light *.

HE obſerved, that a cat emitted an electric
ſpark, which evidently gave her pain, when
the finger was brought to any part of her
body, after ſhe had been ſtroked, while ſhe
was ſitting on a ſilk cuſhion. This muſt have
appeared very extraordinary, before it was
known, that the electric matter paſſed from
the hand to the cat, in the act of rubbing †.

WITH the electric ſparks, he imagined he
could have fired inflammable ſubſtances; and
he made ſeveral attempts with tinder and
gunpowder, but without ſucceſs: he found
no appearance of real fire. This was a diſcovery reſerved for the Germans ‡.

THE two next capital obſervations of Mr.
Du Fay I ſhall repeat in his own words, becauſe they are important and curious; and yet
the former of them is little more than what
Otto Guericke had obſerved before him. " I
" diſcovered," he ſays, " a very ſimple prin-
" ciple, which accounts for a great part of
" the irregularities, and, if I may uſe the
" term, of the caprices, that ſeem to accom-
" pany moſt of the experiments in electricity.
" This principle is, that electric bodies at-
" tract all thoſe which are not ſo, and repel
" them as ſoon as they are become electric,
" by the vicinity or contact of the electric
" body. Thus leaf gold is firſt attracted by

* Dantzick Memoirs, Vol. i. p. 215, 230.
† Ibid. p. 216.   ‡ Ibid. p. 229.

" the

" the tube; acquires electricity by approach-
" ing it, and, confequently, is immediately
" repelled by it; nor is it re-attracted, while
" it retains its electric quality. But if, while
" it is thus fuftained in the air, it chance to
" light on fome other body, it ftraightway
" lofes its electricity, and confequently is re-
" attracted by the tube; which, after having
" given it a new electricity, repels it a fecond
" time; and this repulfion continues as long
" as the tube keeps its power. Upon apply-
" ing this principle to various experiments of
" electricity, one will be furprifed at the
" number of obfcure and puzzling facts
" which it clears up." By the help of this
principle, he, particularly, endeavours to explain feveral of Mr. Haukfbee's experiments *.

" CHANCE, he fays, has thrown in my
" way another principle more univerfal and
" remarkable than the preceding one; and
" which cafts a new light upon the fubject of
" electricity. The principle is, that there
" are *two kinds of electricity*, very different
" from one another; one of which I call
" *vitreous*, the other *refinous* electricity. The
" firft is that of glafs, rock-cryftal, precious
" ftones, hair of animals, wool, and many
" other bodies. The fecond is that of am-
" ber, copal, gum lac, filk, thread, paper,
" and a vaft number of other fubftances.
" The characteriftics of thefe two electricities

* Phil. Tranf. abridged, Vol. viii. p. 396.

" are

" are, that they repel themfelves, and at-
" tract each other.   Thus a body of the vi-
" treous electricity repels all other bodies
" poffeffed of the vitreous, and on the con-
" trary, attracts all thofe of the refinous
" electricity.   The refinous, alfo, repels the
" refinous, and attracts the vitreous.   From
" this principle, one may eafily deduce the
" explanation of a great number of other
" phenomena; and it is probable, that this
" truth will lead us to the difcovery of many
" other things."

THIS very capital difcovery was, as the ingenious author acknowledges, perfectly accidental, having been made in confequence of
cafually obferving (which, he fays, was to his
great furprize) that, having caufed a piece of
leaf gold to be repelled, and fufpended in the
air, by an excited glafs tube, and meaning
likewife to chafe it about the room by a
piece of excited gum copal, inftead of being
repelled by it, as it was by the glafs tube, it
was eagerly attracted.   The fame was the
cafe with fealing-wax, and the other fubftances enumerated above.   He alfo obferved,
that when a piece of leaf gold was electrified
by excited fealing-wax, &c. it was conftantly
attracted by excited glafs, but repelled by excited fealing-wax, &c. *

OUR ingenious electrician was, however,
too hafty in concluding, as he did, that the
two electricities which he had difcovered were

* Ac. Par. 1733, M. p. 627.

altogether

altogther independent of the fubftance with
which the electrics were rubbed. All the difference, he fays, produced by a change of
the rubber, was that of *more or lefs* of the fame
kind *. We fhall find that, in a much later
period, the contrary was difcovered to be
true by Mr. Canton.

IN order to know, immediately, to which
of the two claffes of electricity any body be-
longed, he made a filk thread electrical, and
brought it to the body, when it was excited.
If it repelled the thread, he concluded it was
of the fame electricity with it, viz. refinous;
if it attracted it, he concluded it was vitreous †. He had alfo other ingenions methods
to afcertain the fame thing ‡.

HE alfo obferved, that communicated electricity had the fame property as the excited.
For having electrified, by the glafs tube,
balls of wood or ivory; he found them to repel the bodies which the tube repelled, and to
attract thofe which the tube attracted. If
they had the refinous electricity communicated to them, they obferved the fame rule, by
attracting thofe bodies which had the vitreous
electricity communicated to them, and repelling thofe which had received the refinous.
But, he obferves, the experiment would not
fucceed, if the bodies were not made equally
electrical; for, if one of them was weakly
electrical, it would be attracted by that which

---

* Ac. Par. 1733, M. p. 639.
† Phil. Tranf. abridged, Vol. viii. p 397.
‡ Ac. Par. 1733, M. p. 639.

was much more ſtrongly electrical, of whatever quality it was.

THIS diſcovery of the two electricities was certainly a capital one, but was, notwithſtanding, left very imperfect by Mr. Du Fay. We ſhall ſee that Dr. Franklin found, that, in all probability, the vitreous electricity is poſitive, or a redundancy of electric matter; and the reſinous, negative, or a want of it; and that Mr. Canton has diſcovered, that it depends upon the ſurface of the electric bodies, and of the rubber, whether the electricity be poſitive or negative.

THE doctrine of two different electricities, produced by exciting different ſubſtances, conſiderable as the diſcovery of it was, ſeems to have been dropped after Mr. Du Fay, and thoſe effects aſcribed to other cauſes; which is an inſtance that ſcience ſometimes goes backwards.

MR. DU FAY himſelf ſeems, at laſt, to have adopted the opinion, which generally prevailed to the time of Dr. Franklin; that the two electricities differed only in degree, and that the ſtronger attracted the weaker : not conſidering that, upon this principle, bodies poſſeſſed of the two electricities ought to attract one another leſs forcibly, than if one of them had not been electrified at all, which is contrary to fact.

IT will be ſeen that, many years after, Mr. Kinnerſley of Philadelphia, a friend of Dr. Franklin's, being at Boſton in New England, made ſome experiments which again
ſhewed

shewed the difference of the two electricities. He communicated those experiments to Dr. Franklin, who repeated and explained them *.

Mr. Du Fay was the first person who en- deavoured to excite a tube in which air was condensed, and, to his great surprize, found the attempt ineffectual. Suspecting this might be owing to moisture, which he might have forced into the tube, in using his condensing instrument, he cemented a large copper eoli- pile to his tube, and compressed the air in it, by putting the eolipile upon the fire. After this, he turned a cock, which he had placed to prevent the return of the compressed air, and disengaged the tube from the eolipile; but he still found the excitation to be impos- sible †. The Abbé Nollet, who assisted at most of this gentleman's experiments, declares himself not satisfied even with this precau- tion; thinking that the non-excitation of the tube might still be owing to the moisture, which always exists in the air, and the par- ticles of which must be drawn nearer to- gether by condensation ‡. In answer to this objection, Mr. Boulanger says, that a small glass full of water poured into a tube, and immediately thrown out again, will not de- stroy the excitability of the glass near so much as the condensed air §.

Mr. Du Fay found no difference in the ex- citation of a glass tube whether it was filled with warm *sand* or not; but when the tube was

* See his Letters. † Ac. Par. 1734. M. p. 489.
‡ Nollet's Recherches, p. 258. § Boulanger, p. 132.

F cool

cool it was not fo eafily excited. The excitation was more obftructed by *bran*, and
much more by *water*, warm or cold ; though,
he fays, that the electricity was not quite deftroyed by it *.

MR. DU FAY took a good deal of pains to
afcertain the effect of electricity *in vacuo*,
but his conclufion can hardly be depended
upon. For, he fays, that *glafs*, and other fubftances poffeffed of the fame kind of electricity, are hardly capable of being excited *in
vacuo* ; whereas *amber*, and the fubftances of
that clafs, are excited as eafily, and as vigoroufly *in vacuo*, as in the open air. The
vacuum he made feems to have been as good
as can be made by the better kind of our air-
pumps †.

This philofopher was the firft who obferved
that electric fubftances attract the dew more
than conductors. He obferved that a glafs
veffel, placed on a metal cup, and fet in the
open air all day, will often be wet when the
metal is dry. S. Beccaria accounts for this
fact, by fuppofing that alterations in the electricity of the air eafily produce correfpondent
alterations in the electricity of metals, in
which the electric fluid moves with the utmoft eafe, but not in glafs. Whenever,
therefore, the ftate of the electric fluid in the
air is altered, the glafs is electrified *plus* or
minus, and therefore attracts the vapours in
the air ‡.

* Ac. Par. 1733. M. p. 341.
† Ac. Par. 1734. M. p. 489.
‡ Beccaria del elettricifmo naturale et artificiale, p. 179.

IT

IT muſt be obſerved, that Mr. Granville Wheeler, in the autumn of the year 1732, made ſeveral curious experiments, relating to the repulſive force of electricity. Theſe he repeated to Mr. Grey in the ſummer following, and deſigned to communicate them, through his hands, to the Royal Society; but, deferring the execution of it from time to time, he was informed that Mr. Du Fay had taken notice of the ſame ſolution of the repulſive force. Upon this he laid aſide all thoughts of communicating his diſcovery to the public: but, finding that his experiments were different from thoſe of Mr. Du Fay, he was perſuaded to publiſh them in the Philoſophical Tranſactions for the year 1739.

THE experiments were made by threads of various kinds, and other ſubſtances, hanging down from ſilk lines, and generally made to repel one another by the approach of an excited tube. The reſult of them all he compriſed in the three following propoſitions. 1ſt. That bodies made electrical, by communication with an excited electric, are in a ſtate of repulſion with reſpect to ſuch excited bodies. 2dly. That two, or more bodies, made electrical by communicating with an excited electric, are in a ſtate of repulſion with reſpect to one another. 3dly. Excited electrics do themſelves repel one another *.

ONE of his experiments, to prove the ſecond of theſe propoſitions, deſerves to be

---

* Phil. Tranſ. abridged, Vol. viii. p. 411.

mentioned

mentioned for its curiofity. He tied a number of filk threads together, by a knot at each extremity; when, upon electrifying them, the threads repelled one another, and the whole bundle was fwelled out into a beautiful fpherical figure; fo that he could with pleafure, he fays, obferve the knot at the bottom rifing upwards, as the electricity and mutual repulfion of the threads increafed; and he could not help imagining his bundle of filks to refemble a bundle of mufcular fibres.

By way of corollary to the fame propofition, he obferves, that it fuggefts, more plainly than any other know experiment, a reafon for the diffolution of bodies in menftrua; viz. that the particles of the folvend, having imbibed particles of the menftrua, fo as to be faturated with them, the faturated particles become repulfive of one another, feparate, and fly to pieces *.

* Philofophical Tranfactions abridged, Vol. viii. p. 410.

PERIOD

PERIOD V.

THE CONTINUATION AND CONCLUSION OF
MR. GREY's EXPERIMENTS.

MR. GREY, upon refuming his experiments, expreffes great fatisfaction,
that his former obfervations had been confirmed by fo judicious a philofopher as Mr.
Du Fay ; who, he acknowledges, had made
feveral new ones of his own, particularly that
important *luciferous one*, as he calls it, recited above; which, put him upon making the
experiments which follow, and which were
made in the months of July and Auguft
1734 *.

As Mr. Du Fay had faid, that the fnappings and the fparks, he had mentioned,
were ftrongly excited by a piece of metal,
prefented to the perfon fufpended on filk lines;
Mr. Grey concluded, that if the perfon and
metal fhould change places, the effect would
be the fame. He, accordingly, fufpended
feveral pieces of metal on filk lines, beginning with the common utenfils, which were
at hand, as the poker, tongs, fire fhovel, &c.
and found, that, when they were electrified,
they gave fparks, in the fame manner as the
human body had done in like circumftances.

* Phil. Tranf. abridged, Vol. viii. p. 397.

This

This was the origin of *metallic conductors*, which are in ufe to this day *.

MR. GREY did not, at the time abovementioned, think of making his experiments in the dark, in order to fee the light proceeding from the iron; not imagining, that electricity, communicated to metals would have produced fuch furprifing phenomena, as, he fays, he afterwards found it to do.

CONTINUING his experiments at Mr. Wheeler's, they found, that the flefh of dead animals exhibited, very nearly, the fame appearances as that of living animals, contrary to the affertion of Mr. Du Fay.

BUT what moft furprifed Mr. Grey, and the gentlemen then prefent, in the experiments he made upon that occafion, was the

---

* Phil. Tranf. abridged, Vol. viii. p. 398.

In order the more conveniently to communicate electricity to the iron bar. Mr. Du Fay (who adopted the contrivance from Mr. Grey) faftened to the end of it a bundle of *linen threads*, to which he applied his excited tube. He was led to prefer the thread for this purpofe, in confequence of having found that, of the flexible fubftances, *wool, filk, cotton,* or *linen* ; the laft was moft attracted by an excited electric. He fufpended them all to the fame bar, and brought an excited glafs tube to an equal diftance from them all at the fame time, and obferved that they were attracted in the order in which I have mentioned them, *wool* the leaft, and *linen* the moft. Ac. Par. 1737. M. p. 137. Thefe linen threads of Mr. Du Fay kept their ground in a much improved ftate of the electrical apparatus, when globes were fubftituted in the place of tubes, but now *fmall wires* are univerfally ufed in preference to them.——Mr. Du Fay alfo, in order to determine what *metal* was the moft proper for this purpofe, procured equal cylinders of gold, filver, copper, brafs, lead, iron, and tin, and having placed them fo as to conftitute one cylinder, he drew fparks from each of them in their turn, when the whole was electrified ; but he could not, in any refpect, perceive the leaft difference in them. Ac. Par. 1737. M. p. 132.

pheno-

phenomenon above referred to, and what he
nows calls *a cone*, or *pencil of electric light*;
such as is commonly seen to issue from an electrified point. As this was the first time that
this phenomenon, which is now so common,
was distinctly seen, I shall relate the experiment, of which it was the result, at large.

MR. GREY, and his friends, provided
themselves with an iron rod four feet long,
and half an inch in diameter, pointed at each
end, but not sharp. Suspending this iron
rod upon silk lines in the night ; and applying the excited tube to one end of it, they
perceived not only a light upon that end, but
another issuing from the opposite end, at the
same time. This light extended itself, in the
form of a cone, whose vertex was at the end
of the rod : and Mr. Grey says, that he and
his company could plainly see, that it consisted of separate threads, or rays of light, diverging from the point of the rod, the ex-
terior rays being incurvated. This light
appeared at every stroke they gave the
tube.

THEY likewise observed, that this light
was always attended with a small hissing
noise, which, they imagined, began at the
end next the tube, increasing in loudness till
it came to the opposite end. He says, however, that this noise could not be heard, but
by persons who stood near the rod, and attended to it *.

* Phil. Transf. abridged, Vol. viii. p. 398.

MR.

MR. GREY, repeating thofe experiments in the September following, after his return to London, obferved an appearance, which he fays, furprifed him very much. After the tube had been applied to the iron rod, as before, when the light, which had been feen at both ends, had difappeared; it was vifible again upon bringing his hand near the end of the rod; and, upon repeating this motion of his hand, the fame phenomenon appeared for five or fix times fucceffively; only the rays were, at each time, fhorter than the other. He alfo obferved, that thefe lights, which were emitted by the tube upon the approach of his hand, were, like the others, attended with a hiffing noife.

HE took notice, that the light which appeared on the end next the tube, when it was held oblique to the axis of the rod, had its rays bending towards it; and that, all the time he was rubbing the tube, thofe flafhes of light appeared upon every motion of his hand up or down the tube, but that the largeft flafhes were produced by the motion of his hand downwards *.

WHEN he ufed two or three rods, laying them either in a right line, or fo as to make any angle with each other, and applied the tube to any one of their ends; he obferved, that the fartheft end of the farther rod exhibited the fame phenomena as one fingle rod †.

* Phil. Tranf. abridged, Vol. viii. p. 399.
† Ib. p. 400.

USING

USING a rod pointed only at one end, he obferved, that the other end gave but one fingle fnap, but that it was much louder than the greateſt of thoſe which were given by the point of the rod; alſo that the pain, refembling pricking or burning, was more ſtrongly felt, and that the light was brighter and more contracted.

CONNECTING a pewter plate with the iron rod, and filling the plate with water, he obferved the fame light, the fame puſhing of the finger, as he calls it, and the fame fnapping, as when the experiment was made with the empty plate. And when the experiment was made with water, in the day-light, it appeared to rife in a little hill, under the finger which was prefented to it; and, after the fnapping noiſe, fell down again, putting the water into a waving motion near the place where it had rifen.

THESE effects were the fame with thoſe which he had before obferved top roceed from the immediate action of the tube, but by thefe experiments, he fays, he found (what, no doubt, appeared a real advance in the fcience to him) that an actual flame of fire, together with an explofion, and ebullition of cold water, might be produced by communicative electricity. What he adds is fo remarkable, that I ſhall repeat his own words. " And although thefe " effects are at prefent but *in minimis*, it is " probable, in time, there may be found out " a way to collect a greater quantity of the " electric fire, and confequently to increaſe
" the

" the force of that power; which, by feveral
" of thefe experiments, *fi licet magnis com-*
" *ponere parva*; feems to be of the fame
" nature with that of thunder and light-
" ning *."

How exactly has this prophecy been ful-
filled in the difcoveries of the Leyden electricians, and Dr. Franklin; the former having difcovered the amazing accumulation of
the electric power, in what is called the Leyden phial; and the latter having proved the
matter of lightning to be the very fame with
that of electricity; though Mr. Grey might
poffibly mention thunder and lightning only
by way of common comparifon.

ON February the 18th, 1735, Mr. Grey,
repeating the experiments of the iron rods
with wooden ones, found all the effects to be
fimilar, but much weaker; as it is now well
known muft have been the cafe; wood being
fo imperfect a conductor, and only in proportion to the moifture it contains.

AT the fame time, he relates, that the repeating the electrification of water, he found,
that the phenomena before mentioned were
produced, not only by holding the tube near
the water, but when it was removed, and the
finger afterwards brought near it †.

MAY the 6th of the fame year, he again
fufpended a boy on filk, and found that this
boy was able to communicate the electric fire,

* Phil. Tranf. abridged, Vol. viii. p. 401.
† Ibid. p. 402.

firſt to one, and then to ſeveral perſons ſtanding upon electric bodies.

Mr. Grey ſeems ſtill to have imagined, that electricity depended, in ſome meaſure, upon colour. The boy ſuſpended on blue lines, he ſays, retained his power of attraction fifty minutes; on ſcarlet lines, twenty-five minutes; and on orange coloured lines, twenty-one minutes. By theſe experiments, he ſays, we ſee the efficacy of electricity on bodies ſuſpended upon lines of the ſame ſubſtance, but of different colour *.

But the greateſt deception which this ingenious gentleman ſeems to have lain under, was occaſioned by the experiments which he made with balls of iron, to obſerve the revolution of light bodies about them. The paragraph relating to theſe experiments, being the laſt which Mr. Grey wrote, I ſhall give it at length as a curioſity.

" I have lately made," ſays he, " ſeveral
" new experiments upon the projectile and
" pendulous motion of ſmall bodies by elec-
" tricity; by which ſmall bodies may be
" made to move about large ones, either in
" circles, or in ellipſes; and thoſe either
" concentric, or eccentric to the center of the
" larger body, about which they move, ſo as
" to make many revolutions about them.
" And this motion will conſtantly be the
" ſame way that the planets move about the
" ſun, viz. from the right hand to the left,

* Phil. Tranſ. abridged, Vol. viii. p. 403.

" or

" or from weſt to eaſt. But theſe little pla-
" nets, if I may ſo call them, move much
" faſter in their *apogeon*, than in the *perigeon*
" parts of their orbits; which is directly con-
" trary to the motion of the planets about the
" ſun *."

THESE experiments Mr. Grey had thought
of but a very little while before his laſt ill-
neſs, and had not time to complete them ;
but the progreſs he had made in them he re-
vealed, on the day before his death, to Dr.
Mortimer, then ſecretary to the Royal Society. He ſaid they ſtruck him with new ſurprize every time he repeated them, and hoped
that, if God would ſpare his life a little longer,
he ſhould, from what theſe phenomena pointed out, bring his electrical experiments to the
greateſt perfection. He did not doubt but,
in a ſhort time, he ſhould be able to aſtoniſh
the world with a new ſort of planetarium,
never before thought of ; and that, from
theſe experiments, might be eſtabliſhed a certain theory, to account for the motions of the
grand planetarium of the univerſe. Theſe
experiments, fallacious as they are, deſerve
to be briefly recited, together with thoſe
which were made in conſequence of them after Mr. Grey's death. I ſhall relate them in
Mr. Grey's own words, as they were delivered to Dr. Mortimer, on his death-bed.

PLACE a ſmall iron globe, ſaid he, of an
inch, or an inch and a half in diameter, on

* Phil, Tranſ, abridged, Vol. viii. p. 404.

the

the middle of a circular cake of rofin, feven
or eight inches in diameter, gently excited;
and then a light body fufpended by a very
fine thread, five or fix inches long, held in
the hand over the center of the table, will, of
itfelf, begin to move in a circle round the
iron globe, and conftantly from weft to eaft.
If the globe be placed at any diftance from
the center of the circular cake, it will defcribe
an ellipfe, which will have the fame eccentricity, as the diftance of the globe from the
center of the cake.

If the cake of rofin be of an elliptical form,
and the iron globe be placed in the center of
it, the light body will defcribe an elliptical
orbit, of the fame eccentricity with the form
of the cake.

If the iron globe be placed in, or near, one
of the foci of the elliptical cake, the light body
will move much fwifter in the apogee, than in
the perigee of its orbit.

If the iron globe be fixed on a pedeftal, an
inch from the table, and a glafs hoop, or a
portion of a hollow glafs cylinder, excited, be
placed round it; the light body will move
as in the circumftances mentioned above, and
with the fame varieties.

He faid, moreover, that the light body
would make the fame revolutions, only
fmaller, round the iron globe placed on the
bare table, without any electrical body to
fupport it; but he acknowledged he had not
found the experiment fucceed, if the thread
was fupported by any thing but a human
hand;

hand; though, he fancied, it would have ſucceeded, if it had been ſupported by any animal ſubſtance, living or dead *.

MR. GREY went on to recite to Dr. Mortimer other experiments ſtill more fallacious; which, out of regard to his memory, I ſhall forbear to quote. Let the chimeras of this great electrician teach his followers, in the ſame, and ſtill but newly opened field of philoſophy, a proper degree of caution in their reaſonings from induction. Let not the example, however, diſcourage any perſon from trying what may appear improbable; but let it induce a man to delay the publication of his diſcoveries, till they have been perfectly aſcertained, and performed in the preſence of others. In experiments of great delicacy, a ſtrong imagination will have great influence even upon the external ſenſes; of which we ſhall have frequent inſtances in the courſe of this hiſtory.

DR. MORTIMER himſelf ſeems to have been deceived by theſe experiments of Mr. Grey. He ſays, that, in trying them after his death, he found, that the light body would make revolutions round bodies of various ſhapes and ſubſtances, as well as round the iron globe; and that he had actually tried the experiment, with a globe of black marble, a ſilver ſtandiſh, a ſmall chip box, and a large cork †.

* Phil. Tranſ. abridged, Vol. viii. p. 404, 405.
† Ibid. p. 405.

THESE

THESE experiments of Mr. Grey were tried by Mr. Wheeler, and other gentlemen, at the Royal Society's houfe, and with a great variety of circumftances; but no conclufion could be drawn from what they at that time obferved. Mr. Wheeler himfelf took a great deal of pains to verify them, with various fuccefs; and at laft he gave it as his opinion, that a defire to produce the motion from weft to eaft was the fecret caufe, that determined the pendulous body to move in that direction, by means of fome impreffion from Mr. Grey's hand, as well as his own; though he was, at the fame time, perfuaded, that he was not fenfible of giving any motion to his hand himfelf*.

MR. DU FAY, in the Memoirs of the Academy of Sciences for the year 1737, acknowledges that thefe experiments of Mr. Grey and Dr. Mortimer did not fucceed with him. But fays, they were the only ones of Mr. Grey that had not; and, with a temper becoming a philofopher, adds, that he doth not, therefore, fay, that they never had fucceeded; but feems rather willing to attribute the failure with himfelf, to his omitting fome circumftance, not mentioned by thofe gentlemen, though, unknown to them, it might be of principal confequence to the experiment †. He was afterwards informed of the refult of the laft experiment in England on this fubject, agreeing with his own ‡.

* Phil. Tranf. abridged, Vol. viii. p. 418.
† Dantzick Memoirs, Vol. i. p. 226.
‡ Ac. Par. 1737. M. p. 436.

PERIOD

PERIOD VI.

THE EXPERIMENTS OF DR. DESAGULIERS.

WE are now come to the labours of that indefatigable experimental philosopher Dr. DESAGULIERS, in this new field of science. The reason which he gives why he had avoided entertaining the Royal Society upon this subject before, and why he had not pursued it so far as he might have done; considering, as he says, that he could excite as strong an electricity in glass, by rubbing with his hand, as any body could, is worth mentioning for its curiosity, and for the light that it throws upon the temper and manner of Mr. Grey. He says, that he was unwilling to interfere with the late Mr. Stephen Grey, who had wholly turned his thoughts to electricity; but was of a temper to give it entirely over, if he imagined that any thing was done in opposition to him *.

DR. DESAGULIERS begins with observing very sensibly (and the observation is still true) that the phenomena of electricity are so odd, that, though we have a great many experiments upon that subject, we have not yet been able, from their comparison, to settle such a theory as will lead us to the cause of that property in bodies, or even to judge of

* Phil. Transf. abridged, Vol. viii. p. 419.

all

all its effects, or find out what useful influence electricity has in nature; though certainly, from what we have seen of it, we may conjecture that it muft be of great ufe, becaufe it is fo extenfive.

His firft experiments, of which an account is given in the Philofophical Tranfactions, dated July, 1739, were made with a hempen ftring, extended upon cat-gut. To the end of the hempen ftring, he fufpended various fubftances; and fays, that all thofe which he tried, amongft which were feveral *electrics per fe*, as fulphur, glafs, &c. without exception, received electricity *.

He changed one of the cat-gut ftrings, on which his hempen line of communication was extended, and put various other fubftances in its place, to try what bodies would tranfmit electricity to the fufpended body, and what would not; and from the refult of his experiments, partly concluded, that bodies in which electricity could not be excited intercepted the electric effluvia; and that thofe in which electricity could be excited, did not intercept it, but permitted it to go on to the extremity of the hempen ftring. But ftill he had no juft idea, that, except metals, it was the moifture in the bodies he tried which intercepted the electric effluvia; and his ideas of the manner in which they were intercepted were very imperfect.

* Phil. Tranf. abridged, Vol. viii. p. 420.

To Dr. Defaguliers we are indebted for
fome *technical terms* which have been extremely ufeful to all electricians to this day,
and which will probably remain in ufe as
long as the fubject is ftudied. He firft applied the term *conductor* to that body to which
the excited tube conveys its electricity;
which term has fince been extended to all
bodies that are capable of receiving that virtue. And he calls thofe bodies in which electricity may be excited, by heating or rubbing,
electrics per fe.

In the writings of this author we find many
axioms relating to electrical experiments,
fome of which are expreffed in a more clear,
and diftinct manner than they had been before; but the real improvements which he
made, were very few and immaterial.

On feveral occafions, and particularly in a
paper delivered to the Royal Society, in the
month of January 1741, he lays down,
among others, the following general rules,
which feem to be more accurate than any
which had been delivered before upon the
fubject *.

   " An electric per fe will not receive elec-
" tricity from another electric per fe, in
" which it has been excited, fo as to run
" along its whole length : but will only re-
" ceive it a little way, being, as it were, fa-
" turated with it.

* Phil. Tranf. abridged, Vol. viii. p. 430.

" An

" An electric per se will not lose all its
" electricity at once, but only the electricity
" of those parts near which a non-electric
" has been brought. It, consequently, loses
" its electricity the sooner, the more of those
" bodies are near it. Thus, in moist weather,
" the excited tube holds its virtue but a little
" while, because it acts upon the moist va-
" pours which float in the air. And if the
" excited tube be applied to leaf gold laid
" upon a stand, it will act upon it much
" longer, and more strongly, than if the
" same quantity of leaf gold be laid upon a
" table, which has more non-electric surface
" than the stand*." This, however, seems
not to be the whole reason ; for if the leaf
gold were laid upon a broad surface of glass,
it would not be acted upon so powerfully, as
if it were placed upon a narrow stand of any
kind of matter.

" A non-electric, when it has received
" electricity, loses it all at once, upon the
" approach of another non-electric." This
however could only be the case when the approaching electric was not insulated, but had
a communication with the earth. It must
also be brought into contact with the electrified
body.

" Animal substances are non electrics by
" reason of the fluids they contain †.

" Excited electricity exerts itself in a
" sphere round the electric per se, or

* Phil. Transf. abridged, Vol. viii p. 427.
† Ibid p. 429.

" rather

" rather in a cylinder, if the body be cylin-
" drical *."

FEW of the many experiments which were
made by Dr. Defaguliers (accounts of which
were publifhed in the Philofophical Tranfactions) had, as I obferved before, any thing
new in them. Thofe which were the moft fo
are the following.

ENDEAVOURING to communicate electricity
to a burning tallow candle, he obferved, that
the candle attracted the thread of trial, but
not within two or three inches of the flame;
but that, as foon as the candle was blown out,
the thread was attracted by every part of it,
and even by the wick, when the fire was
quite extinguifhed. He electrified a wax
candle in the fame manner, and the experiment
fucceeded as well, only the electricity came
not fo near the flame in the wax, as in the
tallow candle.

HE fays, that only warming a glafs receiver, without any rubbing, would caufe the
threads of a down feather, tied to an upright
fkewer to extend themfelves, as foon as it was
put over the feather; and that fometimes
rofin and wax would exert their electricity by
being only expofed to the open air.

HE obferved that if a hollow glafs tube,
fupporting the l ne of communication, were
moiftened by blowing through it, it would intercept the electricity.

* Phil. Tranf. abridged, Vol. viii. p. 431.

HE

He fays, that when an excited tube has
repelled a feather, it will attract it again,
after being fuddenly dipped into water, but
in fair weather it will not attract it unlefs it
hath been dipped pretty deep into the water,
a foot of its length at leaft; whereas, in
moift weather, an inch or two will fuffice *.

He fhewed the attraction of water by an
excited tube, in a better manner than it had
been fhewn before, viz. by bringing the tube
to a ftream iffuing from a condenfing fountain : which, thereupon, was evidently bent
towards it.

Dr. Desaguliers feems to have been the
firft who exprefsly faid, that pure *air* might
be ranked amongft electrics per fe, and that
cold air in frofty weather, when vapours rife
leaft of all, is preferable, for electrical purpofes, to warm air in fummer, when the heat
raifes the vapours †. He alfo fuppofed that
the electricity of the air was of the vitreous
kind; and he accounted for the electricity appearing on the infide only of an exhaufted
glafs veffel, by its going where it met with
the leaft refiftance from fo electrical a body as
the air ‡.

He endeavoured to account for the fixing of
air by the fteams of fulphur, according to the
experiment of Dr Hales; by fuppofing that
the particles of fulphur, and thofe of air, being poffeffed of different kinds of electricity,
attracted one another, whereby their repulfive

* Phil. Tranf. abridged, Vol. viii. p. 429.
† Ibid. p. 437.   ‡ Ibid. 438.

power was deſtroyed. He alſo propoſed the following conjecture concerning the riſe of vapour. The air at the ſurface of water being electrical, particles of water, he thought, jumped to it, then, becoming themſelves electrical, they repelled both the air and one another, and conſequently aſcended into the higher regions of the atmoſphere *.

THE laſt paper of Dr. Deſaguliers in the Philoſophical Tranſactions, upon the ſubject of electricity, is dated June 24th, 1742, in which year he publiſhed a diſſertation on electricity, by which he gained the prize of the academy at Bourdeaux. This prize was a medal of the value of 300 livres, propoſed, at the requeſt of Monſieur Harpez de la Force, for the beſt eſſay on electricity, and ſhews how much this ſubject engaged the attention of philoſophers at that time †. The diſſertation is well drawn up, and compriſes all that was known of the ſubject till that period.

* Phil. Tranſ. abridged, Vol. viii. p. 437.
† Dantzick Memoirs, Vol. i. p. 261.

PERIOD VII.

EXPERIMENTS OF THE GERMANS, AND OF DR. WATSON, BEFORE THE DISCOVERY OF THE LEYDEN PHIAL IN THE YEAR 1746.

ABOUT the time that Dr. Defaguliers had concluded his experiments in England, viz. 1742, feveral ingenious Germans began to apply themfelves to the fame ftudies with great affiduity, and their labours were crowned with confiderable fuccefs.

To the Germans we are indebted for many capital improvements in our electrical apparatus within this period, without which, the bufinefs would have gone on very flowly and heavily; but, by the help of their contrivances, we fhall fee that aftonifhing effects were foon produced.

MR. BOZE, a profeffor of philofophy at Wittemburgh, fubftituted the *globe* for the tube, which had been ufed ever fince the time of Haukfbee*. He likewife added a *prime conductor*, which confifted of a tube of iron or tin, at firft fupported by a man ftanding upon cakes of rofin, and afterwards fuf-

* According to other accounts, Chriftian Auguftus Haufen, profeffor of mathematics at Leipfic, was the firft who revived the ufe of Haukfbee's glafs globe, and Mr. Boze, who was excited to make experiments in electricity by the example of Mr. Haufen, borrowed this capital improvement from him. Dantzick Memoirs, Vol. i. p. 278, 279.

pended

pended on filk horizontally before the globe *.

To prevent the tube from doing any harm to the globe, he put a bundle of thread into the end which was next to it, and which was left open for that purpofe. This expedient, befides occafioning various pleafant phenomena, was obferved to make the force of the conductor much ftronger †.

THE ufe of the globe was immediately adopted in the univerfity of Leipfic, where Mr. Winckler, the profeffor of languages, fubftituted a *cufhion* inftead of the hand, which had before been employed to excite the globe. But the beft rubber for the globe, as well as the tube, was, long after this, ftill thought, by all electricians, to be the human hand, dry, and free from moifture ‡.

MR. P. GORDON, a Scotch Benedictine monk; and profeffor of Philofophy at Erford, was the firft who ufed a *cylinder* inftead of a globe. His cylinders were eight inches long, and four inches in diameter. They were made to turn with a bow, and the whole inftrument was portable. Inftead of a cake of rofin, he infulated by means of a frame, furnifhed with net work of filk §.

THE apparatus, likewife, of many of the German electricians was very *various*, and expenfive. Mr. Winckler, in a paper read at the Royal Society, March 21ft, 1745 ‖, de-

---

* Hiftoire de l'electricité, p. 27.
† Phil. Tranf. abridged, Vol. x. p. 271.   ‡ Ibid. 272.
§ Hiftoire, p. 31.
‖ Phil. Tranf. abridged, Vol. x. p. 273.

ſcribes a machine for rubbing tubes, and another for rubbing globes, and compares the
effects of them both. He obſerves, that the
ſparks which are produced from glaſs veſſels
drawn to and fro were larger, and more ve-
hemently pungent, provided that thoſe veſſels
were of the ſame magnitude with the globes;
but that the flux of eſſluvia was not ſo conſtant
as from the globes. Mr. Winckler alſo invented a machine, which he deſcribes at large
in his works, by means of which he could
give his globe ſix hundred and eighty turns
in a minute *. This gentleman likewiſe contrived to rub glaſs, and china veſſels, in the
inſide; and he ſays they acted as ſtrongly on
bodies placed on the outſide of them, as when
they were rubbed on the outſide †.

THE German electricians generally uſed
more globes than one at a time, and imagined they found the effects proportionable,
though this fact was called in queſtion by Dr.
Watſon, and others; and Mr. Nollet preferred globes made blue with zaffre ‡, which
were carefully tried, and rejected by Dr. Watſon afterwards §.

SUCH a prodigious power of electricity
could they excite from theſe globes, whirled
by a large wheel, and rubbed with woollen
cloth, or a dry hand (for we find both theſe
methods were in uſe among them about this

* Hiſtoire, p. 32.
† Dantzick Memoirs, Vol. i. p. 400.
‡ In ſubſequent trials the Abbé himſelf found no advantage
in thoſe blue globes. Ac. Par. 1745. M. p. 162.
§ Phil. Tranſ. abridged, Vol. x. p. 277.

time)

time) that, if we may credit their own accounts, the blood could be drawn from the
finger by an electric spark; the skin would
burst, and a wound appear, as if made by
a cauftic.   They fay, that if feveral globes or
tubes were ufed, the motion of the heart and
arteries of the electrified perfon would be very
fenfibly increafed; and that, if a vien were
opened under the operation, the blood, iffuing from it, would appear like lucid phofphorus, and run out fafter than when the
man was not electrified.   Analogous to this
laft experiment, Mr. Gordon obferved, that
water, running from an artificial fountain
electrified, was fcattered in luminous drops,
that a larger quantity of water was thrown
out in a given time than when the fountain
was not electrified *; and that electrified water evaporated fafter than water not electrified,
when expofed in fimilar glafs veffels †.   Part
of this account we know might be true, but
fome part muft have been exaggerated.   It is
certain that Mr. Gordon increafed the electric
fparks to fuch a degree, that they were felt
from a man's head to his foot, fo that a perfon could hardly take them without falling
down with giddinefs ‡, and fmall birds were
killed by them §.   This he effected by con-
veying electricity, with iron wires, to the
diftance of 200 ells from the place of excitation.

* Phil. Tranf. abridged, Vol. x. p. 277.
† Dantzick Memoirs, Vol. ii. p. 357.
‡ Ibid. p. 358.
§ Nollet's Recherches, p. 172.

He

He alfo found that the fparks were ftronger when the wire was thick than when it was fmall *.

MR. WAITZ made his glafs tubes act ftronger by rubbing them with a waxed cloth and a little oil. He alfo found, that glafs made with very little pot-afh, acted much better than that in the compofition of which much of it was ufed; but it required longer time, and more heat to vitrify it. He got fome glafs made on purpofe to afcertain the fact †.

BY various experiments of attraction and repulfion, which Mr. Waitz made in rubbing a dog (which he had made thoroughly dry for that purpofe) he proved that the flafhes of light, which fometimes appear when animals are ftroked, are electrical. This had been fuppofed, but was not accurately afcertained before ‡. It was this gentleman who gained the prize of 50 ducats, propofed, in the year 1744, by the Academy of Sciences at Berlin, for the beft differtation on the fubject of electricity. It was publifhed along with three others, which were offered at the fame time, and thought worthy of that honour §.

THE thing that ftrikes us moft in their experiments, performed by thefe machines, is their fetting fire to inflammable fubftances. This they were, probably, led to attempt, from obferving the vivid appearance of elec-

* Dantzick Memoirs, Vol. ii. p. 359.
† Ibid. p. 381.   ‡ Ibid. p. 385.   § Ibid. p. 380.

tric

tric light, the burning pain that was felt by a
fmart ftroke from the conductor, and the
many analogies the electric fluid evidently bore to phofphorus and common fire.

THE firft perfon who fucceeded in this attempt was Dr. Ludolf of Berlin, towards the
beginning the year 1744; who kindled, with
fparks excited by the friction of a glafs tube,
the etherial fpirit of Frobenius. This he did
at the opening of the Royal Academy, and in
the prefence of fome hundreds of perfons. He
performed the experiment by electric fparks
proceeding from an iron conductor. Mr.
Winckler did the fame in the May following,
by a fpark from his own finger ; and kindled,
not only the highly rectified fpirit above-mentioned, but French brandy, corn fpirits, and
other fpirits ftill weaker, by previoufly heating them. He alfo fays, that oil, pitch, and
fealing-wax might be lighted by electric
fparks, provided thofe fubftances were firft
heated to a degree next to kindling *. To
thefe it muft be added, that Mr. Gralath
fired the fmoke of a candle juft blown out, and
lighted it again †; and that Mr. Boze fired
gunpowder, melting it in a fpoon, and firft
the vapour that rofe from it.

THE German electricians, likewife, conftructed a machine, by which they could give
friction to a glafs cylinder in vacuo. By thefe
means they contrived to electrify a wire which
terminated in the open air, and there fhewed

* Phil. Tranf. abridged, Vol. x. p. 271.
† Dantzick Memoirs, Vol. ii. p. 438.

a con-

a confiderable electric power. They alfo electrified that end which was in the open air, and
made the other end which was in vacuo exert
its electricity *.

The fame Germans alfo mention an experiment, which, if purfued, would have led
them to difcover, that the friction of the glafs
globe did not produce, but only collect the
electric matter. But that was a difcovery referved, as we fhall find, for Dr. Watfon. It
feems that both Mr. Boze and Mr. Allamand
had fufpended the machine, and the man who
worked it, upon filk; and obferved, that, not
only the conductor, but alfo the man, and
the machine gave figns of electricity ; though
they did not attend accurately to all the circumftances of that curious fact, which did not
at all anfwer their expectations. For, imagining that part of the electric power was
continually going off to the ground by the
machine, they fuppofed that the effect of infulating it, would have been a ftronger electricity †.

In this period it was that Ludolf the
younger demonftrated, that the luminous barometer is made perfectly electrical by the
motion of the quickfilver; firft attracting,
and then repelling bits of paper, &c. fufpended by the fide of the tube, when it was enclofed in another out of which the air was extracted ‡. Before this experiment, thofe ef-

* Phil. Tranf. abridged, Vol. x. p. 275.
† Wilfon's Effay, preface, p. 14.   Watfon's Sequel, p. 34.
‡ Dantzick Memoirs, Vol. iii. p. 495.

fects

fects had been afcribed to the air *. Profeffor Hamberger and Mr. Waitz had difcovered that the motion of quickfilver in a glafs
veffel, out of which the air was extracted,
had the power of moving light bodies; and
Mr. Allamand likewife found, that it made
no difference whether the veffel had air in it
or not †.

ABOUT the fame time alfo, Mr. Boze took
a great deal of pains to determine, whether
the weight of bodies would be affected by
electricity, but he could not find that it
was.

THE electrical *ftar*, made by turning
fwiftly round an electrified piece of tin,
cut with points equidiftant from the center;
and alfo the *electrical bells*, which will be
defcribed hereafter among the furprifing and
diverting experiments performed by the help
of electricity, were of German invention ‡.
The ftar was contrived by Mr. Gordon, and
by turning the points a little obliquely, he
was furprifed to find it began to move of itfelf §. Laftly, to thefe it may be added, that
Mr. Winckler contrived a wheel to move by
electricity; that Mr. Boze conveyed electricity from one man to another by a jet of water, when they were both placed upon cakes of
rofin, at the diftance of fix paces; and that
Mr. Gordon even fired fpirits by a jet of water ‖.

---

* Hiftoire, p 89.
† Dantzick Memoirs, Vol. ii. p. 426.
‡ Nollet's Recherches, p. 187.
§ Dantzick Memoirs, Vol. ii p. 317, 358.
‖ Phil. Tranf. abridged, Vol. x. p. 276.

MR. GOTTFRIED HEINRICK GRUMMERT,
of Biala in Poland, made a curious experiment
upon electric light, which, as we shall see,
was afterwards made and pursued to great
advantage by Dr. Watson and Mr. Canton.
In order to observe whether an exhausted tube
would give light when it was electrified, as
well as when it was excited, he presented one,
eight inches long, and a third of an inch
wide, to the electrified conductor, and was
surprised to find the light dart very vividly
the whole length of the tube. He also observed, that, some time after the tube had been
presented to the conductor, and exposed to
nothing but the air, it gave light again, without being brought to any electrified body.
This light *in vacuo* Mr. Grummert proposed
to make use of in mines and places, where
common fires, and other lights cannot be had,
and for this purpose he mentions several methods of increasing this light *.

I SHALL conclude this account of the discoveries of the German Philosophers in this
period with a very curious one of professor
Kruger, concerning the change made in the
colour of bodies by the electric effluvia. In
order to try, whether there was any thing
of sulphur in these effluvia, he exposed the
red leaves of wild poppies to the electric
spark, and found that they were presently
changed to white. He was not able to produce any change in yellow colours, nor in

* Dantzick Memoirs, Vol. i. p. 417.

blue

blue immediately; but found that when they
had lain a day or two, after being expofed to
this operation they became white. In thefe
experiments the leaves were faftened with
white wax to plates of tin *.

SUCH a general attention was excited to
electricity by thefe curious difcoveries, that,
in the year 1745, electrical experiments were
exhibited, in Germany and Holland, for
money, as a fhow; and public advertifements
appeared in the news-papers for that purpofe †.

The firing of the effluvia of bodies, which
was firft done in Germany, was foon after repeated in England, and among others by
Dr. Miles; who, as appears by a paper of
his, read at the Royal Society, March the
7th, 1745, kindled phofphorus by the application of the excited tube itfelf to it without
the intervention of any conductor ‡.

THIS gentleman's tube happening to be in
excellent order upon this occafion, he obferved, and was perhaps the firft who obferved,
pencils of rays, which he calls *corufcations*,
darting from the tube, without the aid of any
conductor approaching it. Of thefe corufcations he gave a drawing, which anfwers pretty
exactly to the appearance of fuch pencils as
are now very common, particularly fince Mr.
Canton has taught us the ufe of the amal-
gama, by which a tube may be excited

* Dantzick Memoirs, Vol. iii. p. 393.
† Ibid. Vol. ii. p. 399.
‡ Phil. Tranf. abridged, Vol. x. p. 272.

much

much more ftrongly than it could have been before *.

But the moft diftinguifhed name in this period of the hiftory of electricity, is that of Dr. WATSON. He was one of the firft among the Englifh who took up, and improved upon, the difcoveries made by the Germans; and to his ingenuity, and intenfe application, we owe many curious improvements and difcoveries in electricity. His firft letters to the Royal Society on this fubject are dated between March 28th, and October 24th, 1745.

Dr. WATSON's attention to the fubject of electricity feems firft, or principally, to have been engaged by the accounts of the Germans having fired fpirit of wine by it. In this experiment he fucceeded; and, moreover, found that he was able to fire, not only the ethereal fpirit of Frobenius, and rectified fpirit of wine, but even common proof fpirit. He alfo fired air made inflammable by a chemical procefs †. He even fired both fpirit of wine, and inflammable air, by a drop of cold water, thickened with a mucilage made with the feed of flea-wort, and even with ice ‡. He alfo fired thefe fubftances with a hot poker electrified, when it would not fire them in any other ftate §. He fired gunpowder and difcharged a mufket by the power of electricity, when the gunpowder had been ground with a little camphor, or a few drops of fome

* Phil. Tranf. abridged, Vol. x. p. 272.
† Ibid. p. 286.   ‡ Ibid. p. 290.   § Ibid. p. 288.

H   inflam-

inflammable chemical oil *. Laſtly, it was a diſcovery of Dr. Watſon's, that theſe ſub-ſtances were capable of being fired by what he calls *the repulſive power of electricity*; which was performed by the electrified per-ſon holding the ſpoon which contained the ſubſtance to be fired, and another perſon, not electrified, bringing his finger to it †. Be-fore this time, the ſubſtance to be fired had always been held by a perſon not electrified.

In his attempts to fire electrics per ſe, as turpentine, and balſam of capivi, by this re-pulſive power, he thought he confuted an opinion which had prevailed among many perſons, that electricity only floated on the ſurfaces of bodies, for he found that the fume of theſe ſubſtances could not be fired by a ſpark fetched from the ſpoon which contain-ed them. This ſpark muſt therefore paſs through the electric, from the ſurface of the ſpoon below, which was in contact with the electrified conductor.

Electrifying a number of pieces of fine ſpun glaſs, and other pieces of wire, of the ſame length and thickneſs, he was agree-ably amuſed by obſerving, that the threads of glaſs jumped to the electrified body, and adhered to it without any ſnapping; where-as the wires jumped up and down very faſt, giving a ſnap, and a ſmall flame, every time ‡.

---

* Phil. Tranſ. abridged, Vol. x. p. 289.
† Ibid. p. 281.   ‡ Ibid. p. 286.

In a paper read at the Royal Society, February 6th, 1746, he obferved, that electric fparks appeared different in colour and form, according to the fubftances from which they proceeded; that the fire appeared much redder from rough bodies, as rufty iron, &c. than from polifhed bodies, though they were ever fo fharp, as from polifhed fciffars, &c. He judged that the different appearance was owing rather to the different reflection of the electric light from the furface of the bodies from which it was emitted, than to any difference in the fire itfelf *.

He alfo obferved, that electricity fuffered no refraction in pervading glafs; having found, by exact obfervations, that its direction was always in right lines, even through glaffes of different forms, included one within another, and large fpaces left between each glafs†; that if books or other non-electrics were laid upon glafs and interpofed between the excited electric and light bodies, the direction of the virtue was ftill in right lines, and feemed inftantly to pafs through both the books and the glafs. In thefe experiments he conftantly obferved, that the electric attraction through glafs was much more powerful when the glafs was made warm than when it was cold ‡. He fometimes found electricity to pervade, though in fmall quantities, electrics of above four inches thick §.

* Phil. Tranf. abridged, Vol. x. p. 200.   † Ibid. p. 291.
‡ Ibid. p. 292.   § Ibid. p. 295.

He

He says, that in electriying substances of great extent, the attractive power was first observed at that part of it which was most remote from the excited electric.

He made some experiments which showed, that the fire of electricity was affected, neither by the presence, nor the absence of other fire. One of his experiments was made with a chemical mixture, thirty degrees below the freezing point of Fahrenheit's thermometer; from which, when electrified, the flashes were as powerful, and the strokes as smart, as from red hot iron *.

In a sequel to the above experiments, read the 30th of October 1746, Dr. Watson mentions his having lined a glass globe to a considerable thickness with a mixture of wax and rosin; but he found no difference between that and the other globes †.

He also made various experiments with a number of globes, whirled at the same time, and having one common conductor; and concluded from them, that the power of electricity was increased by the number and size of the globes, to a certain degree, but by no means in proportion to their number and size. Yet the Doctor allows a very great increase, in an inference he makes from these very experiments. As bodies to be electrified, he says, will only contain a certain quantity of electricity; when that quantity is acquired, *which is soonest done by a number of globes,* the

* Phil. Transf. abridged, Vol. x, p. 293.
† Ibid. p. 295.

surcharge

furcharge is diffipated as faft as it is excited
So that, it is plain, more fire was collected
by the number of globes, though the form of
the conductor he made ufe of was fuch as
could not retain it. The great power of his
four globes united, is manifeft from his own
account of them. For, he fays, that when two
pewter plates were held, one in the hand of
an electrified perfon, and the other in the hand
of one who ftood upon the floor ; the flafhes
of pure and bright flame were fo large, and
fucceeded each other fo faft, that, when the
room was darkened, he could diftinctly fee the
faces of thirteen perfons who ftood round the
room *.

Lastly, the Doctor found, that the fmoke
of original electrics was a conductor of electricity, and alfo that flame would conduct the
whole of it undiminifhed ; by obferving that
two perfons, ftanding upon electrics, could
communicate the virtue to each other, with
nothing interpofed but the fmoke in the one
cafe, and flame in the other †.

It was in this period that Mr. Du Tour
difcovered that flame would deftroy electricity;
as he informed the Abbé Nollet, in a letter
dated 21ft Auguft 1745. The fame was alfo
difcovered by Mr. Waitz.

* Phil. Tranf. abridged, Vol. x. p. 295.
† Ibid. p. 296.

PERIOD

PERIOD VIII.

THE HISTORY OF ELECTRICITY, FROM
THE DISCOVERY OF THE LEYDEN PHIAL
IN THE YEARS 1745 AND 1746, TO DR.
FRANKLIN's DISCOVERIES.

SECTION I.

THE HISTORY OF THE LEYDEN PHIAL
ITSELF, TILL DR. FRANKLIN's DISCO-
VERIES RELATING TO IT.

THE end of the year 1745, and the beginning of 1746 were famous for the
moſt ſurpriſing diſcovery that has yet been
made in the whole buſineſs of electricity,
which was the wonderful accumulation of its
power in glaſs, called at firſt the LEYDEN
PHIAL; becauſe made by Mr. Cuneus a native of Leyden, as he was repeating ſome experiments which he had ſeen with Meſſrs.
Muſchenbroeck, and Allamand, profeſſors in
the univerſity of that city *. But the perſon
who firſt made this great diſcovery, was Mr.
Von Kleiſt, dean of the cathedral in Camin;
who, on the 4th of November 1745, ſent an
account of it to Dr. Lieberkuhn at Berlin.
This account, as taken by Mr. Gralath out

* Dalibard's Hiſtoire abrigée, p. 33.

of

of the regifter of the academy at Berlin, to which it had been communicated, is as follows. " When a nail, or a piece of thick " brafs wire, &c. is put into a fmall apothe- " cary's phial and electrified, remarkable " effects follow : but the phial muft be very " dry, or warm. I commonly rub it over " before-hand with a finger, on which I put " fome pounded chalk. If a little mercury " or a few drops of fpirit of wine, be put " into it, the experiment fucceeds the better. " As foon as this phial and nail are removed " from the electrifying glafs, or the prime " conductor, to which it hath been expofed, " is taken away, it throws out a pencil of " flame fo long, that, with this burning ma- " chine in my hand, I have taken above fixty " fteps, in walking about my room. When " it is electrified ftrongly, I can take it into " another room, and there fire fpirits of wine " with it. If while it is electrifying, I put " my finger, or a piece of gold, which I " hold in my hand, to the nail, I receive a " fhock which ftuns my arms and fhoulders.

" A TIN tube, or a man, placed upon " electrics, is electrified much ftronger by this " means than in the common way. When " I prefent this phial and nail to a tin tube, " which I have, fifteen feet long, nothing but " experience can make a perfon believe how " ftrongly it is electrified. I am perfuaded, " he adds, that, in this manner, Mr. Boze " would not have taken a fecond electrical " kifs. Two thin glaffes have been broken

H 4   " by

" by the fhock of it.   It appears to me very
" extraordinary, that when this phial and nail
" are in contact with either conducting or
" non-conducting matter, the ftrong fhock
" does not follow.   I have cemented it to
" wood, metal, glafs, fealing-wax, &c. when
" I have electrified without any great effect.
" The human body, therefore, muft contri-
" bute fomething to it.   This opinion is con-
" firmed by my obferving, that, unlefs I hold
" the phial in my hand, I cannot fire fpirits
" of wine with it *."

Notwithstanding Mr. Kleift immediately communicated an account of this
famous experiment (which indeed it is evident he has but imperfectly defcribed) to Mr.
Winckler at Leipfick, Mr. Swiettiki of Dantzick, Mr. Kruger of Hall, and to the profef-
fors of the academy of Lignitz, as well as to
Dr. Lieberkuhn of Berlin above-mentioned,
they all returned him word, that the experiment did not fucceed with them.   Mr. Gralath of Dantzick, was the firft with whom it
anfwered ; but this was not till after feveral
fruitlefs trials, and receiving farther inftructions from the inventor †.

The Abbé Nollet had information of this
difcovery, and, in confequence of it, fays, in
a letter to Mr. Samuel Wolfe, of the Society
of Dantzick, dated March 9th, 1746, that
the experiment at Leyden was upon principles
fimilar to this made with a phial half full of

* Dantzick Memoirs, Vol. i. p. 407.   † Ibid. p. 411.

water,

water, and a nail dipped in it; and that this
difcovery would have been called the Dantzick experiment, if it had not happened to
have got the name of that of Leyden *.

THE views'which led to this difcovery in
Holland were, as I have been informed, as
follows. Profeffor Mufchenbroeck and his
friends, obferving that electrified bodies, expofed to the common atmofphere, which is
always replete with conducting particles of
various kinds, foon loft their electricity, and
were capable of retaining but a fmall quantity
of it, imagined, that, were the electrified
bodies terminated on all fides by original electrics, they might be capable of receiving a
ftronger power, and retaining it a longer
time. Glafs being the moft convenient electric for this purpofe, and water the moft convenient non-electric, they firft made thefe
experiments with water, in glafs bottles:
but no confiderable difcovery was made, till
Mr. Cuneus, happening to hold his glafs veffel in one hand, containing water, which had
a communication with the prime conductor,
by means of a wire; and, with the other
hand, difengaging it from the conductor
(when he imagined the water had received as
much electricity as the machine could give it)
was furprifed by a fudden fhock in his arms
and breaft, which he had not in the leaft expected from the experiment.

* Dantzick Memoirs, Vol. i. p. 409.

MR.

MR. ALLAMAND and Mr. Muſchenbroeck were the firſt who repeated and publiſhed an account of this experiment in Holland, the Abbé Nollet and Monſieur Monnïer in France, and Meſſrs. Gralath and Rugger in Germany *.

IT is extremely curious to obſerve the deſcriptions which philoſophers, who firſt felt the electriſical ſhock, give of it ; eſpecially as we are ſure we can give ourſelves the ſame ſenſation, and thereby compare their deſcriptions with the reality. Terror and ſurprize certainly contributed not a little to the exaggerated accounts they gave of it ; and, could we not have repeated the experiment, we ſhould have formed a very different idea of it from what it really is, even when given in greater ſtrength than thoſe who firſt felt this electrical ſhock were able to give it. It will amuſe my readers if I give them an example or two.

MR. MUSCHENBROECK, who tried the experiment with a very thin glaſs bowl, ſays, in a letter to Mr. Reaumur, which he wrote ſoon after the experiment, that he felt himſelf ſtruck in his arms, ſhoulder and breaſt, ſo that he loſt his breath, and was two days before he recovered from the effects of the blow and the terror. He adds, that he would not take a ſecond ſhock for the kingdom of France †.

* Dantzick Memoirs, Vol ii. p. 433.
+ Hiſtoire, de l'electricité, p. 30.

THE firſt time Mr. Allamand made this experiment (which was only with a common beer glaſs) he ſays, that he loſt the uſe of his breath for ſome moments; and then felt ſo intenſe a pain all along his right arm, that he at firſt apprehended ill conſequences from it, though it ſoon after went off without any inconvenience *. But the moſt remarkable account is that of Mr. Winckler of Leipſic. He ſays, that the firſt time he tried the Leyden experiment, he found great convulſions by it in his body; and that it put his blood into great agitation; ſo that he was afraid of an ardent fever, and was obliged to uſe refrigerating medicines. He alſo felt an heavineſs in his head, as if a ſtone lay upon it. Twice, he ſays, it gave him a bleeding at his noſe, to which he was not inclined. His wife (whoſe curioſity, it ſeems, was ſtronger than her fears) received the ſhock only twice, and found herſelf ſo weak, that ſhe could hardly walk; and, a week after, upon recovering courage to receive another ſhock, ſhe bled at the noſe after taking it only once †.

WE are not, however, to infer from theſe inſtances, that all the electricians were ſtruck with this panic. Few, I believe, would have joined with the cowardly profeſſor, who ſaid that he would not take a ſecond for the kingdom of France. Far different from theſe were the ſentiments of the magnanimous Mr. Boze, who with a truly philoſophical heroiſm, worthy

* Phil. Tranſ. abridged, Vol. x. p. 321.
† Ibid. p. 327.

of

of the renowned Empedocles, faid he wifhed he might die by the electric fhock, that the account of his death might furnifh an article for the memoirs of the French Academy of Sciences *. But it is not given to every electrician to die in fo glorious a manner as the juftly envied Richman.

IT was this aftonifhing experiment that gave eclat to electricity. From this time it became the fubject of general converfation. Every body was eager to fee, and, notwithftanding the terrible account that was reported of it, to *feel* the experiment; and in the fame year in which it was difcovered, numbers of perfons, in almoft every country in Europe, got a livelihood by going about and fhowing it.

WHILE the vulgar of every age, fex, and rank were viewing this prodigy of nature and philofophy with wonder and amazement, we are not furprized to find all the electricians of Europe immediately employed in repeating this great experiment, and attending to the circumftances of it. Mr. Allamand remarked, that, when he firft tried it, he ftood fimply upon the floor, and not upon cakes of rofin. He faid, that it did not fucceed with all kinds of glafs; for that, though he had tried feveral, he had perfect fuccefs with none but that of Bohemia, and that he had tried Englifh glaffes without any effect at all †. Profeffor Mufchenbroeck at that time only

* Hiftoire. p. 164.
† Phil. Tranf. abridged, Vol. x. p. 321.

observed,

obferved, that the glafs muft not be all wet on the outfide.

IT is no wonder that fo few of the properties of glafs charged with electrical fire were known at firft, notwithftanding the attention that was immediately given to the fubject by all the electricians in Europe. The experiment is, to this day, juftly viewed with aftonifhment by the moft profound electricians: for, though fome remarkable phenomena of it have been excellently accounted for by Dr. Franklin, and others, much remains to be done; and, in many refpects, the circumftances attending it are ftill inexplicable. What will refult from more attention being given to it, time only can fhow.

To begin the farther illuftration of this difcovery with fuch of the phenomena as were obferved in Germany, where it was made. Mr. Gralath made the fhock much ftronger by ufing a glafs veffel five inches in diameter, with a narrow neck, ten inches long;·by fubftituting an iron wire with a knob of tin for the iron nail, and water for fpirit of wine*. He firft found, that the fame fhock could be communicated to a number of perfons, who took hold of one another's hands; if the perfon at one extremity of the line they made, touched the outfide of the phial, and he at the other touched a wire communicating with the infide. In this manner, on the 10th of April, 1746, he gave

* Dantzick Memoirs, Vol. ii. p. 411.

a fhock

a fhock to twenty perfons; and he fays, he did not doubt, but it might be given to a thoufand *. When thefe perfons were con-nected by pieces of metal, and did not hold one another's hands, they found the fame fhock, but not when they held wood, and other imperfect conductors †. This gentle-man, alfo, gave a fhock, by means of long wires, to a perfon ftanding in a garden, while he himfelf, who directed the experiment, had the machine in a part of the houfe at a confi-derable diftance ‡; and he was the firft who made what we now call an *electrical battery*; for he increafed the fhock by charging feveral phials at the fame time §. Laftly he obferv-ed that if the phial had the leaft crack in it, it could never give a fhock; and alfo that when a phial was difcharged it acquired a fmall charge by ftanding, without receiving any thing from the machine, fo as to give a fmall fhock ||. This is what we now call the *refi-duum* of a charge, and is properly that part of the charge that lay on the uncoated part of the phial, which doth not let go all its electricity at once; fo that it is, afterwards, gradually diffufed to the coating.

Mr. Winckler found out the method of making the difcharge of the phial without feeling the fhock himfelf, by not bringing his own body into the direct circuit ¶. He alfo gave the fhock when feveral ells of run-

* Dantzick Memoirs, Vol. ii. p. 439.   † Ibid. p. 440.
‡ Ibid.   § Ibid. p. 552.
|| Ibid. Vol. i. p. 514, 516.   ¶ Ibid. Vol. ii. p. 459.

ning water, in his garden, made part of the circuit. This he did on the 28th of July 1746, about the fame time that Monfieur Monnier performed the fame experiment in France *. And, laftly, he found, that the more globes were ufed, and the larger they were, the ftronger was the fhock†. This muft be the confequence of increafing the power of excitation.

WHEN Mr. Jallabert made the Leyden experiment with hot water, the phial broke by a fpontaneous difcharge, and a circular piece, two lines and a half in diameter, was thrown from the place of the rupture, againft a wall, which was at the diftance of five feet. The veffel, he fays, had no crack, or other injury ‡.

DR. WATSON, who gives an account of this famous experiment in the Philofophical Tranfactions, obferves, that it fucceeded beft when the phial, which contained the water, was of the thinneft glafs, and the water warmer than the ambient air. He fays he tried the effect of increafing the quantity of water in glafs veffels of different fizes, as far as four gallons, without in the leaft increafing the ftroke. He alfo obferved, that the force of the ftroke did not increafe in proportion to the fize of the globe, or the number of globes employed upon the occafion; for that he had been as forcibly ftruck with a phial

---

* Dantzick Memoirs, Vol. iii. p. 504.
† Ibid. p. 526.　　　　‡ Jallabert's Experiences, p. 128.

charged

charged by means of a globe of feven inches
in diameter, as from one of fixteen, or from
three of ten; and that, at Hamburgh, a fphere
had been employed of a Flemifh ell in diameter, without the expected increafe of
power. But, in both thefe·obfervations, there
muft have been fome miftake. He found,
that if mercury was ufed inftead of water,
the ftroke was by no means increafed in proportion to its fpecific gravity. He alfo firft obferved, that feveral men, touching each other,
and ftanding upon electrics, were all fhocked,
though only one touched the gun barrel; but
that no more fire was vifible from them
all, than if one had only difcharged it.

SEVERAL of thefe obfervations fhow how
imperfectly this great experiment was underftood, for fome time after it was firft made.
Dr. Watfon, however, obferved a circumftance
attending the charging of the phial, which, if
purfued, would have led him to the difcovery,
which was afterwards made by Dr. Franklin.
He fays, that " when the phial is well elec-
" trified, and you apply your hand thereto,
" you fee the fire flafh from the outfide of
" the glafs, wherever you touch it, and it
" crackles in your hand *."

HE alfo obferved, that when a fingle wire
only was faftened round a phial, properly
filled with warm water, and charged; upon
the inftant of its explofion, the electrical cor-
rufcations were feen to dart from the wire,

* Philofophical Tranfactions abridged, Vol. x. p. 298.

and

and to illuminate the water contained in the phial.

SEVERAL other very important circumstances, relating to the difcharge of the phial, were obferved by Dr. Watfon. He found that the ftroke was, *cæteris paribus*, as the points of contact of the non-electrics on the outfide of the glafs. And upon fhowing Dr. Bevis the experiments which proved this affertion, the Doctor fuggefted a more clear and fatiffactory method of proving it, and which has been the means of accumulating and increafing the force of charged glafs, far beyond what was expected from the firft difcovery of it. This method was, *coating* the outfide of the phial, very near to the neck, with fheet-lead, or tinfoil. When a bottle was prepared in this manner, and nearly filled with water, they obferved, that a perfon who only held in his hand a fmall wire communicating with that coating, felt as ftrong a fhock as he would have felt, if his hand had been in actual contact with every part of the phial touched by the coating *.

DR. WATSON alfo difcovered, that the electrical power, in the difcharge of the phial, darts *rectiffimo curfu*, as he ftyles it, between the gun-barrel and the phial; and, though it is not ftrictly true, that the fhock goes the neareft way, yet it does fo *cæteris paribus*, which alone was a confiderable difcovery for that time. He obferved, that, in a company

* Phil. Tranf. abridged, Vol. x. p. 299.

I

joining hands, a perſon touching two other perſons in the circle, who did themſelves touch one another, felt nothing of the ſhock, his body making no neceſſary part of the circle; and alſo, if a man, holding a wire, which communicated with the outſide of the phial, as it hung upon the conductor, ſhould touch the conductor with it; the exploſion was made, but the man felt nothing *.

In a paper read at the Royal Society, January 21ſt, 1748, Dr. Watſon mentions another diſcovery relating to the Leyden phial, which Dr. Bevis ſuggeſted, and he completed. Having been before fully ſatisfied, that the ſhock from the phial was not in proportion to the quantity of matter contained in the glaſs, but was increaſed by it, and likewiſe by the number of points of non-electric contact on the outſide of the glaſs; he procured three jars, into which he put round leaden ſhot, and, joining their wires and coating, diſcharged them all as one jar. Upon this he obſerved, that the electrical exploſion from two or three of thoſe jars was not double or treble to that from one of them; but that the exploſion from three was much louder than that from two, and the exploſion from two much louder than that from one †.

This experiment had induced him to imagine, that the exploſion from thoſe jars was owing to the great quantity of non-electric matter contained in them. And whilſt he was

* Phil. Tranſ. abridged, Vol. x. p. 301.
† Ibid. p. 374.

confidering of fome certain method of affur-
ing himfelf whether the fact was fo, Dr. Bevis
informed him, that he had found the electrical explofion to be as great from covering the
fides of a pane of glafs, within about an inch
of the edge (which was a curious improvement of Mr. Smeaton's), as it could have been
from an half pint phial of water. Upon this
Dr. Watfon coated large jars with leaf filver,
both infide and outfide, within an inch of the
top, and from the great expofion he produced, when fo little non-electric matter was contained in them, he was of opinion, that the
effect of the Leyden bottle was greatly increafed by, if it was not principally owing to,
not fo much the quantity of non-electric matter contained in the glafs, as the number of
points of non-electric contact within the glafs,
and the denfity of the matter of which thofe
points confifted; provided the matter was, in
its own nature, a ready conductor of electricity. He alfo obferved, that the explofion
was greater from hot water inclofed in glaffes,
than from cold; and from his coated jars
warmed, than when cold *.

THE Doctor obferved, that when the circle
for the difcharge was not through perfect
conductors, the explofion was made flowly,
and not all at once. This law, he fays, was
invariable, but he was not able to account for
it. But to prove that the electricity paffed
with its whole force through the circle of

* Phil. Tranf. abridged, Vol. x. p. 377.

non-

non-electrics, he made a circuit confifting of
iron bars, and fpoons filled with fpirits between each bar (but at fome fmall diftance
from them), and, upon the explofion, all the
fpoons were on fire at once. This was the
firft time, as he obferves, that fpirits were
fired without either the fpirits, or the non-
electric on which they were placed, being infulated, or put upon original electrics. And
yet, he fays, though we know, from its effects, that the electricity goes through the
whole circuit of non-electrics, with all its
vigour, its progrefs is fo quick, as not to affect, by attracting or otherwife, any light
bodies difpofed very near the non-electrics,
through which it muft neceffarily pafs *.

IT is curious to obferve in what manner
Dr. Watfon explained the fhock of the Leyden phial, about the time that he firft made
the experiment with it. He had then been
led (by a courfe of experiments which will be
mentioned hereafter) to the notion both of the
afflux, and *efflux* of electric matter in all electrical experiments. To apply this principle
to the cafe in hand, he fuppofed, that the
man who felt the fhock parted with as much
of the fire from his body, as was accumulated in the water and the gun-barrel; and that
he felt the effect in both arms, from the fire
which was in his body, rufhing through one
arm to the gun barrel, and through the other
to the phial. He imagined alfo, that as much

---

* Phil. Tranf. abridged, Vol. x. p. 378.

fire

fire as the man parted with was inftantly replaced from the floor of the room, and that
with a violence equal to the manner in which
he loft it. It alfo appears, from Dr. Watfon's
remarks on fome fubfequent experiments of
Mr. Monnier, that he then imagined, that
though a confiderable quantity of the electric
matter pervaded the glafs (as he thought was
feen upon prefenting a non-electric body to
it, when it ftood upon the glafs ftand, and
without which it could not be charged at all)
yet, that the lofs of the electric matter this
way was not equal to what came in by the
wire; the thinnefs of the glafs permitting it
not wholly, but partially to ftop the electricity *.

AFTERWARDS, when (from a courfe of
experiments, which will alfo be recited in
their proper place) Dr. Watfon changed his
opinion about this afflux and efflux of electric matter, with a generofity and franknefs
becoming every inquirer after truth, he retracted this hypothefis; and, in refutation of
it, he farther adds, that the charged phial
will explode with equal violence, if the hoop
of the wire be bent, fo as to come near the
coating of the phial, without any other non-
electric body being near, from which fuch a
quantity could be fupplied. He had alfo obferved, that if a man ftood upon glafs, and
difcharged the phial, he felt the fame fhock
as if he had ftood upon the floor. I fhall fub-

* Phil. Tranf. abridged, Vol. x. p. 348.

join

join a remarkable paragraph of the Doctor himfelf upon this occafion, as I think it very applicable even to us, in this more advanced ftate of the fcience.

" I TAKE notice of thefe," fays the Doctor, " in as much as, notwithftanding the " very great progrefs which has been made " in our improvements in this part of natural " philofophy, within thefe few years; pofte- " rity will regard us as only in our *noviciate*; " and therefore it behoves us, as far as we " can be juftified therein by experiment, to " correct any conclufions we may have " drawn, if others yet more probable prefent " themfelves *." The Doctor has lived to fee, not only that *pofterity* would confider him and his affiftants at that time, as in their noviciate; but he *himfelf*, already in the courfe of a few years, looks upon both himfelf and them in the fame light. And, confidering the quick advances ftill making in this fcience, it is to be hoped he may ftill live to fee, even the electricians of the prefent year to have been only in their noviciate.

HAVING feen what was done by Dr. Watfon towards explaining the electric fhock, before it was undertaken by Dr. Franklin; let us fee what obligations we are under to other Englifh electricians, and particularly Mr. Wilfon.

MR. WILSON fays that, as early as the year 1746, he difcovered a method of giving

---

* Phil. Tranf. abridged, Vol. x. p. 373.

the

the fhock to any particular part of the body without affecting the reft *. He increafed the ftrength of the fhock by plunging the phial in water, thereby giving it a coating of water on the outfide, as high as it was filled on the infide †.

In a letter to Mr. Smeaton, dated Dublin October 6th, 1746, he mentions his having made fome experiments, in order to difcover the law of accumulation of the electric matter in the Leyden bottle; and found, that it was always in proportion to the thinnefs of the glafs, the furface of the glafs, and that of the non-electrics in contact with the infide and outfide thereof. The experiments, he fays, were made with water a little warmed, which was poured into the bottle, while the outfide was immerged in a veffel filled with water, but a little colder; leaving three inches, or thereabout, uncovered, which was preferved dry and free from duft. An account of this experiment he wrote to Mr. Folkes, and it was read before the Royal Society, October 23d, 1746, as appears by their minutes of that day, though the original was loft or miflaid.

ANOTHER curious experiment Mr. Wilfon made, in order to prove an hypothefis, which he conceived very early, of the influence of a fubtle medium furrounding all bodies, and refifting the entrance or exit of the electric fluid. To determine this, he made

* Wilfon's Effay, p. 83.　　† Ibid. p. 71.

　　the

the Leyden experiment with a chain, and
confidered each link of it as having two furfaces, at leaft; fo that lengthening or fhorten-
ing the chain, in each experiment, would occafion different refiftances; and the event, he
fays, proved accordingly. When he made
the difcharge with one wire only, he found
the refiftance to be lefs than when a chain was
ufed. But to leave no room for doubt, he
caufed the chain to be ftretched with a weight,
that the links might be brought nearer into
contact, and the event was the fame as when
a fingle wire had been ufed *.

Two circuits being made, one confifting of
the arms of a man, and the other of the links
of a chain; he found, that the fire would
take the arms of the man; but that if the
chain were ftretched, it would take the chain.
No perfon, he fays, who has not made the
experiment, would imagine, with how much
force the chain muft be ftretched before the
experiment will anfwer, and the electric fluid
pafs through it without producing a fpark at
any of the links; that is, before the links can
be brought into abfolute contact with one
another, their own weight being by no means
fufficient †.

MR. WILSON obferved, that if one part of
the Leyden phial wss ground very thin, and
covered with fealing-wax till it was charged,
and then had the fealing-wax taken off, and
a conductor communicating with the earth

* Letter to Hoadley.   † Wilfon and Hoadley, p. 65.

touched

touched the thin part, the charge would be diffipated in nearly half the time that it otherwife would have been *.

HE obferved that bodies, placed without the electric circuit, would be affected with the fhock, if they were only in contact with any part of it, or very near it. To fhew this to the moft advantage, he fet a charged phial upon a glafs ftand, and placed feveral pieces of brafs upon the ftand, one of them in contact with the chain that formed the circuit, and others a twentieth of an inch from it, or from one another; and, upon making the difcharge, there was a fpark vifible between each of them †.

ANALOGOUS, in fome refpects, to this, was Mr. Wilfon's obfervation, that if the circuit was not made of metals, or other very good conductors, the perfon who laid hold of them, in order to perform the experiment, felt a confiderable fhock in that arm which was in contact with the circuit.

HE alfo obferved, that when the phial was coated, within and without, with metals, the firft explofion bore the greateft proportion to the fubfequent ones, the whole charge being diffipated almoft at once; whereas, when water was ufed, the fubfequent explofions were more in number, and more confiderable; and that when the phial was charged with nothing but a wire inferted into it, the firft explofion

* Wilfon's Effay, p. 74.　　† Ibid. p. 90.

and

and the fubfequent ones were ftill more nearly equal.

MR. WILSON once happening to break a
fmall wire by the convulfive fhock given to
his arms by the Leyden phial, he faftened to
his hands, well guarded with leather, a large
wire, of the thicknefs of a flender knitting
needle, and placed himfelf in fuch a manner,
that it would neceffarily be ftretched, if his
arm fhould be convulfed again. He accordingly difcharged the phial, and this wire was
broken, like the former *.

MR. GEORGE GRAHAM fhewed how feveral circuits for the difcharge of the Leyden
phial might be made at the fame time, and
the fire be made to pafs through them all. He
made a number of perfons take hold of a
plate of metal, communicating with the outfide of the phial; and all together, likewife,
laid hold of a brafs rod with which the difcharge was made; when they were all fhocked at the fame time, and in the fame degree †.

LASTLY, Mr. Canton found, that if a
charged phial was placed upon electrics, the
wire and the coating would give a fpark or
two alternately ; and that, by continuing this
operation, the phial would be difcharged ‡.
This difcovery, which is the firft that I
find recorded of this excellent philofopher, to
whom the fcience of electricity owes fo much,
has a near affinity to the great difcovery of

---

* Wilfon's Effay, p. 84.   † Ibid. p. 128.
‡ Ibid. p 64.

Dr.

Dr. Franklin; but he did not then obferve, that thofe alternate fparks proceeded from the two contrary electricities. This hiftory will furnifh many more inftances of perfons being on the eve of great difcoveries, without actually making them. Both Mr. Gralath and Mr. Richman obferved, in feveral cafes, a ftronger fpark between two bodies, when both of them were electrified, than when only one of them was in that ftate; but neither of them fufpected that the electricities were of a different kind *.

We have feen what obfervations the Englifh philofophers had made upon the Leyden experiment before the time of Dr. Franklin; let us now take a view of what was done by electricians in other parts of the world, within the fame period.

As Mr. Mufchenbroeck's letter to Mr. Reaumur, concerning the experiment of the phial, came at a time when many learned men were employed about electricity, the Abbé Nollet, and Mr. De Monnier, gentlemen of the academy, zealous to fearch into fo an extraordinary a phenomenon, divefting themfelves of the fear with which the profeffor's letter had juftly infpired them, made the experiment upon themfelves, and, in like manner, faid they found the commotion very terrible. The report of it inftantly fpread through the court and the city, from whence all ranks of men crouded to fee this new

* Wilcke's Preface to the German Verfion of Franklin's Letters.

kind

kind of thunder, and to experience the effect
of it *.

THE Abbé Nollet was the firft who made
experiments upon the phial in France, and
the relult of many of them was the fame
with what Dr. Watfon had difcovered, for
which reafon I fhall not recite them here.
They may all be feen at one view in his
Leçons de phyfique, p. 481. The circumftances
which the Englifh philofophers had not attended to, are the following.

THE Abbé received a fhock from a bottle
out of which the air had been exhaufted, and
into which the end of his conductor had been
inferted. As he was amufing himfelf with
obferving the beautiful irradiations of the
electric light in the veffel, it immediately occurred to him, that, being fo ftrongly electrified, it could not fail to give a fhock fimilar
to that of the Leyden phial, and without any
farther reflection, laying one hand on the veffel, and bringing the other to the conductor,
his conjecture was verified, but in a manner
that gave him more pain than he could have
wifhed. The blow he received was greater,
he fays, than he ever felt from the Leyden
experiment in any other form †.

IN the fame place he obferves, that he
never confidered the water in the phial as of
any ufe, but to convey the electric matter into the infide of the glafs ; and that he afcribed the force of the glafs in giving a fhock, to

* Nollet's Leçons de Phyfique, p. 452. Ac. Par. 1746. M.
p. 5. † Recherches, p. 426.

that

that property of it, whereby it retained it more ftrongly than conductors do, and was not fo eafily divefted of it as they are. The Abbé alfo gave the fhock with porcelain, and obferved, that fome perfons were much more fenfible to it than others in whatever part of the circuit they were placed *.

MR. MONNIER is faid, by Mr. Buffon, to have been the firft who difcovered that the Leyden phial would retain its electricity a confiderable time after it was charged, and to have found it do fo for thirty-fix hours, in time of froft. He frequently electrified his phial at home, and brought it in his hand, through many ftreets, from the college of Harcourt to his apartments in the King's garden, without any confiderable diminution of its efficacy †.

In France as well as in Germany experiments were made to try how many perfons might feel the fhock of the fame phial. The Abbé Nollet, whofe name is famous in electricity, gave it to one hundred and eighty of the guards, in the King's prefence; and at the grand convent of the Carthufians in Paris, the whole community formed a line of nine hundred toifes, by means of iron wires between every two perfons (which far exceeded the line of one hundred and eighty of the guards) and the whole company upon the difcharge of the phial, gave a fudden fpring, at

* Ac. Par. 1746, M. p. 11, 26.
† Phil. Tranf. abridged, Vol. x. p. 333.

the

the fame inftant of time, and all felt the
fhock equally *.

Mʀ. Nᴏʟʟᴇᴛ alfo tried the effect of the
electric fhock upon two birds, one of which
was a fparrow, and the other a chaffinch,
which, as far as I can find, were the firft
brute animals of any kind that ever received
it.   The confequence was, that upon the firft
fhock, they were both inftantaneoufly ftruck
motionlefs, and, as it were, lifelefs, though
for a time only ; for they recovered fome few
minutes after.   Upon the fecond fhock, the
fparrow was ftruck dead, and, upon examination, was found livid without, as if it had
been killed with a flafh of lightning ; moft of
the blood veffels in the body being burft by the
fhock.   The chaffinch revived as before †.
Fifhes were alfo killed with the electric fhock,
by the Abbé, and others.

Tʜᴇ circumftance of the blood veffels of
the fparrow being burft is pretty fingular.   I
have feen no fuch effect, when fmaller animals have been killed by a fhock fifty times
as great as, it is probable, the Abbé ufed upon this occafion.

Tʜᴇ Abbé Nollet, as well as Mr. Jallabert,
mentions the burfting of glafs veffels by the
electric explofion.   They were pierced, he
fays, with round holes, three or four lines in
diameter ‡.

Iᴛ feems that the French philofophers, as
well as the Englifh, had obferved, that, if the

* Phil. Tranf. abridged, Vol. x. p. 335.   † Ibid p. 336.
Ac. Par. 1746. M. p. 32.   ‡ Nollet's Lettres, Vol. i. p. 42.

phial ftood upon glafs, it could not be charged, except a perfon's hand, or fome other
non-electric fubftance were brought near to it.
Upon this they imagined the fire ftreamed
out of the hand, and paffed through the fubftance of the phial into the water *. This fact
furprifed them very much, as it well might.
Mr. Monnier obferved, that a light body would
be attracted by a charged phial, as it ftood
upon the table, and produced a fpark if any
perfon touched the wire; but that the light
body muft be fufpended by a non-electric fubftance †. He likewife found, that when the
charged phial ftood upon glafs, it might be
handled with all fafety ‡. Thefe experiments feem not to have been made with proper circumfpection: for by an attention to
thefe very circumftances, Dr. Franklin was
afterwards led to the great difcovery of the
different quality of the electricity, on different
fides of the glafs.

* Phil. Tranf. abridged, Vol. x. p. 334.
† Ac. Par. 1746, M. p. 684.
‡ Phil. Tranf. abridged, Vol. x. p. 337.

SECTION

SECTION II.

THE METHODS USED BY THE FRENCH AND
ENGLISH PHILOSOPHERS, TO MEASURE
THE DISTANCE TO WHICH THE ELEC-
TRIC SHOCK CAN BE CARRIED, AND THE
VELOCITY WITH WHICH IT PASSES.

WE are now come to an ampler field of
electrical experiments, in which we
shall be spectators, not of what might be exhibited in a private room, and by a few operators,
but where we shall find an amazing apparatus
necessary, and a great number of assistants in
the management of it; as well as the greatest
judgment, and the most unwearied patience
in the conduct of it.

THE French philosophers were the first to
appear in this field, but they excited the
English to go far beyond them in these great
undertakings. It has been said already, that
a circuit was made of nine hundred toises,
consisting of men holding iron wires betwixt
each two, through which the electric shock
was sensibly felt. At another time, they made
the shock pass through a wire two thousand
toises in length, that is near a Paris league,
or about two English miles and a half;
though part of the wires dragged upon wet
grass, went over charmil hedges, or pali-
sades, and over ground newly ploughed up.
Into another chain they took the water of the
bason

bafon in the Thuilleries, the furface of which was about an acre, and the phial was difcharged through it *. Mr. Monnier, who made this experiment, mentioning the quantity of furface in the bafon of water, as if it was of confequence to the experiment, and faying it was *electrified,* (tho' all he meant by this was, that it received and tranfmitted the electric charge †.) Mr. Gralath made feveral experiments, which prove, that bodies which form the circuit of the fhock are not properly electrified ‡.

MR. MONNIER the younger, alfo endeavoured to determine the velocity of the electric matter; and for this purpofe, made the fhock pafs through an iron wire of nine hundred and fifty toifes in length, but he could not obferve, that it fpent a quarter of a fecond in paffing it. He alfo found, that when a wire of one thoufand three hundred and nineteen feet, with its extremities brought near together, was electrified; the electricity ceafed at one end, the moment it was taken off at the other. This fact refuted the opinion of thofe who maintained, that it was the force of the electrical *fhock*, which threw the electric matter with fo great velocity §.

Thefe attempts of the French gave occafion to the greater, the more accurate, and the more numerous experiments of the Englifh.

* Phil. Tranf. abridged, Vol. x. p. 336.
† Ac. Par. 1746. M. p. 678.
‡ Dantzick Memoirs, Vol. iii. p. 552.
§ Ac. Par. 1746, M. p. 686.

The names of the Englifh gentlemen, animated with a truly philofophical fpirit, and who were indefatigable in this bufinefs, deferve to be tranfmitted to pofterity in every work of this nature.

The principal agent in this great fcene was Dr. Watfon. He planned and directed all the operations, and never failed to be prefent at every experiment. His chief affiftants were Martin Folkes, Efq. prefident of the Royal Society, Lord Charles Cavendifh, Dr. Bevis, Mr. Graham, Dr. Birch, Mr. Peter Daval, Mr. Trembley, Mr. Ellicott, Mr. Robins, and Mr. Short. Many other perfons, and fome of diftinction, gave their attendance occafionally.

Dr. Watson, who wrote the hiftory of their proceedings, in order to lay them before the Royal Society, begins with obferving (what was verified in all their experiments) that the electric fhock is not, ftrictly fpeaking, conducted in the fhorteft manner poffible, unlefs the bodies through which it paffes conduct equally well; for that, if they conduct unequally, the circuit is always formed through the beft conductors, though the length of it be ever fo great.

The firft attempt thefe gentlemen made, was to convey the electric fhock acrofs the river Thames, making ufe of the water of the river for one part of the chain of communication This they accomplifhed on the 14th and 18th of July 1747, by faftening a wire all along Weftminfter bridge, at a confiderable

height

height above the water. One end of this wire communicated with the coating of a charged phial, the other being held by an obferver, who, in his other hand, held an iron rod, which he dipped into the river. On the oppofite fide of the river, ftood a gentleman, who, likewife, dipped an iron rod in the river, with one hand; and in the other held a wire, the extremity of which might be brought into contact with the wire of the phial.

Upon making the difcharge, the fhock was felt by the obfervers on both fides the river, but more fenfibly by thofe who were ftationed on the fame fide with the machine; part of the electric fire having gone from the wire down the moift ftones of the bridge, thereby making feveral fhorter circuits to the phial; but ftill all paffing through the gentlemen who were ftationed on the fame fide with the machine. This was, in a manner, demonftrated by fome perfons feeling a fenfible fhock in their arms and feet, who only happened to touch the wire, at the time of one of the difcharges, when they were ftanding upon the wet fteps which led to the river. In one of the difcharges made upon this occafion, fpirits were kindled by the fire which had gone through the river *.

Upon this, and the fubfequent occafions, the gentlemen made ufe of wires, in pre-

* Phil. Tranf. abridged, Vol. x. p. 394.

ference

ference to chains, for this, among other reafons, that the electricity which was conducted by chains was not fo ftrong, as that which
was conducted by wires. This, as they well
obferved, was occafioned by the junctures of
the links not being fufficiently clofe, as appeared by the fnapping and flafhing at every
juncture, where there was the leaft feparation. Thefe leffer fnappings, being numerous in the whole length of a chain, very
fenfibly leffened the great difcharge at the
gun-barrel.

THEIR next attempt was to force the electrical fhock to make a circuit of two miles,
at the New River at Stoke Newington. This
they performed on the 24th of July 1747, at
two places; at one of which the diftance by
land was eight hundred feet, and by water
two thoufand: in the other, the diftance by
land was two thoufand eight hundred feet, and
by water eight thoufand. The difpofition of
the apparatus was fimilar to what they before
ufed at Weftminfter bridge, and the effect anfwered their utmoft expectations. But, as in
both cafes, the obfervers at both extremities
of the chain, which terminated in the water,
felt the fhock, as well when they ftood with
their rods fixed into the earth twenty feet
from the water, as when they were put into
the river; it occafioned a doubt, whether the
electric circuit was formed through the wind-
ings of the river, or a much fhorter way, by
the ground of the meadow: for the experi-

ment

ment plainly fhewed, that the meadow-ground, with the grafs on it, conducted the electricity very well.

By fubfequent experiments, they were fully convinced, that the electricity had not, in this cafe, been conveyed by the water of the river, which was two miles in length, but by land, where the diftance was only one mile ; in which fpace, however, the electric matter muft necessarily have paffed over the New River twice, have gone through feveral gravels pits, and a large ftubble field *.

July 28th, they repeated the experiment, at the fame place, with the following variation of circumftances. The iron wire was, in its whole length, fupported by dry fticks, and the obfervers ftood upon original electrics; the effect of which was, that they felt the fhock much more fenfibly than when the conducting wire had lain upon the ground, and when the obfervers had likewife ftood upon the ground, as in the former experiment.

Afterwards, every thing elfe remaining as before, the obfervers were directed, inftead of dipping their rods into the water, to put them into the ground, each one hundred and fifty feet from the water. They were both fmartly ftruck, though they were diftant from each other above five hundred feet †.

* Phil. Tranf. abridged, Vol. x. p. 360.
† Ibid. p. 357.

THE

THE same gentlemen, pleased with the success of their former experiments undertook another, the object of which was, to determine, whether the electric virtue could be conveyed through dry ground; and, at the same time, to carry it through water to a greater distance than they had done before. For this purpose, they pitched upon Highbury-barn beyond Islington, where they carried it into execution on the 5th of August 1747. They chose a station for their machine, almost equally distant from two other stations for observers upon the New River; which were somewhat more than a mile asunder by land, and two miles by water. They had found the streets of London, when dry, to conduct very strongly, for about forty yards; and the dry road at Newington about the same distance. The event of this trial answered their expectations. The electric fire made the circuit of the water, when both the wires and the observers were supported upon original electrics, and the rods dipped into the river. They also both felt the shock, when one of the observers was placed in a dry gravelly pit, about three hundred yards nearer the machine than the former station, and one hundred yards distant from the river: from which the gentlemen were satisfied, that the dry gravelly ground had conducted the electricity as strongly as water.

FROM the shocks which the observers received in their bodies, when the electric power was conducted upon dry sticks, they

were

were of opinion, that, from the difference of distance simply considered, the force of the shock, as far as they had yet experienced, was very little, if at all impaired. When the observers stood upon electrics, and touched the water, or the ground, with the iron rods, the shock was always felt in their arms or wrists; when they stood upon the ground with their iron rods, they felt the shock in their elbows, wrists, and ancles; and when they stood upon the ground without rods, the shock was always felt in the elbow and wrist of that hand which held the conducting wire, and in both ancles *.

THE last attempt of this kind which these gentlemen made, and which required all their sagacity and address in the conduct of it, was to try whether the electric shock was perceptible at twice the distance to which they had before carried it, in ground perfectly dry, and where no water was near; and also to distinguish, if possible, the respective velocity of electricity and sound.

FOR this purpose, they fixed upon Shooter's-hill, and made their first experiments on the 14th of August 1747, a time, when, as it happened, but one shower of rain had fallen during five preceding weeks. The wire communicating with the iron rod, which made the discharge, was six thousand seven hundred and thirty-two feet in length, and was supported all the way upon baked sticks;

* Philosophical Transactions abridged, Vol. x. p. 360.

K 4

as was alſo the wire which communicated with the coating of the phial, which was three thouſand eight hundred and ſixty-eight feet long, and the obſervers were diſtant from each other two miles. The reſult of the exploſion demonſtrated, to the . ſatisfaction of the gentlemen preſent, that the circuit performed by the electric matter was four miles, viz. two miles of wire, and two of dry ground, the ſpace between the extremities of the wires ; a diſtance which, without trial, as they juſtly obſerved, was too great to be credited. A gun was diſcharged at the inſtant of the exploſion, and the obſervers had ſtop watches in their hands, to note the moment when they felt the ſhock : but, as far as they could diſtinguiſh, the time in which the electric matter performed that vaſt circuit might have been inſtantaneous *.

In all the exploſions where the circuit was made of conſiderable length, it was obſerved, that though the phial was very well charged, yet that the ſnap at the gun barrel, made by the exploſion, was not near ſo loud as when the circuit was formed in a room; ſo that a by-ſtander, ſays Dr. Watſon, though verſed in thoſe operations, would not imagine, from ſeeing the flaſh, and hearing the report, that the ſtroke, at the extremity of the conducting wire, could have been conſiderable ; the contrary whereof, when the wires were properly managed, he ſays, always happened.

* Phil. Tranſ. abridged, Vol. x. p. 363.

STILL the gentlemen, unwearied in thefe purfuits, were defirous, if poffible, to afcertain the abfolute velocity of electricity at a certain diftance; becaufe though, in the laft experiment, the time of it's progrefs was certainly very fmall, if any, they were defirous of knowing, fmall as that time might be, whether it was meafureable, and Dr. Watfon had contrived an excellent method for that purpofe.

ACCORDINGLY, on the 5th of Auguft 1748, the gentlemen met once more, and the laft time, at Shooter's-hill; when it was agreed to make an electric circuit of two miles, by feveral turnings of the wire, in the fame field. The middle of this circuit, they contrived to be in the fame room with the machine, where an obferver took in each hand one of the extremities of the wires, each of which was a mile in length. In this excellent difpofition of the apparatus, in which the time between the explofion and the fhock might have been obferved to the greateft exactnefs, the phial was difcharged feveral times; but the obferver always felt himfelf fhocked at the very inftant of making the explofion. Upon this the gentlemen were fully fatisfied, that through the whole length of this wire, which was 12276 feet, the velocity of the electric matter was inftantaneous *.

THESE experiments excited the admiration of all foreign electricians. Profeffor Mufchen-

---

* Phil. Tranf. abridged, Vol. x. p. 368.

broeck,

broeck, who was greatly satisfied with the
extent and success of them, said, in a letter to
Dr. Watson, upon the occasion, *Magnificen-*
tissimis tuis experimentis superasti conatus om-
nium.

IT is said by some, that the last of these
experiments go upon a wrong supposition,
and therefore can be of no use; it being supposed that the very same particles of the electric fluid, which were thrown on one side of
the charged glass, actually made the whole
circuit of the intervening conductors, and arrived at the opposite side: whereas Dr. Franklin's theory only requires that the deficiency
on one side of the glass be supplied from the
neighbouring conductors; which may, in return, receive as much as they parted with,
from the side of the glass that was overcharged. So that, to be a little more particular,
the redundancy of electric matter on the
charged side of a pane of glass, only passes
into the bodies which form that part of the
circuit which is contiguous to it, driving forward that part of the fluid which was natural
to them; till, at length, the fluid which re-
sided in those conductors which formed the
last part of the circuit, passes into the exhausted side of the glass.

BUT should this be the case (though in great
discharges it supposes the natural quantity of
electricity in bodies to be very considerable)
and should Dr. Watson, and other philosophers at that time, have conceived otherwise;
it does not follow, that the experiments could
poffibly

poffibly determine *nothing:* for there ftill remains fomething to be meafured, viz. the
time required for the fucceffive diflodging
the electric fluid in the whole length of the
circuit.

WERE the whole mafs of the electric matter contained in all the intervening conductors
abfolutely folid, no motion could be made at
one extremity, without producing an inftantaneous motion at the other; juft as if one
end of a rod be ftruck, the motion is inftantly
communicated to the other end. But this
cannot be the cafe in an elaftic medium, the
parts of which yield to one another. In this
cafe, the motion is communicated in a real
fucceffion, like a vibration, running the whole
length of the circuit; which muft therefore
take up time, and be meafurable. The motion of found may be meafured, though nô
particle of the vibrating air be finally difplaced. Thefe great experiments of Dr. Watfon,
therefore, had a real object, only it appeared
to be too fmall to be afcertained by them.

SECTION

S E C T I O N III.

MISCELLANEOUS DISCOVERIES OF DR. WATSON, AND OTHERS, BEFORE THE TIME OF DR. FRANKLIN.

THE firſt of theſe diſcoveries in order of time, and in importance ſecond to none (except that of the ſhock itſelf, and Dr. Franklin's diſcovery of the different electricity of the oppoſite ſides of the charged glaſs) was that of Dr. Watſon, proving, that the glaſs tubes and globes did not contain the electric power in themſelves, but only ſerved as *firſt movers*, and *determiners*, as he calls it, of that power.

HE was firſt led to this diſcovery by obſerving, that, upon rubbing the glaſs tube, while he was ſtanding upon cakes of wax (in order, as he expected, to prevent any of the electric power from diſcharging itſelf through his body upon the floor) the power was, contrary to his expectation, ſo much leſſened, that no ſnapping could be obſerved upon another perſon's touching any part of his body; but that if a perſon not electrified held his hand near the tube, while it was rubbed, the ſnapping was very ſenſible *.

THE event was the ſame when the globe was whirled in ſimilar circumſtances. For if

---

* Phil. Tranſ. abridged, Vol. x. p. 303.

the

the man who turned the wheel, and who, together with the machine was fufpended upon filk, touched the floor with one foot, the electric fire appeared upon the conductor; but if he kept himfelf free from any communication with the floor, no fire was produced.

DR. WATSON by this, and the following experiments in conjunction, difcovered, what he calls, the complete circulation of the electric matter. He obferved, that only a fpark or two would iffue from his hand to the infulated machine, unlefs he, at the fame time, formed a communication between the conductor and the floor; but that then there was a conftant and copious flux of the electric matter to the machine.

OBSERVING, that while his hand was in contact with the conductor, the man who turned this infulated machine gave fparks, which would fire inflammable fubftances, and perform other electrical experiments which were ufually performed at the conductor; he naturally imagined, that the fire iffued from the man, for the very fame reafon that all electricians had before imagined that it came from the conductor; and feeing that the man gave no fire unlefs there was a communication between the floor and the conductor, he concluded that, in this cafe, the fire was fupplied by that communication, fo that the courfe of the electricity was inverted, as he expreffes it *.

* Phil. Tranf. abridged, Vol. x. p 305.

IT was not then fufpected, that the eye could not diftinguifh in what direction an electric fpark proceeds. Electricians natu-rally imagined that all electric powers, and confequently the electric fluid, which they fuppofed to be the caufe of thefe powers, exifted in the excited electric, whatever it was; and that whatever powers were exerted by electrified bodies, proceeded from a real communication of electric matter to them. Accordingly, when Dr. Watfon found that, by cutting off the communication of the elec-tric with the floor, all electrical operations were ftopped, he concluded, that the electric fluid was collected from the floor to the rub-ber, and thence conveyed to the globe. For the fame reafon, feeing the rubber, or the man who had a communication with it, give no fparks but when the conductor was con-nected with the floor, he would as naturally conclude that the globe was fupplied from the conductor, as he had before concluded that it was fupplied from the rubber.

COMPARING both thefe experiments to-gether, Dr. Watfon was led to infer, that, in all electrical operations, there was both an *afflux* of electric matter to the globe, and the conductor, and likewife an *efflux* of the fame electric matter from them *.

FINDING that a piece of leaf filver was fuf-pended between a plate electrified by the con-ductor, and another communicating with the

---

* Phil. Tranf. abridged, Vol. x, p. 311.

floor, he reasons from it in the following manner. "No body can be suspended in "equilibrio but by the joint action of two "different directions of power: so here, the "blast of electric ether from the excited "plate blows the silver towards the plate un-"excited, and this last, in its turn, by the "blast of electric ether from the floor setting "through it, drives the silver towards the "plate electrified. We find from hence, "likewise, that the draught of electric ether "from the floor is always in proportion to "the quantity thrown by the globe over the "gun barrel, or the equilibrium by which "the silver is suspended could not be main-"tained *."

DR. WATSON observes, that the Abbé Nollet, two years before he made this communication, had given it as his opinion (though without any experiment which proved it) that the electric matter did not only proceed from the electrified bodies, but from all others about them, to a certain distance †.

SOME time after this, Dr. Watson observes, in a paper read at the Royal Society, January 21st, 1748, that Dr. Bevis had carried his experiment, to prove that rubbing the tube or the globe, only conveyed, and did not produce the electric matter, farther than he had done. For he had observed, above a year before, that placing one man upon electrics, to rub the tube or globe, and another

* Phil. Transf. abridged, Vol. x. p. 310.
† Ibid. p. 315.

alſo upon electrics to touch them, as the conductor; both the man who rubbed, and the
man who touched the excited glaſs would
give a ſpark; and farther, that if they touched one another, the ſnapping was much
greater than if either of them touched a perſon
ſtanding upon the floor. Upon this the Doctor ſeems to have corrected his former opinion of the afflux and efflux of electric matter: for he accounts for this fact by ſuppoſ-
ing, that as much electricity as was taken
from the perſon rubbing was given to him
who touched the conductor, being conveyed
by the globe. By this means the electricity
of the former of theſe perſons, he obſerves,
was more rare than it naturally was, and that
of the latter more denſe; ſo that the denſity
of electricity between theſe two perſons differed more than that between either of them,
and another perſon ſtanding upon the floor.
In this manner did Dr. Watſon diſcover, what
Dr. Franklin obſerved, about the ſame time,
in America, and called the *plus* and *minus* in
electricity *.

DR. WATSON obſerved that the flame at
the end of an electrified wire was ſenſible to
the hand, as a cool blaſt of wind, and that
when light ſubſtances were attracted and repelled between an electrified plate and one
communicating with the floor, the ſucceſſion
of theſe alternate attractions and repulſions
was extremely quick, ſo that ſometimes the

* Phil. Tranſ. abridged, Vol. x. p. 369.

eye

eye could hardly keep pace with it; and that
when a glafs globe, of about an inch in diameter, very light and finely blown, was put
upon a plate of metal, and another plate
hung on the conductor over it, the ftrokes
from the alternate attractions and repulfions
were almoft too quick for the ear. From
this laft experiment he likewife deduced an
argument to prove the extreme velocity with
which thefe glafs globes were attracted and repelled. He fays, that if they were let fall from
the height of fix feet or more upon a wooden
floor, or even a plate of metal, they were
rarely broken; but that by the attraction and
repulfion of them between thefe plates, though
at the diftance of no more than one fixth of
an inch, they were frequently beaten to pieces *.

THE Doctor alfo proved, that the electric
matter paffed through the fubftances of the
metal of communication, and not over the
furface of it, by covering a wire with a mixture of wax and rofin, and difcharging a phial
through it.

I MUST here obferve, that Mr. Monnier the younger difcovered, that electricity is not communicated to homogeneous
bodies in proportion to their maffes or
quantity of matter, but rather in proportion to their furfaces; and yet that all equal
furfaces do not receive equal quantities of
electricity, but that thofe receive the moft
which are moft extended in length; that a

---

* Phil. Tranf. abridged, Vol. x. p. 309.

fquare

fquare fheet of lead, for inftance, received a much lefs quantity of electricity than a fmall ftrip of the fame metal with a furface equal to that of a fquare fheet *.

MR. WILSON, whofe curious obfervations on the Leyden phial have been mentioned in a former fection, claims no fmall fhare of honour in this. As early as the latter end of the year 1746, he made the fame difcovery that Dr. Watfon had done, viz. that the electric fluid did not come from the globe, but from the earth itfelf, and from all other non-electric bodies about the apparatus. He fuggefted a method of proving this in a letter to Mr. Ellicott from Chefter ; and mentions his having completed the experiment himfelf foon after, in a letter to Mr. Smeaton, from Dublin.

HAVING conceived that the difference between electric and non-electric bodies was owing to the different refiftance which a *fubtle medium*, as he calls it, on the furfaces of all bodies gave to the paffage of the electric fluid ; and conceiving that heat would rarify this medium, and thereby convert electrics into non-electrics, he made fome experiments which confirmed him in that fuppofition. He found that one perfon might communicate electricity to another, notwithftanding the intervention of a confiderable quantity of red-hot glafs. He alfo made other experiments of a fimilar nature, as difcharging phials by means of hot glafs, hot amber,

* Phil. Tranf. abridged, Vol. x. p. 338.

and

and various other heated electrics. Thefe, however, as Mr. Canton afterwards obferved, might be owing to the hot air upon the furfaces of thofe bodies, which he found to tranfmit electricity very well. But another experiment, which Mr. Wilfon made upon melted rofin, does not feem liable to that objection. He poured the melted rofin into a phial, and found that he could give fhocks with it; but he obferved, that thefe fhocks diminifhed as the rofin grew cold, and that when it was quite cold, they entirely ceafed *.

MR. WILSON mentions a curious experiment (of which, however, he does not fay that he was the inventor) which he made with paper vanes ftuck in a cork, and fufpended by a magnet. Thefe, he fays, if they were brought near the point of any body proceeding from the prime conductor, would turn round very fwiftly, but would not turn at all in vacuo. This blaft he thought was occafioned by the iffuing of the electric matter out of the point, which caufed a current in the air; but he did not try what would be the confequence of prefenting the vanes to a point which received the electric fluid †.

LASTLY, Mr. Wilfon obferved, that if a needle were prefented to a piece of down hanging to the conductor, it would cling clofe to it; but that, upon prefenting any thing that was blunt, it would be repelled again; and fays that Mr. Canton made

* Wilfon's Effay, p. 143. † Ibid. p. 141.

feveral

feveral curious experiments of the fame
kind *.

Mr. Smeaton, within this period, obferved, that if a man who was infulated pref-
ed againft the globe with the flat part of his
hand, while another perfon, ftanding on the
floor, did the fame, in order to excite it, the
perfon who was infulated would hardly be
electrified at all; but that, if he only laid his
fingers lightly on the globe, he would be
electrified very ftrongly †. The fame ingenious perfon alfo obferved, that upon heating
the middle of a large bar of iron to a glowing
heat, and electrifying it, the electric power of
the part that was heated was as ftrong as that
of the cold part ‡.

For feveral curious difcoveries relating to
electricity, made within this period, we
are indebted to Dr. Miles. In a paper
read at the Royal Society, January 25th,
1746, he fays, that having excited a ftick
of black fealing-wax with white and brown
paper, or clean dried flannel, he was able
to kindle common lamp-fpirits with it. Comparing the ftick of wax with the glafs tube,
he obferved a remarkable difference between
the appearance of fire from both, though he
did not underftand the reafon of it. He fays
he found the luminous effluvia to proceed in
a much greater quantity from the top of his
finger to the ftick of wax, than they did to
the glafs. He feveral times obferved a fmall

---

* Wilfon's Effay, p. 141. † Ibid. p. 153.
‡ Ibid. p. 129.

globular

globular spot of fire to appear first on his finger, from which issued regular streams towards the wax, in the form of a comet's tail. This is now well known to be the constant appearance of the electric fire between an unelectrified body and an electric excited negatively *.

DR MILES found a stick of sulphur to perform very well; but not at all, when he had put an iron rammer in the center of it, to strengthen it. It is remarkable, that after setting this stick upright in a cupboard, it lost all its electric virtue, and could never afterwards be excited in the least degree. This effect the Doctor attributed to its being put up without any cover.

DR. MILES also mentions his having got a a tube of green glass, which he could never excite but with great difficulty, and then but to a small degree †.

THE same ingenious gentleman, some time after, made an experiment upon pieces of leaf brass in a bottle hermetically sealed. To these he found he could give motion by the approach of the excited tube, in the same manner as if they had been in the open air; but one appearance struck him, of which he by no means gives a satisfactory account. He observed that when he removed the tube from the exhausted glass slowly, no commotion was seen in the leaf brass, but a very brisk one

* Wilson's Essay, p. 317.
† Phil. Transf. abridged, Vol. x. p. 320.

upon

upon removing it fuddenly. Indeed this fact could not have been underftood but by comparing it with other facts depending upon the fame principle, and which were not difcovered till fome years after *.

FROM England, to which, as an Englifh-man, I would give the preference only in matters of abfolute indifference, I pafs over to France, where, next to thofe made in England, the moft important difcoveries, and greateft number of them were made in the period of which I am treating. And, without all difpute, the greateft name in France, in this or any other period, except that of Mr. Du Fay, his friend and affociate, is that of the Abbé Nollet.

THE favourite obfervation of Mr. Nollet, on which he built his darling theory of afflu-ences and effluences was, that bodies not in-fulated, plunged in electric atmofpheres, fhewed figns of electricity. He obferved a fenfible blaft from the hand of a perfon not electrified, in the above mentioned circum-ftances, alfo the attraction and repulfion of light bodies by them, the appearance of flame, the diminution of their weight by in-creafed evaporation and perfpiration, and al-moft every other appearanc and effect of elec-tricity. Moreover obferving that his globe contracted a foulnefs while it was whirling, even when rubbed with a clean hand, he had the curiofity to collect a quantity of the mat-

* Phil. Tranf. abridged, Vol. x. p. 326.

ter which formed that foulnefs; and finding that, when it was put into the fire, it had the fmell of burnt hair, he concluded that it was an animal fubftance; and that it had been carried by the affluent electricity from his own body to the globe *.

THE only miftake of this ingenious philofopher in thefe experiments, and which was the fource of many others, which, in the end, greatly bewildered and perplexed him, was, that the electricity of the body, which was plunged in the atmofphere of an electrified body, was of the fame nature with that of the electrified body. Had he but preferved the diftinction, which Mr. Du Fay had difcovered, between the two electricities, and imagined that the body electrified, and that which was plunged in its atmofphere were poffeffed of thefe two different and oppofite electricities, he might have been led to the great difcoveries made by Mr. Canton, Dr. Franklin, and Mr. Wilcke; which, we fhall find, arofe from that fingle obfervation; and he would have avoided a great deal of debate and contention, which has not ended to his advantage.

THIS partial difcovery of Mr. Nollet is by no means the only one of his, that the hiftory of electricity prefents in this period. He made feveral experiments on pointed bodies, and obferved, that thofe which had the fmalleft points fooneft threw out brufhes of

* Nollet's Recherches, p. 142.

electric

electric light, but did not show other signs of electricity so strong as bodies that were not pointed *.

He took a great deal of pains in making experiments, in order to determine the degree in which different substances conducted the electric fluid; and found that the smoke of gum lac, turpentine, karabé, and sulphur did not carry away the electricity of an excited tube so soon as the smoke of linen, wood, and more especially the steam of water, and the effluvia of burning tallow, and of other fatty substances. In short, he found, that vapours which were not watery did very little, or no injury to electrical experiments, provided the tube was not exposed to them near the fire which caused them. A smoky room did not prevent his performing experiments, at least in any great degree; nor were odoriferous effluvia at all prejudicial to them †.

Several curious observations were made by the Abbé upon heat, and heated bodies. He found, that a piece of iron glowing hot, so as to throw off ignited particles, did not leave the smallest trace of electricity in an excited tube, to which it had been brought within five or six inches, and only held there two or three seconds; but it ceased to affect the tube at the same distance before it ceased to be red, and had no influence at all long before it was cold. The electricity of the tube, in this instance, was probably conveyed through

* Recherches, p. 146.   † Ibid. p. 194, &c.

the

the air heated by the iron; as it can hardly
be suppofed, that the iron emitted any effluvia
capable of producing that effect *.

HE found that the excited tube loft nothing
of its electricity in the focus of a burning
mirror. That the flame of a candle, or the
near approach of it, would deftroy electricity
had been known before: he obferved, that
the flame was fenfibly difturbed by the approach of the excited tube, and he mentions
Mr. Du Tour, and the Abbé Needham's having found, that the interpofition of the
thinneft piece of glafs, or of any other fubftance, between the candle and the tube prevented the diffipation of the electricity. From
this fact it was inferred, that the diffipation
was owing to fome effluvia proceeding from
the candle †.

CONTINUING his obfervations on what
increafed or impeded electrical experiments,
he found, that a light body, placed on a
non-electric ftand, moved more brifkly upon
the approach of an electrified body, than
when it was placed upon an electric ftand ‡.
Several electrical experiments, he obferved,
fucceeded beft when there was a number of
fpectators prefent, and when they drew near,
and ftood clofe together to fee his experiments; provided they did not occafion fo
great a perfpiration as made his glaffes moift §.
This obfervation we fhall find accounted for
hereafter by Mr. Wilcke.

* Recherches, p. 216.   † Ibid. p. 219.
‡ Ibid. p. 122.   § Ibid. p. 123.

THE

THE Abbé moiftened, with water or fpirit of wine, a flender and pointed bar of iron, and thought that the blaft from the point of it was more fenfible than when it was not moiftened; which he attributed to the electric fluid carrying away with it fome of the particles of the water, and of the fpirit of wine *.

SOME few obfervations the Abbé made on the difference between excited and communicated electricity, and between the electricity of glafs and that of fulphur. He obferved, that the electricity of an excited globe or tube, caufed an odd fenfation upon the face, as if a fpider's web were drawn over it; whereas that effect was feldom produced by communicated electricity. Excited electricity, he alfo fays, might be perceived by the fmell, at more than a foot diftance, when communicated electricity could not †.

HE melted fulphur in a glafs globe, by turning it over a chafing difh of burning coals; when he obferved, that fmall pieces of fulphur, before they were melted, were attracted and repelled by the glafs within, at the fame time that the afhes of the coals were attracted without ‡. Holding a piece of excited fulphur in one hand, with a piece of down fticking to it, and ready to fly off, the down, he fays, would cling faft to the fulphur, upon prefenting to it an excited glafs, tube, which he held in his other hand §.

---

* Recherches, p. 140.　　　† Ibid. p. 136.
‡ Ibid. p. 134.　　§ Ibid. p 124.

I SHALL

I SHALL, in the laſt place, recite the Abbé Nollet's experiments made in vacuo. He found that glaſs, and other electrics, might be excited in vacuo, but not ſo ſtrongly as in the open air *. He obſerved that there was a remarkable difference between the appearance of the electric light in vacuo, and in the open air; being much more diffuſe, and unbroken in vacuo †. Inſerting the extremity of his conductor into an exhauſted glaſs veſſel, he obſerved the veſſel to be full of light, when-ever he brought his hand to it; that the light was conſiderably increaſed when he ſpread his hand over it; and that when a ſpark was taken from the conductor, the whole veſſel ſeemed to be full of light. He alſo obſerv-ed, that ſmall pieces of metal, incloſed in the veſſel, adhered cloſe to the glaſs; but de-tached themſelves from it, on the approach of the finger, or of any conductor on the outſide.

M. MONNIER attempted, in an ingenious method, to be certain whether the quantity of electricity communicated to a body was in proportion to its ſolid or ſuperficial contents. He firſt found that an anvil which weighed two hundred pounds, gave but an inconſider-able ſpark, while the ſpark from a ſpeaking-trumpet of tin, which weighed but ten pounds, but was eight or nine feet long, was almoſt equal to the ſhock of the Leyden phial. He then obſerved, that a ball of

* Recherches, p. 236.　　　† Ibid. p. 243.

lead

lead four inches in diameter, gave a fpark of
the fame force with another from a thin piece
of lead of the fame fuperficies, in the form of
a hoop. And, laftly, he took a thin and long
piece of lead, and obferved, that when it was
electrified in its whole length, it gave a very
ftrong fpark, but a very fmall one when it
was rolled into a lump. But, becaufe a fquare
piece of lead did not give a fpark equal to
one from a piece of the fame quantity of furface, but of greater length, he concluded
that, though electrification is ftronger in proportion to the furfaces of electrified bodies,
yet that, of equal furfaces, that which is
drawn out to the greateft length will have the
advantage *.

THERE are a few other names of electricians in France, whofe experiments and obfervations, made within this period, deferve
to be mentioned. Of thefe is Mr. Boulanger.
He took great pains to determine the degree
in which different fubftances are capable of
being excited. The experiments, he fays,
were made with the greateft care: and though
the ftate of the fcience did not admit of this
bufinefs being determined with greater accuracy, it may not be difagreeable to fee the refult of them; which he has comprifed in the
following table, beginning with thofe that are
leaft excitable in every column.

* Ac. Par. 1746, M. p. 693.

FIRST

FIRST COLUMN.

Ebony.
Guiacum.
Box wood.
Sandal wood.
Oak.
Elm.
Aſh.
Linden tree.
Roſe.
Willow.
Ozier.
Cork.
Dry wood of all kinds.
All dry plants.

SECOND COLUMN.

Shells of all kinds.
Whalebone.
Bones.
Ivory.
Horn.
Scales.
Parchment.
Hair.
Wool.
Feathers.
Cotton.
Silk.

THIRD COLUMN.

Alum.
Sugar Candy.

The Phoſphorus of
 Berne.
Yellow and white wax.
Japan varniſh.
Sandarac.
Maſtich.
Amber.
Jet.
Pitch.
Gum copal.
Gum lac.
Colophonia.
Sulphur.
Sealing-wax.
All ſalts which have
 ſufficient conſiſt-
 ence.
All reſins.

FOURTH COLUMN.

Loadſtone.
Hand-ſtone.
Marble of all colours.
Slate.
Free-ſtone.
Granite.
Porphyry.
Jaſper.
Varniſhed earth.
Cornelians.
Agates.
All opaque precious
 ſtones.
Porcelaine.

FIFTH

FIFTH COLUMN.

Hyacinth.
Opal.
Emerald.
Amethyſt.
Topaz.
Ruby.
Sapphire.
Cat's eye.
Peridote.
Granite.
Rock cryſtal.

Venice and Muſcovy talc.
Coloured diamonds, eſpecially yellow.
White diamonds, eſpecially the brilliant.
All tranſparent precious ſtones.
Glaſs, and all vitrifications without excepting thoſe of metals.

THE inference which this author draws from this catalogue is, that the moſt brittle, and the moſt tranſparent ſubſtances, are always the moſt electric; and he has recourſe to an awkward hypotheſis to account for the marcaſites not being excitable at all, notwithſtanding they are both brittle and tranſparent. He ſays it is owing to condenſed air contained in thoſe ſubſtances, which is known to prevent excitation *.

THE ſame author ſays, that mineral waters are much more ſenſibly affected with electricity than common water; that black ribbons are much ſooner attracted than thoſe of other colours; and, next to them, the brown, and deep red †.

* Boulanger, p. 74.   † Ibid. p. 124.

MR.

MR. LE CAT, a phyfician at Rouen, who has diftinguifhed himfelf by feveral perform-ances in the learned world, fufpended feveral pieces of leaf gold at his conductor, and ob-ferved that they hung at different diftances, according to their fizes, the fmaller pieces placing themfelves nearer the conductor, and the larger receding farther from it. This he compares to the diftances at which the planets make their revolutions round the fun, and he fuppofed the caufe to be the fame in both. The fame author very particularly compares the electric fhock, which had juft been difcover-ed, to thunder *.

GERMANY affords but few articles for the electrical hiftory of this period; one of them, however, is curious, and well deferves to be tranfmitted to pofterity. Mr. Gordon of Er-ford excited the electricity of a cat fo ftrongly, that, when it was communicated by iron chains, it fired fpirit of wine †.

IT has been mentioned before, that feveral gentlemen in Germany, as well as in Eng-land, had found, that if the man who rubbed the globe ftood upon electrics, fparks were perceived upon touching him; but Mr. Klin-genftierna, a Swede, and Mr. Stroema, were the firft who properly electrified by the rub-ber; and their experiments were publifhed in the Acts of the Royal Academy of Sciences at Stockholm for the year 1747 ‡.

* Hiftore, p. 84—85. † Nollet's Recherches, p. 98.
‡ Wilcke, p. 112.

MR.

MR. JALLABERT, profeffor of philofophy at Geneva, found that a coating of pitch did not prevent the conductor from being electrified, which proved that the electric fluid enters the fubftance of metals. He alfo proved, that ice was a conductor of electricity, by making the Leyden experiment with a bottle in which water was frozen *.

THE amazing and extenfive effects of electricity now began to make philofophers look for it where it had not been fufpected before. The firft account that is given of woollen garments being obferved to exhibit figns of electricity, when they were put off, after the flafhes of light they gave were known to be owing to electricity, was fent to the Royal Society by Mr. Coke of the Ifle of Wight, who fays, that a lady of his acquaintance obferved it; and that it was alfo at laft found, that it was only new flannel, and after fome time wearing, which gave that appearance, and that this property was loft when it was wafhed †.

THE fame appearance, he obferves, upon another occafion, was moft confpicuous in frofty weather; in which feafon he takes notice, that there is generally, not only a greater purity of the air, and abfence of moifture, but that all hairy and horny fubftances (for hairs, as he fays, are only fmall horns) are more elaftic, and confequently fufceptible of, and more capable of exciting ftrong vi-

---

* Hiftoire, p. 95, 96.
† Phil. Tranf. abridged, Vol. x. p. 343.

brations.

brations. He fays, that the flannel being rendered damp with fea water, and afterwards dry, would heighten the electric appearances *.

BUT though this was the firft appearance of the kind that was obferved, after it was known to arife from electricity, fimilar appearances had been feveral times noted before. Bartholin, who flourifhed in 1650, wrote a book *De luce animalium,* in which he fuppofes, that unctuous effluvia had a great fhare in thofe appearances. The fame writer fays, that Theodore Beza might be feen by a light proceeding from his eye-brows; and that fparks would flafh from the body of Charles Gonzaga, Duke of Mantua, upon being gently rubbed. But he does not fay whether he had any particular hairy, or fcaly fuperficies to his fkin †.

DR. SIMPSON, who publifhed a philofophical difcourfe on fermentation, dedicated to the Royal Society in 1675, alfo takes notice of the light proceeding from animals on frication, or pectation as he calls it, and inftances in the combing of a woman's head, the currying of a horfe, and the ftroking of a cat's back ‡.

MR. CLAYTON alfo, in a letter to Mr. Boyle, dated June 23d, 1684, at James-town in Virginia, gives him an account of a ftrange accident, as he calls it, which happened to one Mrs. Sewall, whofe wearing apparel emit-

---

* Phil. Tranf. abridged, Vol. x. p. 344.   † Ibid. p. 344.
‡ Ibid. p. 357.

ted

ted a flafhing of fparks, which were feen by feveral perfons. The like happened to Lady Baltimore her mother-in-law *.

I SHALL conclude this fection with what I can find, in this period, about increafing the power of electricity, and meafuring its effects.

MR. MONNIER the younger, whofe name has been frequently mentioned in the courfe of this hiftory, ufed glafs fpheroids inftead of globes, and endeavoured to increafe his electrical power by ufing feveral of thefe fpheriods at a time; but he found, upon trial, that they did not anfwer his expectations; and was thence difpofed to conclude, that there might be a *ne plus ultra* in the intenfity of electricity, as well as in the heat communicated to boiling water †.

THE power of glafs in electrifying being found to be fo great, it is no wonder that philofophers fhould endeavour to find what kind of glafs was capable of being excited to the greateft degree. Among other propofals we find a very memorable one communicated to the Royal Society, April 6th, 1749, by Mr. Boze. He fays, that a glafs ball which has often been employed in violent diftillations, and other chemical operations fends forth electricity incomparably more ftrong, than any glafs which had never been expofed to fo violent a fire. This article is the more curious, as it fhews us how much philofophers at this

* Phil. Tranf. abridged, Vol. x. p. 278.
† Ibid. p. 330.

time piqued themfelves upon difcoveries in electricity. He afferts his being the firft perfon who ever mentioned this notable circumftance, as he calls it, and defires Dr. Watfon, to whom he communicated it, to let him have the honour of that improvement in the Philofophical Tranfactions *.

IT was within this period that Dr. Watfon contrived to improve the ftrength of electricity by moiftening the rubber of his globe, though he was not aware of all the reafons for it. He obferved that the man who ftood on the floor, to excite the globe by his hand, did it more ftrongly than a cufhion. This, he fays, he could not conceive to be owing to any other difference, than to his hand being more moift, and confequently more readily conducting the electricity from the floor; wherefore he ordered his machine, and even his cufhion, to be made damp; and then found that the electricity was as ftrong as when the globe was rubbed by the hand †.

A GENTLEMAN at Chartres in France, greatly increafed the effects of electricity by means of moifture, for afferting which he is very much ridiculed by the author of *Hiftoire de l'Electricité*.

MR. WILSON fays, that if the cufhion (which he made of leather) was gilt with filver, brafs, or copper, it would do very well; and that the filk line on which the conductor

* Phil. Tranf. abridged, Vol. x, p. 329.
† Ibid. p. 312.

hung

hung fhould be red or yellow *. The table, he fays, fhould ftand on moift ground, or a wire pafs from the machine to the moift ground †.

DR. WATSON alfo found, that though no electricity could be produced by rubbing the globe with original electrics perfectly dry, yet that they anfwered very well when they had been made moift; the water imbibed by thofe fubftances ferving as a canal of communication to the electricity between the hand, or the cufhion, and the globe; in the fame manner as the air, replete with vapours in damp weather, prevents the accumulation of the electric matter in any confiderable degree, by conducting it as faft as it is excited to the neareft non-electrics. He obferved, on the contrary, that moft vegetable fubftances, though made as dry as poffible, furnifhed electricity, but fmall in quantities. He excited electricity not only from linen, cotton, &c. but even from fheet lead and a deal board ‡.

THE Abbé Nollet fays, that he found oil of turpentine upon a piece of woollen cloth excited glafs very powerfully, but that the leaft water mixed with it prevented the excitation §.

MR. BOULANGER fays, that if two cylinders be made of the fame kind of glafs, and of the fame fafhion, one of them tranfparent, and the other tinged with any colour, the tranfparent cylinder will be excited more eafily

---

* Wilfon's Effay, p. 5, 6.   † Ibid. p. 8.
‡ Ibid. 380.   § Recherches, p. 168.

than

than the coloured one *. He acknowledges, however, that fometimes the moft tranfparent, and the moft brittle glafs is capable of acquiring but little electricity †. In another place he fays, that a cylinder of three or four lines in thicknefs will acquire a ftronger, and a more lafting electricity than a cylinder of one line thick ‡. He alfo fays, that a perfon's two hands, or one cufhion, is better than more §.

ABOUT the fame time that Dr. Watfon made his firft experiments upon the Leyden phial, Mr. Canton difcovered a method by which the quantity of electricity accumulated in the phial might be meafured to a good degree of exactnefs. He took the charged phial in his hand, and made it give a fpark to an infulated conductor, which fpark he took off with his other hand. This operation he repeated till the whole was difcharged, and he eftimated the height of the charge by the number of the fparks. This is a pretty certain and exact method of knowing how high a phial *has been* charged; but what electricians chiefly want is a method of afcertaining how high a phial *is* charged, or the exact force of the charge while it is contained in the glafs.

SOMETHING of this kind was done by Mr. Ellicott, in the fame year 1746. He propofed to eftimate the ftrength of common

---

* Poulanger, p. 64.   † Ibid. p. 164.
‡ Ibid. p. 135.   § Ibid. p. 136.

electrification, by its power to raise a weight
in one scale of a balance, while the other
should be held over the electrified body,
and pulled to it by its attractive power *. Mr.
Gralath also constructed an electrometer upon
the same principle †.

THE Abbe Nollet applied the threads that
Mr. Grey and Du Fay had used in electrical
experiments, to shew the degree of electricity.   He hung two of them together, and observed the angle of their divergence, by means
of the rays of the sun, or the light of a candle, and their shadow upon a board placed
behind them.   Mr. Waitz also thought of the
same kind of electrometer, with this improvement, that he loaded the ends of the threads
with small weights ‡.

* Boulanger, p. 324.
† Dantzick Memoirs, Vol. i. p. 525.
‡ Histoire, p. 58.

SECTION

SECTION IV.

EXPERIMENTS ON ANIMAL, AND OTHER
ORGANIZED BODIES IN THIS PERIOD; AND
OTHER EXPERIMENTS CONNECTED WITH
THEM, MADE CHIEFLY BY THE ABBE
NOLLET.

HITHERTO the effect of electricity upon human bodies had not been attended to, farther than the mere shock of the
Leyden phial. But we shall now see a curious set of experiments on this subject exhibited by the Abbé Nollet. The English philosophers, who led the way in almost every
other application of electricity, were among
the last to try its effects upon animals, and
other organized bodies. The only article
that I can find upon this subject, before the
discoveries of the Abbé Nollet, is one of Mr.
Trembley's; who says that several persons
had observed, that while they were electrified,
their pulse beat a little faster than before. He
says, that he himself, after having been electrified a long time together, had felt an odd
sensation all over his body, and that some persons had felt very sharp pains after being
electrified *.

* Phil. Tranf. abridged, Vol. x. p. 321.

M 4   THE

THE ingenious Abbé Nollet begins his experiments with the evaporation of fluids by electricity. They were made with the greatest attention, and the following observations were the result of them.

" 1. ELECTRICITY augments the natural
" evaporation of fluids; since, excepting mer-
" cury, which is too heavy, and the oil of
" olives, which is too viscous, all the others
" which were tried suffered a diminution
" which could not be ascribed to any other
" cause than electricity.

" 2. ELECTRICITY augments the evapo-
" ration of those fluids the most, which are
" most subject to evaporate of themselves. For
" the volatile spirit of sal ammoniac suffered a
" greater loss than spirit of wine, or turpen-
" tine ; these two more than common water;
" and water more than vinegar, or the solu-
" tion of nitre.

" 3. ELECTRICITY has a greater effect
" upon fluids when the vessels which contain
" them are non-electrics; the effects always
" seeming to be a little greater when the
" vessels were of metal, than when they were
" of glass.

" 4. THIS increased evaporation was more
" considerable when the vessel which contain-
" ed the liquor was more open, but the ef-
" fects did not increase in proportion to their
" apertures. For when these liquors were
" electrified in vessels, whose aperture was
" four inches in diameter, though they pre-
" sented to the air a surface sixteen times
" larger

" larger than when they were contained in
" veffels whofe aperture was one inch in dia-
" meter, they were, neverthelefs, far from
" fuffering a diminution proportioned to that
" difference.

" 5. ELECTRIFICATION does not make
" any liquors evaporate through the pores,
" either of metal, or of glafs ; fince after ex-
" periments which were continued ten hours,
" there was found no diminution of their
" weight, when the veffels in which they were
" contained were well ftopped *."

AFTER having made experiments on fluias,
the Abbé began another courfe on folids of various kinds, the refult of which was, that they
loft weight only in proportion to the moifture they contained, and the opennefs of their
pores †.

THE Abbé alfo extended his experiments
to other fenfible qualties of bodies, as their
fmell, their tafte, and chemical properties ;
but found no change in any of them, after a
ftrong and continued electrification of a variety of fubftances. Electrification did not affect the power of the magnet, and neither
retarded nor accelerated the heating or cooling of bodies ‡.

HE then proceeded to the electrification of
capillary tubes, full of water ; it having been
obferved by Mr. Boze, who communicated
the obfervation to Mr. Nollet ‖, that the water would iffue in a conftant ftream when they

* Nollet's Recherches, p. 327.   † Ibid. p. 335.
‡ Ibid. p. 341.   ‖ Ibid. p. 343.

                                        were

were electrified; whereas it would only drop very flowly without that operation. Every perfon, at firft fight, would judge that the ftream was accelerated, and that the electrified veffel would foon be empty : but this accurate philofopher was unwilling to rely on firft appearances, and therefore refolved to afcertain the fact, by meafuring the time, and the quantity of liquor running out. And, in order to know if the acceleration, fuppofing there were any, was uniform, during the whole time of the running out, he made ufe of veffels of different capacities, terminating in pipes of different bores, from three lines in diameter, to the fmalleft capillaries.

As the Abbé did not find it fo eafy a matter to draw a fafe conclufion in this cafe as might at firft be imagined, he gives us in grofs the following refult of above an hundred experiments *.

" 1. The electrified ftream, though it " divides, and carries the liquid farther, is " neither fenfibly accelerated nor retarded, " when the pipe through which it iffues is " not lefs than a line in diameter.

" 2. Under this diameter, if the tube is " wide enough to let the liquid run in a con- " tinued ftream, electricity accelerates it a " little; but lefs than a perfon would ima- " gine, if he judged by the number of jets " which are formed, and by the diftance to " which they go.

* Recherches, p. 327. Phil. Tranf. abridged, Vol. x. p. 382.

" 3. If

" 3. IF the tube be a capillary one, from
" which the water only drops naturally, the
" electrified jet not only becomes a continu-
" ed stream, and even divided into several
" streams, but is also considerably accelerat-
" ed; and the smaller the capillary tube
" is, the greater, in proportion, is this ac-
" celeration.

" 4. So great, is the effect of the electric
" virtue, that it drives the water in a con-
" stant stream out of a very small capillary
" tube, out of which it had not before been
" able even to drop."

THE most unaccountable of these experiments, as the ingenious Abbé acknowledges,
are those which suppose a retardation of the
electrified current, and he long doubted the
fact; but a great number of experiments,
carefully noted in his journal, obliged him to
admit it, though still with hesitation, and to
account for it in the best manner he could;
which, indeed, is not very satisfactory *.

THE beautiful appearance of these streams
of electrified water, when the experiment
was exhibited in the dark, is particularly described by this author, after Messrs. Boze and
Gordon, who first observed it †.

THESE last experiments served as a basis to
the Abbé's future inquiries. He considered
all organized bodies as assemblages of capillary tubes, filled with a fluid that tends to run
through them, and often to issue out of them.

* Recherches, p. 351.   † Ibid. p. 354.

In

In confequence of this idea, he imagined, that the electric virtue might poffibly communicate fome motion to the fap of vegetables, and alfo augment the infenfible perfpiration of animals. He began with the following experiments, the refult of which confirmed his fuppofition *.

He electrified for four or five hours together, fruits, green plants, and fpunges, dipped in water which he had carefully weighed ; and found that, after the experiment, all thofe bodies were remarkably lighter than others of the fame kind, weighed with them, both before and after the experiment, and kept in the fame place and temper †.

The electrification of growing vegetables was firft begun in Britain. Mr. Maimbray at Edinburgh electrified two myrtle trees, during the whole month of October 1746; when they put forth fmall branches and bloffoms fooner than other fhrubs of the fame kind, which had not been electrified. Mr. Nollet, hearing of this experiment, was encouraged to try it himfelf ‡

He took two garden pots, filled with the fame earth, and fowed with the fame feeds, He kept them conftantly in the fame place, and took the fame care of them ; except that one of the two was electrified fifteen days together, for two or three, and fometimes four hours a day. The confequence was, that the

* Recherches, p. 355.
† Phil Tranf. abridged, Vol. x. p. 383.
‡ Recherches, 356.

electri-

electrified pot always shewed the sprouts of its seeds two or threee days sooner than the other. It also threw out a greater number of shoots, and those longer in a given time; which made him believe, that the electric virtue helped to open and display the germs, and thereby to facilitate the growth of plants. This, however, our cautious philosopher only calls a conjecture, which required farther confirmation. The season, he says, was then too far advanced to allow him to make as many experiments as he could have wished, but he says the next course of experiments had greater certainty, and they are not less interesting *.

THE same experiments were carrying on about the same time by Mr. Jallabert, Mr. Boze, and the Abbé Menon, principal of the college of Bueil at Angers, who all drew the same conclusions from them †.

THE Abbé chose several pairs of animals of different kinds, cats, pigeons, chaffinches, sparrows, &c. All these he put into separate wooden cages, and weighed them. One of each pair he electrified for five or six hours together, and then weighed them again. The result was, that the electrified cat was commonly sixty-five or seventy grains lighter than the other, the pigeon from thirty-five to thirty-eight grains, the chaffinch or sparrow six or seven grains. In order to have nothing to charge upon the difference that

* Recherches, p. 358, &c. Phil. Transf. abridged, Vol. x. p. 383. † Recherches, p. 357.

might

might arife from the temperament of the individuals he happened to pitch upon, he repeated the fame experiments, by electrifying that animal of each pair which had not been electrified before; and, notwithftanding fome fmall varieties the electrified animal was conftantly lighter than the other in proportion *.

AFTER thefe experiments, he had no doubt but that electricity increafed the infenfible perfpiration of animals, but it was not certain whether this increafe was in the ratio of their bulks, or in that of their furfaces. The Abbé's opinion was, that it was neither in the one, nor the other, ftrictly fpeaking, but in a ratio much more nearly approaching the latter than the former; fo that he imagined, there was no room to apprehend, that a human perfon electrified would lofe near a fiftieth part of his weight, as it appeared to him to have happened to one fort of bird; nor 140th part, as to the pigeon, &c. All that he had then obferved upon that head was, that a young man or woman, between the ages of twenty and thirty, from being electrified five hours together, had loft feveral ounces of their weight, more than they were wont to lofe when they were not electrified †.

THE Abbé obferves, that no inconvenience whatever was felt by the perfons who fubmitted to be electrified in this manner. They

* Recherches, p. 366, &c.
† Phil. Tranf. abridged, Vol. x. p. 384. Recherches, p. 382.

only

ónly found themfelves a little exhaufted, and had got a better appetite. He adds, that none of them found themfelves fenfibly warmer, and that he could not perceive that their pulfe was encreafed *.

THESE laft experiments on human bodies, he juftly obferves, are difficult to purfue with exactnefs, becaufe the cloathing, which cannot ftrictly be compared to the hairs or feathers of animals, retains a confiderable fhare of the perfpired matter, and prevents our forming a good judgment of the whole effect of the electric virtue.

THE foregoing experiments, he fays, convinced him of the reality of the *effluent* matter, carrying away with it the perfpirable parts of bodies, and what could be evaporated from their furfaces. And he was convinced of the *affluent* matter, by obferving all thofe effects produced, if, inftead of electrifying bodies themfelves, they were only brought near a large body which was electrified. He moiftened a thick fpunge in water, and cut it into two pieces, and then weighed the parts feparately, and placing the whole near a large electrified body; he found that, after an electrification of five or fix hours, that part of the fpunge which was nearer to the electrified body had loft more weight than the other. From this fact he concluded, that if any part of an animal body was prefented to a large electrified fubftance, it would perfpire more

* Recherches, p. 389.

than

than the other, and that perhaps obſtructions might by this means be removed from the pores of it *.

THE experiments above recited of Mr. Nollet by no means ſatisfied the Engliſh philoſophers, and particularly Mr. Ellicott, who made experiments to refute the theory which the author had deduced from them. He obſerved that the ſyphon, though electrified, would only deliver the water by drops, if the baſon in which the water was contained was electrified too. But this does not invalidate Mr. Nollet's curious experiments upon the ſubject of evaporation and perſpiration. For when an animal body is electrified, there is always non-electric matter enough in the atmoſphere, to anſwer the purpoſe of the unelectrified baſon, in the experiment of the capillary tube; thereby to cauſe a continual exhalation of the perſpirable matter from the pores of the ſkin. Beſides, the capillary tube will, in fact, unite the water in a conſtant ſtream, when it has only the open air to throw it into. In all debates upon ſubjects in natural philoſophy, facts ought only to be oppoſed to facts. The veracity of the Abbé Nollet is not to be called in queſtion; though it muſt be acknowledged, that, in his later writings, at a time when his favourite ſyſtem was in danger, he makes miſtakes with reſpect to the facts that nearly affect it.

* Phil. Tranſ. abridged, Vol. x. p. 385.

To

To account for the appearance of light, which feems, in fome cafes, to iffue from a non-electric body prefented to an excited electric, and which Mr. Nollet thought to be the affluent matter, Mr. Ellicott fuppofes that it was the light which had come from the electric. In accounting for the fufpenfion of leaf gold between an electrified and an unelectrified plate, Mr. Ellicott's theory made it neceffary to fuppofe (what Dr. Franklin afterwards found not to be fact) that the leaf gold will always be fufpended nearer the unelectrified than the electrified plate.

In his anfwer to Mr. Nollet, Mr. Ellicott alfo endeavours to account for the electric matter iffuing from a point at the extremity of the conductor, more fenfibly than if it had terminated round or flat. He fays that the effluvia, in rufhing from the globe along the conductor, as they approached the point, were brought nearer together, and therefore were denfer there than in any part of the rod. Confequently, he fays, if the light be owing to the denfity and velocity of the effluvia, it will be vifible at the point, and no where elfe. This, as far as I can find, was the firft attempt to account for this phenomenon; but it by no means accounts for the whole virtue of the conductor being diffipated from fuch points. Indeed, it is no wonder that the influence of points which are but imperfectly underftood even at this day, furnifhed too difficult a problem fo many years ago *.

* Phil. Tranf. abridged, Vol. x. p. 393.

It

IT will, now, be univerfally acknowledged, that there was very great merit in thefe
experiments of the Abbé Nollet, made upon
animal and other organized bodies. He opened a new and noble field of electrical difcoveries, and he purfued them with great attention, perfeverance, and expence. This laft
circumftance, I fuppofe, may have been the
reafon why his experiments have not, as far as
I can find, been refumed and purfued by any
electrician fince his time, though there feems
to be great room to improve upon what he
began. The only method in which they can
be conducted to any purpofe, would be by the
the help of a machine for perpetual electrification, to go by wind or water; which would,
likewife, ferve for many other capital experiments in electricity. This application of
electricity, in particular, may perhaps be of
more ufe in medicine, than any other mode in
which it has hitherto been adminiftered.

MR. JALLABERT of Geneva carried the
experiments on plants farther than the Abbé
Nollet had done; and, by electrifying bottles
in which the plants were growing in water,
and placing in the fame expofure other bottles, containing plants of the fame kind; he
proved, in the cleareft manner, that the electrified plants always grew fafter, and had finer
ftems, leaves, and flowers than thofe which
were not electrified, and confumed more of
their water *.

* Beccaria dell' elettricifmo naturale et artificiale, p. 125.

SECTION

SECTION V.

THE HISTORY OF THE MEDICATED TUBES,
AND OTHER COMMUNICATIONS OF MEDI=
CINAL VIRTUES BY ELECTRICITY, WITH
THEIR VARIOUS REFUTATIONS:

IN the courſe of this hiſtory we have ſeen
frequent inſtances of ſelf-deception, for
want of perſons attending to all the eſſential
circumſtances of facts; but nothing we have
yet ſeen equals what was exhibited in the
years 1747 and 1748. Mr. Grey's decep-
tions were chiefly owing to his miſtaking the
cauſe of real appearances; but in this caſe
we can hardly help thinking, that, not only
the imagination and judgment, but even all
the external ſenſes of philoſophers muſt have
been impoſed upon. It was aſſerted by Signior Pivati at Venice (who has all the merit
of theſe extraordinary diſcoveries), and, after
him, by Mr. Verati at Bologna, Mr. Bianchi
at Turin, and Mr. Winckler at Leipſick, that
if odorous ſubſtances were confined in glaſs
veſſels, and the veſſels excited, the odours
and other medicinal virtues would tranſpire
through the glaſs, infect the atmoſphere of
the conductor, and communicate the virtue
to all perſons in contact with it; alſo that
thoſe ſubſtances, held in the hands of perſons
electrified, would communicate their virtues
to them; ſo that medicines might be made to

N 2 operate

operate without being taken into the ſtomach.
They even pretended to have wrought many
cures by the help of electricity applied this
way. Some of the more curious of theſe pretended experiments deſerve to be recorded,
for the entertainment and inſtruction of poſte-
rity.

THE forementioned Signior Johannes Fran-
ciſco Pivati, a perſon of eminence at Venice,
ſays, in an Italian epiſtle, printed at Venice
with all the uſual licences, in the year 1747,
that a manifeſt example of the virtue of electricity was ſhown in the balſam of Peru,
which was ſo concealed in a glaſs cylinder,
that, before the excitation of it, not the leaſt
ſmell could by any means be diſcovered. A
man who, having a pain in his ſide, had applied hyſſop to it, by the advice of a phyſician, approached the cylinder thus prepared,
and was electrified by it. The conſequence
was, that when he went home, and fell aſleep,
he ſweated, and the power of the balſam was
ſo diſperſed, that even his cloaths, the bed,
and chamber, all ſmelled of it. When he had
refreſhed himſelf by his ſleep, he combed his
head, and found the balſam to have penetrated his hair; ſo that the very comb was
perfumed *.

The next day, Signior Pivati ſays, he electrified a man in health in the ſame manner,
who knew nothing of what had been done before. On his going into company half an

* Phil. Tranſ. abridged, Vol. x. p. 400.

hour

hour afterwards, he found a gradual warmth
diffuling itfelf through his whole body, and
he grew more lively and chearful than ufual.
His companion was furprifed at an odour, and
could not imagine whence it proceeded, but
he himfelf perceived that the fume arofe from
his own body, at which he alfo was much
furprifed, not having the leaft fufpicion that
it was owing to the operation which had been
performed upon him by Signior Pivati*.

MR. WINCKLER of Leipfick, being ftruck
with fo extraordinary a relation, fays, that he
was defirous of trying the power of electricity on certain fubftances in the fame manner,
and that he found the event to confirm what
had been related †.

HE put fome pounded fulphur into a glafs
fphere, fo well covered and ftopped, that, on
turning it over the fire, there was not the
leaft fmell of fulphur perceived. When the
fphere was cold he electrified it; and, immediately, a fulphureous vapour iffued from
it, and, on continuing the electricity, filled
the air, fo as to be fmelled at the diftance of
more than ten feet. He called in a friend
well verfed in electricity, profeffor Haubold,
and feveral others, as witneffes and judges
of this fact; but they were prefently driven
away by the ftench of the fulphur. He ftaid
a little longer himfelf in this fulphureous atmofphere, and was fo impregnated thereby,
that his body, cloath's, and breath retained

* Phil. Tranf. abridged, Vol. x. p. 401.   † Ibid.

the

the odour even the next day. On repeating this experiment in the prefence of a perfon who was converfant with the effects of ful-phur, the figns of an inflamed blood were vi-fible in his mouth on the third day *.

AFTER this he tried the effect of a more agreeable fmell, and filled the fphere with cinnamon. When he had heated this as be-fore, the fmell of cinnamon was foon perceiv-ed by the company, and the whole room was in a fhort ime fo perfumed by it, that it im-mediately affected the nofes of all who came in, and the odour remained the next day.

HE tried the balfam of Peru with the like fuccefs, when his above mentioned friend (whofe teftimony, he fays, he did not care to be without) after he had received the power of the balfam, fmelled fo ftrong of it, that going abroad to fupper, he was often afked by the company what prefume he had about him. The next day, when Mr. Winckler was drinking tea, he fays, he found an un-ufual fweet tafte, owing to the fumes of the balfam that ftill remained in his mouth †.

IN a few days, when the fphere had loft all the fcent of the balfam, they let a chain out of the chamber window, and extended it through the open air, into another room de-tached from the former. Here they fufpend-ed the chain on filken lines, and gave it into the hand of a man, who alfo ftood on extend-ed filken lines, and knew nothing of their

* Phil. Tranf. abridged, Vol. x. p. 401.   † Ibid.

purpofe.

purpofe. When the electricity had been excited for fome time, the man was afked
whether he fmelled any thing; and, on fnuf-
fing up his nofe, he faid he did. Being afked again what fmell it was, he faid he did
not know. When the electrification had been
continued for about a quarter of an hour, the
room fmelled fo ftrong of it, that the man,
who knew nothing of the balfam, faid his
nofe was filled with a fweet fmell, like that
of fome fort of balfam. After fleeping in a
houfe, a confiderable diftance from the room
where the experiment was tried, he rofe very
chearfully in the morning, and found a more
pleafant tafte than ordinary in his tea .

I SHALL only give an account of two inftances of the effect of medicine applied in
this manner. The affiftance of Signior Pivati, the celebrated inventor of this improvement in electricity, was implored by a young
gentleman, who was miferably afflicted by a
quantity of corrupted matter collected in his
foot, that eluded all the attempts of the phyficians. Signior Pivati filled a glafs cylinder
with proper materials; and, having electrified it, drew fparks from the part affected,
and continued the operation for fome minutes.
When the patient went to bed, he had a good
night, and a mitigation of his pain. When
he awaked in the morning, he found a fmall
red tubercle on his foot, which only itched,
as if a cold humour had flowed through the

* Phil. Tranf. abridged, Vol. x. p. 401.

inner

inner part of his foot. He fweated every night for eight days together, and at the end of that time was perfectly well.

AFTER this, Signior Donadoni, bifhop of Sebenico, came to Signior Pivati, attended by his phyfician and fome friends. His lordfhip was at that time feventy-five years old, and had been afflicted with pains in his hands and fe et for feveral years. The gout had fo affected his fingers, that he was not able to move them; and his legs, fo that he could not bend his knees. In this deplorable fituation, the poor old bifhop intreated Signior Pivati to try the effects of electricity on him. The electrician undertook it, and proceeded after the following manner. He filled a glafs cylinder with difcutient medicines, and managed it fo, that the electric virtue might enter into the patient, who prefently felt fome unufual commotions in his fingers; and the action of electricity had been continued but two minutes, when his lordfhip opened and fhut both his hands, gave a hearty fqueeze to one of his attendants, got up, walked, fmote his hands together; helped himfelf to a chair, and fat down, wondering at his own ftrength, and hardly knowing whether it was not a dream. At length he walked out of the chamber down ftairs, without any affiftance, and with all the alacrity of a young man *.

⁎ Philofophical Tranfactions abridged, Vol. x. p. 403.

A variety of facts of this nature being publifhed, and feemingly well attefted, enr gaged all the electricians of Europe to repeat thefe experiments ; but none of them could fucceed but thofe mentioned above. An excellent remark of Mr. Baker's, who advifed trying all thefe experiments, notwithftanding their feeming very improbable, deferves to be quoted here. " Romantic as thefe things " may feem, they fhould not be abfolutely " condemned without a fair trial, fince we " all, I believe remember the time, when " thofe phenomena in electricity, which are " now the moft common and familiar to us, " would have been thought deferving as little " credit as the cafes under confideration may " feem to do, had accounts of them been fent " to us from Rome, Venice, or Bologna, " and had we never experienced them our- " felves *."

To fee thefe wonders, and to be affured of their truth or fallacy, Mr. Nollet, who was deeply interefted in every thing that related to his favourite ftudy, and who fet no bounds to his labour or expences, in the purfuit of truth, even paffed the Alps, and travelled into Italy, where he vifited all the gentlemen who had publifhed any account of thefe experiments. But though he engaged them to repeat their experiments in his prefence, and upon himfelf ; and though he made it his bufinefs to get all the beft information he could

* Phil. Tranf. abridged, Vol. x. p. 406.

concerning them, he returned, convinced that the accounts of cures had been much exaggerated; that in no one inftance had odours been found to tranfpire through the pores of excited glafs; and that no drugs had ever communicated their virtues to perfons who only held them in their hands while electrified.

HE had no doubt, however, but that, by continued electrification, without drugs, feveral perfons had found confiderable relief in various diforders; particularly, that a paralytic perfon had been cured at Geneva, and that a perfon deaf of one ear, a footman who had a violent pain in his head, and a woman who had a diforder in her eyes, were cured at Bologna *.

THE Englifh philofophers fhowed no lefs attention to this fubject than the Abbé Nollet. The Royal Society had received an account from Mr. Winckler of his experiments, to prove the tranfudation of odoriferous matter through the pores of excited glafs; and none of them fucceeding here, the fecretary was defired to write to Mr. Winckler, in the name of the fociety, defiring him to tranfmit to them, not only a circumftantial account of his manner of making the experiments, but likewife fome globes and tubes, fitted up by himfelf, for that purpofe.

THESE veffels, and directions how to ufe them, Mr. Winckler actually fent, and the

* Phil. Tranf. abridged, Vol. x. p. 413, &c.

experi-

experiments were made with every poffible precaution, at the houfe of Dr. Watfon (the moft interefted and active perfon in the king-dom in every thing relating to electricity) on the 12th of June 1751. There were prefent Martin Folkes, prefident of the Royal Society, Nicholas Mann, Efq. vice prefident, Dr. Mortimer, and Peter Daval, Efq. fecretaries, Mr. Canton a fellow, and Mr. Shroder, a gentleman of diftinction, well known to, and correfponding with Mr. Winckler. But, notwithftanding all the pains thefe gentlemen took, purfuing, with the utmoft exactnefs, the directions of Mr. Winckler, and alfo ufing methods of their own, which they thought ftill better adapted to force the effluvia through the glafs, they were unfuccefsful. They were not able to verify Mr. Winckler's experiments even in one fingle inftance[*].

But perhaps the moft fatisfactory refutation both of this pretended tranfudation of odours, and the medicinal effects of electricity above mentioned, was made at Venice, the very place where this medical electricity took its rife. The experiments were made by Dr. Bianchini, profeffor of medicine, in the prefence of a great number of witneffes, many of them prejudiced in favour of the pretended difcoveries; but they were all forced to be convinced of their futility, by the evidence of facts, and by experiments made with the greateft care and accuracy[†].

---

[*] Phil. Tranf. abridged, Vol. xlvii. p. 321.
[†] Ibid. Vol. xlviii. p. 399.

After

AFTER the publication of thefe accounts
properly attefted, every unprejudiced perfon
was fatisfied, that the pretended difcoveries
from Italy and Leipfick, which had raifed
the expectation of all the electricians in Europe, had no foundation in fact; and that
no method had yet been difcovered whereby
the power of medicine could by electricity
be made to infinuate itfelf into the human
body *.

LASTLY, I would obferve, that Dr. Franklin alfo fhowed, by feveral experiments, the
impoffibility of mixing the effluvia or virtue
of medicines with the electric fluid †.

IN fome refpects fimilar to the experiments
with the *medicated tubes* (as thofe mentioned
above were ufually called) was that of profeffor Boze, which he termed the *beatification*;
and which, for a long time, employed other
electricians to repeat after him, but to no
purpofe. His defcription of this famous experiment was, that if, in electrifying, large
globes were employed, and the electrified
perfon were placed upon large cakes of pitch,
a lambent flame would by degrees arife from
the pitch, and fpread itfelf round his feet;
and that from thence it would be propagated
to his knees and body, till, at laft, it afcended to his head; that then, by continuing the
electrification, the perfon's head would be
furrounded by a glory, fuch a one, in fome

* Phil. Tranf. abridged, Vol. xlviii. p. 406.
† Franklin's Letters, p. 82.

meafure,

meafure, as is reprefented by painters in their ornamenting the heads of faints *.

THIS experiment, as well as that of the medicated tubes, fet all the electricians in Europe to work, and put them to a great deal of expence ; but none of them could fucceed, fo as to produce an appearance any thing like that defcribed by Mr. Boze. No perfon took more pains in this bufinefs than Dr. Watfon. He himfelf underwent the operation feveral times, fupported by folid electrics three feet high. Upon being electrified very ftrongly, he found, as he fays feveral other perfons alfo did, a tingling upon the fkin of his head, and in many parts of his body, or fuch a fenfation as would be felt from a vaft number of infects crawling over him at the fame time; and he conftantly obferved the fenfation to be the greateft in thofe parts of his body which were neareft to any non-electric, but ftill no light appeared upon his head, though the experiment was feveral times made in the dark, and with fome continuance †.

AT length the Doctor, wearied with thefe fruitlefs attempts, wrote to the profeffor, and his anfwer fhowed that the whole had been a mere trick. He candidly acknowledged, that he had made ufe of a fuit of armour, which was decked with many bullions of fteel, fome pointed like nails, fome like wedges, and fome pyramidal; and that when the electrization was very vigorous, the edges of the

* Phil. Tranf. abridged, Vol. x. p. 411.   † Ibid.

helmet

helmet would dart forth rays, fomething like thofe which are painted on the heads of faints. And this was all his boafted bea-tification *.

THIS fame Mr. Boze, who feems to have had a fingular affectation of fomething myfte-rious and marvellous in his experiments, in a letter to the Royal Society at London, faid that he had been able, by electricity only, to in-vert the poles of a natural magnet, to deftroy their virtue, and to reftore it again, but he did not defcribe his method †. Confidering that no perfon in England could fucceed in this attempt, and that we are now able to do it but imperfectly, it is hardly probable that he did it at all.

THERE feems to have been fome decep-tion in an experiment which the worthy and excellent Dr. Hales communicated to the Royal Society this year, when he fays, that he obferved the electric fpark from warm iron to be of a bright light colour; from warm copper, green ; and from a warm egg, of a yellowifh flame colour, Thefe experiments, he faid, feemed to argue, that fome particles of thofe different bodies were carried off in the electric flafhes, whence thofe different colours were ex-hibited ‡.

I SHALL conclude this fection, which might juftly be intitled the *marvellous*, with

* Phil. Tranf. abridged, Vol. x. p. 413.
† Wilfon's Effay, p. 219.
‡ Phil. Tranf. abridged, Vol. x. p. 406.

mention-

mentioning the furprifing effect of an electric fpark in fetting fire to a fuftian frock,
on a fon of Mr. Robert Roche, when he
was electrified for fome diforder. I do not
queftion the fact. The experiment was
repeated, and it anfwered again as well as
at the firft time, when it was merely accidental. The paper containing this account
was read at the Royal Society on the 29th of
May 1748 *.

PERIOD IX.

THE EXPERIMENTS AND DISCOVERIES OF DR. FRANKLIN.

SECTION I.

DR. FRANKLIN's DISCOVERIES CONCERN-ING THE LEYDEN PHIAL, AND OTHERS CONNECTED WITH THEM.

WE have hitherto feen what had been
done in electricity by the Englifh
philofophers, and thofe on the continent of
Europe, till about the year 1750; but our
attention is now ftrongly called to what was
doing on the continent of America; where
Dr. Franklin and his friends were as affiduous
in trying experiments, and as fuccefsful in

---

* Phil. Tranf. abridged, Vol. x. p. 406.

making
4

making difcoveries, as any of their brethren
in Europe. For this purpofe, we muft look
back a few years. As Dr. Franklin's difcoveries were made intirely independent of any
in Europe, I was unwilling to interrupt the
former general account, by introducing them
in their proper year. For the fame reafon, I
imagine, it will be generally more agreeable,
to fee, at one view, what was done in America for fome confiderable fpace of time, without interrupting this account with what was
doing, in the mean time, in Europe. I fhall,
therefore, digeft, in the beft manner I can,
the three firft publications of Dr. Franklin,
entitled *New Experiments and Obfervations on
Electricity, made at Philadelphia in America*,
communicated in feveral letters to Peter Col-
linfon, Efq. of London, fellow of the Royal
Society; the firft of which is dated July 28th,
1747, and the laft April 18th, 1754.

NOTHING was ever written upon the fubject of electricity which was more generally
read and admired in all parts of Europe than
thefe letters. There is hardly any European
language into which they have not been tranflated; and, as if this were not fufficient to
make them properly known, a tranflation of
them has lately been made into Latin. It is
not eafy to fay, whether we are moft pleafed
with the fimplicity and perfpicuity with
which thefe letters are written, the modefty
with which the author propofes every hypothefis of his own, or the noble franknefs
with which he relates his miftakes, when
they

they were corrected by fubfequent experiments.

THOUGH the Englifh have not been backward in acknowledging the great merit of this philofopher, he has had the fingular good fortune to be, perhaps even more celebrated abroad than at home; fo that to form a juft idea of the great and deferved reputation of Dr. Franklin, we muft read the foreign publications on the fubject of electricity; in many of which the terms *Franklinifm*, *Franklinift*, and the *Franklinian fyftem* occur in almoft every page. In confequence of this, Dr. Franklin's principles bid fair to be handed down to pofterity, as expreffive of the true principles of electricity; juft as the Newtonian philofophy is of the true fyftem of nature in general.

THE zeal of Dr. Franklin's friends, and his reputation, were confiderably increafed by the oppofition which the Abbé Nollet made to his theory. The Abbé, however, never had any confiderable feconds in the controverfy, and thofe he had, I am informed, have all deferted him.

THE rife of Dr. Franklin's fame in France was firft occafioned by a bad tranflation of his letters falling into the hands of Mr. Buffon, intendant of the French King's gardens, and author of the Natural Hiftory for which he is famous. This gentleman, having fuccefsfully repeated Dr. Franklin's experiments, engaged a friend of his, Mr. Dalibard, to revife the tranflation; which was afterwards publifh-

O   ed,

ed, with a fhort hiftory of electricity prefix-
ed to it, and met with a very favourable reception from all ranks of people. What contributed not a little to the fuccefs of this publication, and to bring Dr. Franklin's principles into vogue in France, was a friend of
Mr. Dalibard's exhibiting Dr. Franklin's experiments for money. All the world, in a
manner, flocked to fee thefe new experiments,
and all returned full of admiration for the inventor of them *.

   DR. FRANKLIN had difcovered, as well as
Dr. Watfon, that the electric matter was not
created, but collected by friction, from the
neighbouring non-electric bodies. He had
obferved, that it was impoffible for a man to
electrify himfelf, though he ftood upon glafs
or wax ; for that the tube could communicate
to him no more electricity than it had received
from him in the act of excitation. He had
obferved, that if two perfons ftood upon wax,
one of which rubbed the tube, and the other
took the fire from it, they would both appear
to be electrified; that if they touched one another after that operation, a ftronger fpark
would be perceived between them, than when
any other perfon touched either of them; and
that fuch a fpark would take away the electricity of both †.

   THESE experiments led the Doctor to think,
that the electric fluid was conveyed from the
perfon who rubbed the tube to him who touch-

* Nollet's Letters, Vol. i. p. 4.
† Franklin's Letters, p. 14.

ed

ed it; which introduced some terms in electricity that had not been used before, but have continued in use ever since. The person who touched the tube was said, by Dr. Franklin, to be electrified *positively*, or *plus*; being supposed to receive an additional quantity of electric fire: whereas the person who rubbed the tube was said to be electrified *negatively*, or *minus*; being supposed to have lost a part of his natural quantity of the electric fluid *.

THIS observation was necessary to explain the capital discovery which Dr. Franklin made with respect to the manner of charging the Leyden phial; which is, that when one side of the glass is electrified positively, or *plus*, the other side is electrified negatively, or *minus*; so that whatever quantity of fire is thrown upon one side of the glass, the same is thrown out of the other; and there is really no more electric fire in the phial after it is charged than before; all that can be done by charging, being to take from one side, and convey to the other. Dr. Franklin also observed, that glass was impervious to electricity, and that, therefore, since the equilibrium could not be restored to the charged phial by any internal communication, it must be done by conductors externally, joining the inside and the outside †.

THESE capital discoveries he made by observing, that when a phial was charged, a cork ball suspended on silk would be attracted

* Franklin's Letters, p. 15.   † Ibid. p. 3.

by

by the outfide coating, when it was repelled
by a wire communicating with the infide;
and that it would be repelled by the outfide,
when it was attracted by the infide*. But
the truth of this maxim appeared more evident
when he brought the knob of the wire communicating with the outfide coating within a
few inches of the wire communicating with
the infide coating, and fufpended a cork ball
between them; for, in that cafe, the ball was
attracted by them alternately, till the phial
was difcharged †.

The European electricians had obferved,
that a phial could not be charged unlefs fome
conductor was in contact with the outfide;
but Dr. Franklin made the obfervation more
general, and alfo was able, by the principle
above mentioned, to give a better account of
it. As no more electric fire, he fays, can be
thrown into the infide of a phial when all is
driven from the outfide; fo, in a phial not
yet charged, none can be thrown into the
infide when none can be got from the outfide. He alfo fhowed, by a beautiful experiment, that, when the phial was charged, one
fide loft exactly as much as the other gained,
in reftoring the equilibrium. Hanging a
fmall linen thread near the coating of an electrified phial, he obferved, that every time he
brought his finger near the wire, the thread
was attracted by the coating. For as the fire
was taken from the infide by touching the

* Franklin's Letters, p. 4.   † Ibid. p. 5.

8.   wire,

wire, the outfide drew in an equal quantity by the thread *.

HE proved that, in difcharging the phial, the giving from one fide was exactly equal to the receiving by the other, by placing a perfon upon electrics, and making him difcharge the phial through his body; when he obferved, that no electricity remained in him after the difcharge †. He alfo hung cork balls upon an infulated conductor at the time of the difcharge of a phial hanging to it; and obferved, that if they did not repel before the explofion, they did not repel at the time, nor after ‡. But the experiment which moft completely proved, that the coating on one fide received juft as much as was emitted from the difcharge of the other, was the following.

HE infulated his rubber, and then, hanging a phial to his conductor, he found it could not be charged, even though his hand was held conftantly to it; becaufe, though the electric fire might leave the outfide of the phial, there was none collected by the rubber to be conveyed into the infide. He then took away his hand from the phial, and forming a communication, by a wire from the outfide coating to the infulated rubber, he found that it was charged with eafe. In this cafe, it was plain, that the very fame fire which left the outfide coating was conveyed by the way of the rubber, the globe, the conductor,

---

* Franklin's Letters, p. 5.   † Ibid p. 8.
‡ Ibid. p. 84.

and

and the wire of the phial, into the infide *.

DR. FRANKLIN's new theory of charging
the Leyden phial led him to obferve a greater
variety of facts, relating both to charging and
difcharging it, than other philofophers had
attended to. He found that the phial would
be electrified as ftrongly if it were held by
the hook, and the coating applied to the
globe or tube, as if it were held by the coating, and the hook applied; and, confequently, that there would be the fame explofion,
and fhock, if the electrified phial were held
in one hand by the hook, and the coating
touched with the other, as when held by the
coating, and touched at the hook. To take
the charged phial by the hook with fafety,
and not diminifh its force, he obferves,
that it muft firft be fet down upon electrics
per fe †.

DR. FRANKLIN obferved, that if a man
held in his hand two phials, the one fully
electrified, and the other not at all, and
brought their hooks together, he would have
but half a fhock: for the phials would both
remain only half electrified, the one being
half charged, and the other half difcharged ‡.

IF two phials were charged both through
their hooks, a cork ball fufpended on filk,
and hanging between them, would firft be attracted, and then repelled by both; but if
they were electrified, the one through the

----

* Franklin's Letters, p. 83.   † Ibid. p. 19.
‡ Ibid. p. 21.

wire,

wire, and the other through the coating, the ball would play vigoroufly between them both, till they were nearly difcharged *. The Doctor did not, at that time, take notice, that if the phials were both charged through their coatings (by which both the hooks would have been electrified minus) the ball would be repelled by them both, as when they were electrified plus. And when he, afterwards, obferved that two bodies electrified minus repelled one another, he feems to have been furprifed at the appearance, and acknowledged that he could not fatisfactorily account for it †.

Ir was known to every electrician, that a globe or tube wet on the infide would afford little or no fire; but no good reafon was given for it, before Dr. Franklin attempted its explanation by the help of his general maxim. He fays, that when a tube lined with any non-electric is rubbed, what is collected from the hand by the downward ftroke enters the pores of the glafs, driving an equal quantity out of the inner furface, into the non-electric lining; and that the hand, in pafling up to take a fecond ftroke, takes out again what had been thrown into the outward furface, the inner furface at the fame time receiving back again what it had given to the non-electric lining; fo that the particles of the electric fluid go in and out of their pores, upon every ftroke given to the tube ‡.

* Franklin's Letters, p. 21. † Ibid. p. 34.
‡ Ibid. p. 76.

O 4

IF,

If, in thefe circumftances, a wire was put into the tube, he obferved, that, if one perfon touched the wire, while another was rubbing the tube, and took care to withdraw his finger as foon as he had taken the fpark, which had been made to fly from the infide, it would be charged *.

If the tube was exhaufted of air, he obferves, that a non-electric lining in contact with the wire was not neceffary; for that, in vacuo, the electric fire would fly freely from the inner furface, without a non-electric conductor †.

Upon the fame principle he accounts for the effects of an excited electric being perceived through the glafs in the vacuum beyond it. The tube and its excited atmofphere, being brought near a glafs veffel, repels the electric fluid from the inner furface of the glafs; and this fluid, iffuing from the inner furface acts upon light bodies in the vacuum, both in its paffage from the glafs, and likewife in its return to it, when the excited electric on the outfide is withdrawn ‡.

This maxim, that whatever the phial takes in at one furface it lofes at the other, led Dr. Franklin to think of charging feveral phials together with the fame trouble, by connecting the outfide of one with the infide of another; whereby the fluid that was driven out of the firft would be received by the fecond,

* Franklin's Letters, p. 77.   † Ibid.
‡ Ibid. p. 78.

and

and what was driven out of the fecond would be received by the third, &c. By this means he found, that a great number of bottles might be charged with the fame labour as one only; and that they might be charged equally high, were it not that every bottle receives the new fire, and lofes its old with fome reluctance, or rather gives fome fmall refiftance to the charging. This cirumftance, he fays, in a number of bottles, becomes more equal to the charging power, and fo repels the fire back again on the globe fooner than a fingle bottle would do *.

Upon this principle Dr. Franklin conftructed an *electrical battery*, confifting of eleven panes of large fafh glafs, coated on each fide, and fo connected, that charging one of them would charge them all. Then having a contrivance to bring all the giving fides in contact with one wire, and all the receiving fides with another, he united the force of all the plates, and difcharged them all at once †.

When Dr. Franklin firft began his experiments upon the Leyden phial, he imagined that the electric fire was all crowded into the fubftance of the non-electric in contact with the glafs; but he afterwards found, that its power of giving a fhock lay in the glafs itfelf, and not in the coating, by the following ingenious analyfis of the bottle.

In order to find where the ftrength of the charged bottle lay, he placed it upon glafs;

---

* Franklin's Letters, p. 12.   † Ibid. p. 26.

then

then firft took out the cork and the wire, and
finding the virtue was not in them; he touched the outfide coating with one hand, and
put the finger of the other into the mouth of
the bottle; when the fhock was felt quite as
ftrong as if the cork and wire had been in it.
He then charged the phial again, and pouring out the water into an empty bottle infulated, expected that if the force refided in
the water it would give the fhock, but he
found it gave none. He then judged that
the electric fire muft either have been loft in
decanting, or muft remain in the bottle; and
the latter he found to be true; for, filling the
charged bottle with frefh water, he found
the fhock, and was fatisfied that the power of
giving it refided in the glafs itfelf *.

THE Doctor made the fame experiment
with panes of glafs, laying the coating on
lightly, and changing it, as he had before
changed the water in the bottle, and the refult was the fame in both †. This experiment is more fatisfactory than the former;
becaufe, when the water is poured out of the
phial, there ftill remains a thin coating of the
fluid, which might be thought to contain the
power of giving a fhock.

THAT the electric fire refided in the glafs,
was alfo farther evident from this confideration, that when glafs was gilt, the difcharging of it would make a round hole, tearing
off a part of the gilding, which, the Doctor

* Franklin's Letters p. 24.   † Ibid. p 25.

thought,

thought, could only have been done by the fire coming out of the glafs through the gilding. He alfo fays, that when the gilding was varnifhed even with turpentine, this varnifh, though dry and hard, would be burned by the fpark driven through it, yielding a ftrong fmell, and a vifible fmoke. Alfo, that when a fpark was driven through paper, it would be blackened by the fmoke, which fometimes penetrated feveral of the leaves, and that part of the gilding which had been torn off was found forcibly driven into the hole made in the paper by the ftroke. He alfo obferved, that when a thin bottle was broken by a charge, the glafs was broken inwards, at the fame time that the gilding was broken outwards *.

LASTLY, Dr. Franklin difcovered, that feveral fubftances which would conduct electricity in general, would not conduct the fhock of a charged phial. A wet packthread, for inftance, though it tranfmitted electricity very well, fometimes failed to conduct a fhock; as alfo did a cake of ice. Dry earth too rammed into a glafs tube intirely failed to conduct a fhock, and indeed would convey electricity but very imperfectly †.

* Franklin's Letters, p. 32.   † Ibid. p. 33.

SECTION

SECTION II.

DR. FRANKLIN's DISCOVERIES CONCERNING THE SIMILARITY OF LIGHTNING AND ELECTRICITY.

THE greatest difcovery which Dr. Franklin made concerning electricity, and which has been of the greatest practical ufe to mankind, was that of the perfect fimilarity between electricity and lightning. The analogy between thefe two powers had not been wholly unobferved by philofophers, and efpecially by electricians, before the publication of Dr. Franklin's difcovery. It was fo obvious, that it had ftruck feveral perfons. I fhall give one inftance, in the fagacious Abbé Nollet.

THE Abbé fays*, " If any one fhould " take upon him to prove, from a well con- " nected comparifon of phenomena, that " thunder is, in the hands of nature, what " electricity is in ours, that the wonders " which we now exhibit at our pleafure are " little imitations of thofe great effects which " frighten us, and that the whole depends " upon the fame mechanifm; if it is to be de- " monftrated, that a cloud, prepared by the " action of the winds, by heat, by a mix- " ture of exhalations, &c. is oppofite to a

---

* Leçons de Phyfique, Vol. iv. p. 34.

terreftrial

" terreftrial object; that this is the electrized
" body, and, at a certain proximity from
" that which is not; I avow that this idea, if
" it was well fupported, would give me a
" great deal of pleafure; and in fupport of
" it, how many fpecious reafons prefent
" themfelves to a man who is well acquaint-
" ed with electricity. The univerfality of the
" electric matter, the readinefs of its action,
" its inflammability, and its activity in giv-
" ing fire to other bodies, its property of
" ftriking bodies externally and internally,
" even to their fmalleft parts, the remarkable
" example we have of this effect in the ex-
" periment of Leyden, the idea which we
" might truly adopt in fuppofing a greater
" degree of electric power, &c. all thefe
" points of analogy, which I have been fome
" time meditating, begin to make me be-
" lieve, that one might, by taking electrici-
" ty for the model, form to one's felf, in re-
" lation to thunder and lightning, more per-
" fect and more probable ideas than what
" have been offered hitherto, &c."

MR. WINCKLER alfo enumerated many
particulars, in which electricity and lightning
refemble one another *.

BUT though the Abbé, and others, had
been ftruck with the obvious analogy between lightning and electricity, they went no
farther than thefe arguments *a priori*. It was
Dr. Franklin who firft propofed a method of

---

* Dantzick Memoirs, Vol. iii. p. 528.

verifying

verifying this hypothefis, entertaining the bold thought, as the Abbé Nollet expreffes it, of bringing lightning from the heavens, of thinking that pointed iron rods, fixed in the air, when the atmofphere was loaded with lightning, might draw from it the matter of the thunderbolt, and difcharge it without noife or danger into the immenfe body of the earth, where it would remain as it were abforbed.

MOREOVER, though Dr. Franklin's directions were firft begun to be put in execution in France, he himfelf completed the demonftration of his own problem, before he heard of what had been done elfewhere: and he extended his experiments fo far as actually to imitate almoft all the known effects of lightning by electricity, and to perform every electrical experiment by lightning.

BUT before I relate any of Dr. Franklin's experiments concerning lightning, I muft take notice of what he obferved concerning the power of *pointed bodies*, by means of which he was enabled to carry his great defigns into execution. For he was properly the firft who obferved the intire and wonderful effect of pointed bodies, both in drawing, and throwing off the electric fire.

IT was a fmall ftep towards difcovering the effect of pointed bodies, that Carolus Auguftus van Bergen, profeffor of medicine at Frankfort on the Oder, obferved that fparks taken from a polifhed body were ftronger than thofe from a rough one. He could fire fpirit eafily

with

with a polished conductor, but with difficulty by means of one not polished *.

Mr. Jallabert was perhaps the first who observed that a body, pointed at one end, and round at another, produced different appearances upon the same body, according as the pointed, or round end was presented to it. But as Mr. Nollet, in whose presence he made the experiment, says, the effect was not constant, and nothing was inferred from it †. And the Abbé acknowledges, that Dr. Franklin was the first who shewed the property of pointed bodies, in drawing off electricity more effectually, and at greater distances than other bodies could do it ‡.

He electrified an iron shot, three or four inches in diameter, and observed, that it would not attract a thread, when the point of a needle was presented to it; but that this was not the case, unless the pointed body had a communication with the earth; for, presenting the same pointed body, stuck on a piece of sealing wax, it had not that effect; though the moment the pointed body was touched with his finger, the electricity of the ball to which it was suspended was discharged. The

---

* Dantzick Memoirs, Vol. ii. p. 378.

† Lettres, Vol. i. p. 130.

‡ Recherches, p. 132. Dr. Franklin, in the new edition of his Letters, p. 5, says, that the power of points to throw off the electric fire, was communicated to him by his friend Mr. Thomas Hopkinson, who electrified an iron ball of three or four inches diameter, with a needle fastened to it, expecting to draw a stronger spark from the point, as from a kind of focus, but was surprised to find little or none.

converse

converfe of this he proved, by finding it impoffible to electrify the iron fhot when a fharp
needle lay upon it *.

BY obferving points of different degrees of
acutenefs, Dr. Franklin corrected the conclufion of Mr. Ellicott, and other Englifh
electricians, that a pointed body, as a piece
of leaf gold, would always be fufpended
nearer to the plate which was unelectrified
than that which was electrified, if it were
put between them. For the Doctor obferved, that it always removed fartheft from that
plate to which its fharpeft point was prefented, whether it was electrified or not; and if
one of the points was very blunt, and the
other very fharp, it would be fufpended in
the air by its blunt end, near the electrified
body, without any unelectrified plate being
held below it at all †.

DR. FRANKLIN endeavoured to account
for this effect of pointed bodies, by fuppofing that the bafe on which the electric fluid
at the point of an electrified body refted, being fmall, the attraction by which the fluid
was held to the body was flight; and that,
for the fame reafon, the refiftance to the entrance of the fluid was proportionably weaker
in that place than where the furface was
flat ‡. But he himfelf candidly owns, that
he was not quite fatisfied with this hypothefis.
Whatever we think of Dr. Franklin's theory
of the influence of pointed conductors in

* Franklin's Letters, p. 56, &c.   † Ibid. p. 67.
‡ Ibid. p. 56.

drawing

drawing and throwing off the electric fluid,
the world is greatly indebted to him for the
practical ufe he made of this doctrine *.

THE manner in which Dr. Franklin firft
conceived the practicability of drawing lightning from the clouds may be feen in an
extract which he has given us from his me
morandums, November 7th, 1749. After
enumerating all the known points of refemblance between lightning and electricity, he
concludes with faying, "The electric fluid is at-
" tracted by points. We do not know whether
" this property be in lightning, but fince they
" agree in all the particulars in which we can
" already compare them, it is not probable that
" they agree likewife in this. Let the experi-
" ment be made." Every circumftance relating
to a difcovery of fo much importance as this,
is interefting and pleafing †.

DR. FRANKLIN begins his account of the
fimilarity of the electric fluid and lightning
by cautioning his readers not to be ftaggered
at the great difference of the effects in point
of degree; fince that is no argument of any
difparity in their nature. It is no wonder,
fays he, if the effects of the one fhould be fo
much greater than thofe of the other. For if
two gun barrels electrified will ftrike at two
inches diftance, and make a loud report, at
how great a diftance will ten thoufand
acres of electrified cloud ftrike, and give

* Franklin's Letters, p. 62.
† Letters, New Edit. p. 323.

P   its

its fire, and how loud muſt be that crack * !

I SHALL digeſt all Dr. Franklin's obſervations concerning lightning under the ſeveral points of reſemblance which he obſerved between it and electricity, mentioned theſe points of ſimilarity in the order in which he himſelf remarked them; only bringing into one place the obſervations which may happen to lie in different parts of his letters, when they relate to the ſame ſubject.

1. FLASHES of lightning, he begins with obſerving, are generally ſeen crooked, and waving in the air. The ſame, ſays he, is the electric ſpark always, when it is drawn from an irregular body at ſome diſtance †. He might have added, when it is drawn by an irregular body, or through a ſpace in which the beſt conductors are diſpoſed in an irregular manner, which is always the caſe in the heterogeneous atmoſphere of our globe.

2. LIGHTNING ſtrikes the higheſt and moſt pointed objects in its way preferably to others, as high hills, and trees, towers, ſpires, maſts of ſhips, points of ſpears, &c. In like manner, all pointed conductors receive or throw off the electric fluid more readily than thoſe which are terminated by flat ſurfaces ‡.

3. LIGHTNING is obſerved to take the readieſt and beſt conductor. So does electri-

* Franklin's Letters, p. 44.   † Ibid. p. 46.
‡ Ibid. p. 47.

city in the difcharge of the Leyden phial. For this reafon, the Doctor fuppofes that it would be. fafer, during a thunder ftorm, to have one's cloaths wet than dry, as the lightning might then, in a great meafure, be tranfmitted to the ground, by the water, on the outfide of the body. It is found, fays he, that a wet rat cannot be killed by the explofion of the electrical bottle, but that a dry rat may *.

4. LIGHTNING burns. So does electricity. Dr. Franklin fays, that he could kindle with it hard dry rofin, fpirits unwarmed, and even wood. He fays, that he fired gun-powder, by only ramming it hard in a car-tridge, into each end of which pointed wires were introduced, and brought within half an inch of one another, and difcharging a fhock through them †.

5. LIGHTNING fometimes diffolves metals. So does electricity, though the Doctor was miftaken when he imagined it was by a cold fufion, as will appear in its proper place. The method in which Dr. Franklin made elec-tricity melt metals was by putting thin pieces of them between two panes of glafs bound faft together, and fending an electric fhock through them. Sometimes the piece of glafs, by which they were confined, would be fhattered to pieces by the difcharge, and be broken into a kind of coarfe fand, which once happened with pieces of thick looking-glafs; but if they remained whole, the piece

* Franklin's Letters, p. 47.   † Ibid. p. 48, 92.

of

of metal would be miffing in feveral places where it had lain between them, and inftead of it, a metallic ftain would be feen on both the glaffes, the ftains on the under and upper glafs being exactly fimilar in the minuteft ftroke *.

A PIECE of leaf gold treated in this manner appeared not only to have been melted, but, as the Doctor thought, even vitrified, or otherwife fo driven into the pores of the glafs, as to be protected by it from the action of the ftrongeft aqua regis. Sometimes he obferved that the metallic ftains would fpread a little wider than the breadth of the thin pieces of metal. True gold, he obferved, made a darker ftain, fomewhat reddifh, and filver a greenifh ftain †.

MR. WILSON fuppofes that, in this experiment, the gold was not driven into the pores of the glafs, but only into fo near a contact with the furface of the glafs, as to be held there by an exceedingly great force; fuch an one, he fays, as is exerted at the furface of all bodies whatever ‡.

6. LIGHTNING rends fome bodies. The fame does electricity §. The Doctor obferves, that the electric fpark would ftrike a hole through a quire of paper. When wood, bricks, ftone, &c. are rent by lightning, he takes notice, that the fplinters will fly off on that fide where there is the leaft refiftance.

* Franklin's Letters, p. 48, 65.　　† Ibid. p. 68.
‡ Hoadley and Wilfon, p. 68.
§ Franklin's Letters, p. 49.

In

In like manner, he fays, when a hole is ftruck through a piece of pafteboard by an electrified jar, if the furfaces of the pafteboard are not confined and compreffed, there will be a bur raifed all round the hole on both fides of the pafteboard ; but that if one fide be confined, fo that the bur cannot be raifed on that fide, it will all be raifed on the other fide, which way foever the fluid was directed. For the bur round the outfide of the hole is the effect of the explofion, which is made every way from the center of the electric ftream, and not an effect of its direction *.

7. Lightning has often been known to ftrike people blind. And a pigeon, after a violent fhock of electricity, by which the Doctor intended to have killed it, was obferved to have been ftruck blind likewife †.

8. In a thunder ftorm at Stretham, defcribed by Dr. Miles ‡, the lightning ftripped off fome paint which had covered a gilded molding of a pannel of wainfcot, without hurting the reft of the paint. Dr. Franklin imitated this, by pafting a flip of paper over the filleting of gold on the cover of a book, and fending an electric flafh through it. The paper was torn off from end to end, with fuch force, that it was broken in feveral places ; and in others there was brought away part of the grain of the Turkey leather in which the book was bound. This convinced

* Franklin's Letters, p. 124.   † Ibid. p. 63.
‡ Phil. Tranf. abridged, Vol. xlv, p. 387.

the

the Doctor, that if it had been paint, it would have been ftripped off in the fame manner with that on the wainfcot at Stretham *.

9. LIGHTNING deftroys animal life. Animals have likewife been killed by the fhock of electricity. The largeft animals which Dr. Franklin and his friends had been able to kill were a hen, and a turkey which weighed about ten pounds †.

10. MAGNETS have been obferved to lofe their virtue, or to have their poles reverfed by lightning. The fame did Dr. Franklin by electricity. By electricity he frequently gave polarity to needles, and reverfed them at pleafure. A fhock from four large jars, fent through a fine fewing needle, he fays, gave it polarity, fo that it would traverfe when laid on water. What is moft remarkable in thefe electrical experiments upon magnets is, that if the needle, when it was ftruck, lay Eaft and Weft, the end which was entered by the electric blaft pointed North, but that if it lay North and South, the end which lay towards the North, would continue to point North, whether the fire entered at that end or the contrary; though he imagined, that a ftronger ftroke would have reverfed the poles even in that fituation, an effect which had been known to have been produced by lightning. He alfo obferved, that the polarity was ftrongeft when the needle was ftruck ly-

---

* Phil. Tranf. abridged, Vol. xlv. p. 64.
† Franklin's Letters, p. 86, 153.

ing

ing North and South, and weakeft when it lay Eaft and Weft. He takes notice that, in thefe experiments, the needle, in fome cafes, would be finely blued, like the fpring of a watch, by the electric flame; in which cafe the colour given by a flafh from two jars only might be wiped off, but that a flafh from four jars fixed it, and frequently melted the needles. The jars which the Doctor ufed held feven or eight gallons, and were coated and lined with tinfoil *.

To demonftrate, in the completeft manner poffible, the famenefs of the electric fluid with the matter of lightning, Dr. Franklin, aftonifhing as it muft have appeared, contrived actually to bring lightning from the heavens, by means of an electrical kite, which he raifed when a ftorm of thunder was perceived to be coming on. This kite had a pointed wire fixed upon it, by which it drew the lightning from the clouds. This lightning defcended by the hempen ftring, and was received by a key tied to the extremity of it ; that part of the ftring which was held in his hand being of filk, that the electric virtue might ftop when it came to the key. He found, that the ftring would conduct electricity even when nearly dry, but that when it was wet, it would conduct it quite freely ; fo that it would ftream out plentifully from the key, at the approach of a perfon's finger †.

---

* Franklin's Letters, p 90, &c.   † Ibid. p. 106.

AT

AT this key he charged phials, and from electric fire thus obtained, he kindled spirits, and performed all other electrical experiments which are usually exhibited by an excited globe or tube.

As every circumstance relating to so capital a discovery as this (the greatest, perhaps, that has been made in the whole compass of philosophy, since the time of Sir Isaac Newton) cannot but give pleasure to all my readers, I shall endeavour to gratify them with the communication of a few particulars which I have from the best authority.

THE Doctor, after having published his method of verifying his hypothesis concerning the sameness of electricity with the matter lightning, was waiting for the erection of a spire in Philadelphia to carry his views into execution; not imagining that a pointed rod, of a moderate height, could answer the purpose; when it occurred to him, that, by means of a common kite, he could have a readier and better access to the regions of thunder than by any spire whatever. Preparing, therefore, a large silk handkerchief, and two cross sticks, of a proper length, on which to extend it, he took the opportunity of the first approaching thunder storm to take a walk into a field, in which there was a shed convenient for his purpose. But dreading the ridicule which too commonly attends unsuccessful attempts in science, he communicated his intended experiment to no body

but

but his fon, who affifted him in raifing the kite.

THE kite being raifed, a confiderable time elapfed before there was any appearance of its being electrified. One very promifing cloud had paffed over it without any effect; when, at length, juft as he was beginning to defpair of his contrivance, he obferved fome lofe threads of the hempen ftring to ftand erect, and to avoid one another, juft as if they had been fufpended on a common conductor. Struck with this promifing appearance, he immediately prefented his knucle to the key, and (let the reader judge of the exquifite pleafure he muft have felt at that moment) the difcovery was complete. He perceived a very evident electric fpark. Others fucceeded, even before the ftring was wet, fo as to put the matter paft all difpute, and when the rain had wetted the ftring, he collected electric fire very copioufly. This happened in June 1752, a month after the electricians in France had verified the fame theory, but before he had heard of any thing that they had done.

BESIDES this kite, Dr. Franklin had afterwards an infulated iron rod to draw the lightning into his houfe, in order to make experiments whenever there fhould be a confiderable quantity of it in the atmofphere; and that he might not lofe any opportunity of that nature, he connected two bells with this apparatus, which gave him notice,

6   by

by their ringing, whenever his rod was electrified *.

THE Doctor being able, in this manner,
to draw the lightning into his house, and
make experiments with it at his leisure; and
being certain that it was in all respects of the
same nature with electricity, he was desirous
to know if it was of the positive or negative
kind. The first time he succeeded in making
an experiment for this purpose was the 12th
of April 1753, when it appeared that the
lightning was negative. Having found that
the clouds electrified negatively in eight suc-
cessive thunder gusts, he concluded they were
always electrified negatively, and formed a
theory to account for it. But he afterwards
found he had concluded too soon. For, on
the sixth of June following, he met with one
cloud which was electrified positively; upon
which he corrected his former theory, but
did not seem able perfectly to satisfy himself
with any other. The Doctor sometimes
found the clouds would change from positive
to negative electricity several times in the
course of one thunder gust, and he once observed the air to be strongly electrified during
a fall of snow, when there was no thunder
at all †.

BUT the grand practical use which Dr.
Franklin made of his discovery of the sameness of electricity and lightning, was to se-

* Franklin's Letters, p. 112.   † Ibid. p. 112, &c.

cure

cure buildings from being damaged by lightning, a thing of vaft confequence in all parts
of the world, but more efpecially in feveral
parts of North America, where thunder ftorms
are more frequent, and their effects, in that
dry air, more dreadful, than they are ever
known to be with us.

THIS great end Dr. Franklin accomplifhed
by fo eafy a method, and by fo cheap, and
feemingly trifling apparatus, as fixing a
pointed metalline rod higher than any part of
the building, and communicating with the
ground, or rather the neareft water. This
wire the lightning was fure to feize upon,
preferably to any other part of the building;
whereby this dangerous power would be fafely conducted to the earth, and diffipated,
without doing any harm to the building *.

DR. FRANKLIN was of opinion, that a
wire of a quarter of an inch in thicknefs
would be fufficient to conduct a greater quantity of lightning than was ever actually difcharged from the clouds in one ftroke. He
found, that the gilding of a book was fufficient to conduct the charge of five large jars,
and thought that it would probably have
conducted the charge of many more. He alfo found by experiment, that if a wire was
deftroyed by an explofion, it was yet fufficient to conduct that particular ftroke, though
it was thereby rendered incapable of conducting another †.

* Franklin's Letters, p. 62, 124.   † Ibid. p. 124, 125.

THE Doctor also suppoſed, that pointed rods erected on edifices might likewiſe often prevent a ſtroke of lightning in the following manner. He ſays, that an eye ſo ſituated as to view horizontally the underſide of a thunder cloud, will ſee it very ragged, with a number of ſeparate fragments, or petty clouds, one under another, the loweſt ſometimes not far from the earth. Theſe, as ſo many ſtepping ſtones, aſſiſt in conducting a ſtroke between a cloud and a building. To repreſent theſe by an experiment, he directs us to take two or three locks of fine looſe cotton and connect one of them with the prime conductor, by a fine thread of two inches (which may be ſpun out of the ſame lock) another to that, and a third to the ſecond, by like threads. He then bids us to turn the globe, and ſays we ſhall ſee theſe locks extending themſelves towards the table (as the lower ſmall clouds do towards the earth) but, that, on preſenting a ſharp point, erect under the loweſt, it will ſhrink up to the ſecond, the ſecond to the firſt, and all together to the prime conductor, where they will continue as long as the point continues under them. A moſt ingenious and beautiful experiment! May not, he adds, in like manner, the ſmall electrified clouds, whoſe equilibrium with the earth is ſoon reſtored by the point, riſe up to the main body, and by that means occaſion ſo large a vacancy, as that the grand cloud cannot ſtrike in that place *.

* Franklin's Letters, p. 121, &c.

MR.

MR. WILCKE, in his remarks on Dr.
Franklin's letters, fays, that on the 20th of
Auguft 1758, he faw this fuppofition verified; as he was viewing a large fringed cloud,
ftrongly electrified, paffing over a foreft of
tall fir trees. The ragged and depending
parts of the large cloud were firft attracted
lower, and then fuddenly rofe higher, and
joined the large cloud *.

HE was alfo an eye witnefs of two clouds
lying one over the other, approaching, and
flafhing into one another. The lightning
fpread itfelf over all the parts of the blacker
cloud, which was negative, and which immediately began to diffolve in rain †.

DR. FRANKLIN advifes perfons who are
apprehenfive of danger from lightning, to
fit in the middle of a room (provided it be
not under a metal luftre fufpended by a chain)
fitting on one chair, and laying their feet on
another. It is ftill fafer, he fays, to bring
two or three mattreffes, or beds, into the
middle of the room, and folding them double,
to place the chairs upon them, for they not
being fo good conductors as the walls, the
lightning will not chufe to pafs through
them; but the fafeft place of all is in a ham-
mock hung in filken cords, at an equal diftance from all the fides of the room, p. 484.
I would add, that the place of moft abfolute
fafety muft be the cellar, and efpecially the
middle of it; for when a perfon is lower than

* Wilcke's Tranflation, p. 351.
† Franklin's Letters, p. 259.

the

the surface of the earth, the lightning must
strike it before it can possibly reach him.   In
the fields, the place of safety is, within a few
yards of a tree, but not quite near it.

S E C T I O N III.

MISCELLANEOUS DISCOVERIES OF DR. FRANKLIN, AND HIS FRIENDS IN AMERICA, DURING THE SAME PERIOD.

DR. FRANKLIN, retaining the common opinion, that electrified bodies
have real atmospheres of the electric fluid
(consisting of particles at some distance from
the surface of the body, but always going
along with it) observed that these atmospheres
and the air did not seem to exclude one another; though, he says, this be difficult to
conceive, considering that they are generally
supposed to repel one another.

An electric atmosphere, he says, raised
round a thick wire, inserted into a phial,
drives out none of the air it contained ; nor
on withdrawing that atmosphere, will any air
rush in, as he found by a very curious experiment, accurately made ; whence he also
concluded, that the elasticity of the air was
not affected by it *.

THE experiment, as the Doctor informs
me, was made with a small glass syphon,

* Franklin's Letters, p. 98.

one

one leg paffing through the cork into the bottle. The other leg had in it a drop of red ink, which readily moved on the leaft change of heat or cold in the air contained in the phial ; but not at all on the air's being electrified.

HE alfo made an experiment which would feem to prove the immobility, as we may fay, of thefe atmofpheres by any external force, if they have any exiftence at all ; but others may think it is rather an argument againft their exiftence. He electrified a large cork ball faftened to the end of a filk ftring three feet long ; and, taking the other end in his hand, he whirled it round, like a fling, a hundred times in the open air, with the fwifteft motion he could poffibly give it ; and obferved, that it ftill retained its electric atmofphere, though it muft have paffed through eight hundred yàrds of air *.

To fhow that a body, in different circumftances of dilatation and contraction, is capable of receiving, or retaining more or lefs of the electric fluid on its furface, he made the following curious experiment. He electrified a filver cann, in which there were about three yards of brafs chain, one end of which he could raife to what height he pleafed, by means of a pully and a filken cord. He fufpended a lock of cotton by a filken ftring from the ceiling of the room, making it hang near the cup ; and obferved, that every time he drew up the

* Franklin's Letters, p. 97.

chain

chain, the cotton approached nearer to the cup, and as conftantly receded from it when the chain was let down. From this experiment it was evident, he fays, that the atmofphere about the cup was diminifhed by raifing the chain, and increafed by lowering it ; and that the atmofphere of the chain muft have been drawn from that of the cup when it was raifed, and have returned to it again when it was let down *.

To make electric atmofpheres in fome meafure vifible, the Doctor ufed to drop rofin on hot iron plates held under bodies electrified; and, in a ftill room, the fmoke would afcend, and form vifible atmofpheres round the bodies, making them look very beautiful.   In trying in what circumftances, the repellency between an electrified iron ball, and a fmall cork ball would be altered, he obferved, that the fmoke of rofin did not deftroy their repellency, but was attracted both by the iron and the cork †.

THE Doctor obferved, that filver expofed to the electric fpark would acquire a blue ftain, and that iron would feem corroded by it ; but he could never perceive any impreffion made on gold, brafs, or tin.   The fpots on the filver or iron were always the fame, whether they received the fpark from lead, brafs, gold, or filver; and the fmell of the electric fire was the fame, through whatever bodies it was conveyed ‡.

---

* Franklin's Letters, p. 121.   † Ibid. p. 55.
‡ Ibid. p. 81, 98.

WHILE we are attending to what was done by Dr. Franklin at Philadelphia, we muſt by no means overlook what was done by Mr. Kinnerſley, the Doctor's friend, while at Boſton in New England. Some of his obſervations, of which an account is given in the Doctor's letters, are very curious; and ſome later accounts, which he himſelf has tranſmitted to England, ſeem to promiſe, that, if he continue his electrical inquiries, his name, after that of his friend, will be ſecond to few in the hiſtory of electricity.

HE firſt diſtinguiſhed himſelf by re-diſcovering Mr. Du Fay's two contrary electricities of glaſs and ſulphur, with which both he and Dr. Franklin were at that time wholly unacquainted. But Mr. Kinnerſley had a great advantage over Mr. Du Fay; for making his experiments in a more advanced ſtate of the ſcience, he ſaw immediately, that the two contrary electricities of glaſs and ſulphur were the very ſame poſitive and negative electricities, which had juſt been diſcovered by Dr. Watſon and Dr. Franklin.

HE obſerved, that a cork ball, electrified by a conductor from excited glaſs, would be attracted by excited amber and ſulphur, and repelled by excited glaſs and china; that electrifying the ball with the wire of a charged phial, it would be repelled by excited glaſs, but attracted by excited ſulphur; and that when he electrified it by ſulphur or amber, till it became repelled by them, it would be attracted by the wire of the phial, and repelled by its

Q coating.

coating. Thefe experiments furprifed him very much, but by analogy he was led to infer, *a priori*, the following paradoxes, as he calls them, which were afterwards verified by Dr. Franklin at his requeft *.

" 1. If a glafs globe be placed at one end " of a prime conductor, and a fulphur one at " the other, both being equally in good or- " der, and in equal motion, not a fpark of " fire can be obtained from the conductor, " but one globe will draw out as faft as the " other gives in.

" 2. If a phial be fufpended on the con- " ductor with a chain from its coating to the " table, and only one of the globes be made " ufe of at a time, twenty turns of the wheel, " for inftance, will charge it; after which, " as many turns of the other wheel will " difcharge it; and as many more will charge " it again.

" 3. The globes being both in motion, " each having a feparate conductor, with a " phial fufpended on one of them, and the " chain faftened to the other ; the phial will " become charged, one globe charging pofi- " tively, and the other negatively.

" 4. The phial being thus charged, hang " it in like manner, on the other conductor. " Set both wheels a-going again, and the " fame number of turns that charged it be- " fore will now difcharge it, and the fame " number repeated will charge it again.

* Franklin's Letters, p. 99.

" 5. When

" 5. WHEN each globe communicates with
" the fame prime conductor, having a chain
" hanging from it to the table, one of them,
" when in motion (but which I cannot fay)
" will draw fire up through the cufhion, and
" difcharge it, through the chain ; and the
" other will draw it up through the chain,
" and difcharge it through the cufhion *."

WHEN Mr. Kinnerfley was advifing his
friend to try the experiments with the fulphur
globe, he cautions him not to make ufe of
chalk on the cufhion, telling him that fome
fine powdered fulphur would do better. And
he expreffes his hope that if the Doctor fhould
find the two globes to charge the prime conductor differently, he would be able to difcover fome method of determining which it was
that charged pofitively.

DR. FRANKLIN, when thefe experiments
and conjectures were propofed to him, had no
idea of their having any real foundation; but
imagined, that the different attractions and
repulfions obferved by Mr. Kinnerfley proceeded rather from the greater or fmaller
quantities of the electric fire, obtained from
different bodies, than from its being either
of a different kind, or having a different direction. But finding, upon trial, that the
principal of Mr. Kinnerfley's fuppofitions were
verified by fact, he had no doubt of the
reft †.

* Franklin's Letters, p. 100.
† Ibid. p. 102, 103.

In

IN anfwer to the doubt of Mr. Kinnerfley, whether the glafs, or the fulphur electrified pofitively, the Doctor gave it as his opinion, that the glafs globe charged pofitively, and the fulphur negatively, for the following reafons.

1. BECAUSE, though the fulphur globe feemed to work equally well with the glafs one, yet it could never occafion fo large, and fo diftant a fpark between his finger and conductor as when the glafs globe was ufed. But what he adds to confirm this proof does not feem to be fatisfactory. He fuppofes that bodies of a certain bignefs cannot fo eafily part with the quantity of electric fluid which they have, and hold attracted within their fubftance, as they can receive an additional quantity upon their furface, by way of atmofphere; and that therefore fo much could not be drawn out of the conductor, as might be thrown on it *.

2. HE obferved that the ftream or brufh of fire, appearing at the end of the wire connected with the conductor, was long, large, and much diverging when the glafs globe was ufed, and made a fnapping or rattling noife; but that when the fulphur globe was ufed, it was fhort, fmall, and made a hiffing noife. He alfo obferved, that juft the reverfe of both thefe cafes happened when he held the fame wire in his hand, and the globes were worked alternately. The brufh was large,

* Franklin's Letters, p. 104.

long,

long, diverging, and fnapping or rattling, when the fulphur globe was turned; bu fhort, fmall, and hiffing, when the glafs globe was turned. When the brufh was long, large, and much diverging, it feemed to the Doctor, that the body to which it joined was throwing the fire out, and when the contrary appeared, it feemed to be drinking in *.

3. He obferved, that when he held his knuckle before the fulphur globe, while it was turning, the ftream of fire between his knuckle and the globe feemed to fpread on its furface, as if it flowed from the finger, but before the glafs globe it was otherwife.

4. He obferved that the cool wind (or what was called fo) which is felt as coming from an electrified point, was much more fenfible when the glafs globe, than when the fulphur one was ufed. But thefe, though the beft arguments which the fenfes can furnifh, of the courfe of the electric fluid, the Doctor acknowledges were but hafty thoughts. Indeed, confidering that the velocity of the electric fluid has been found, by experiment, to be nearly inftantaneous, in a circuit of many miles, it cannot be fuppofed that the eye fhould be able to diftinguifh which way it goes in the fpace of one or two inches †

I shall conclude this article with obferving that the experiments, which the Doctor made with globes of glafs and fulphur, are

* Franklin's Letters, p. 104.   † Ibid. p. 105.

much

much more eafily exhibited by the conductor
and infulated rubber of either of them, all
the effects being the reverfe of each other.

I MUST now, for the prefent, take leave
of this ingenious writer and his friends, after
having brought the hiftory of their labours to
the year 1754, and muft return to fee what
was doing on the continent of Europe for two
or three years preceding this date, while we
left it to go over to America.

P E R I O D X.

THE HISTORY OF ELECTRICITY, FROM THE
TIME THAT DR. FRANKLIN MADE HIS
EXPERIMENTS IN AMERICA, TILL THE
YEAR 1766.

WE are now entering upon the laft period into which the hiftory of electricity divides itfelf, in which the great variety
of matter prefented to our view muft oblige
an hiftorian to have recourfe to the ftricteft
method; for, otherwife, the narration would
be extremely perplexed and difgufting. As
this period contains the events of a larger
fpace of time than moft of the others, yet
without any convenient refting place; as the
bufinefs of electricity has been confiderably
multiplied in it, and a greater number of
labourers have been employed in gathering in
the harveft of difcoveries, the feeds of which
were fown by Dr. Watfon, Dr. Franklin, and
others,

others, in the preceding periods; I am obliged to fubdivide this into more diftinct parts,
but I hope they will not be found to be more
than were neceffary, in order to prevent confufion.

However, this circumftance, of the great
quantity and variety of materials furnifhed in
this period, in proportion as it tends to em-
barrafs an hiftorian, and exercife his talent
for proper diftribution and arrangement, is
a ftriking demonftration of a truth, which
muft give the greateft pleafure to all the lovers
of electricity and Natural Philofophy. If the
progrefs continue the fame in another period,
of equal length, if the harveft of difcoveries
continue to be more plentiful, and the labourers proportionably more numerous; what
a glorious fcene fhall we fee unfolded, what a
fund of entertainment is there in ftore for us,
and what important benefits may be derived
to mankind!

Q 4   SECTION

SECTION I.

IMPROVEMENTS IN THE ELECTRICAL AP-
PARATUS, WITH EXPERIMENTS AND OB-
SERVATIONS RELATING TO IT.

AS our electrical apparatus has been much improved within this period, I shall first recite what has occurred to me upon this subject; particularly the methods which have, from time to time, been communicated of increasing the power of electricity, by different circumstances of excitation.

So early as the year 1751, upon occasion of trying Mr. Winckler's experiments, notice is taken of Mr. Canton's method of rubbing tubes with silk prepared with linseed oil. These he had found, by the experience of some considerable time, to produce the greatest effect upon tubes, but he had not found that they were proportionably useful in rubbing globes *.

UPON another occasion, Mr. Canton observes, that by means of this rubber, a solid cylinder of glass, which had been set before the fire till it was quite dry, might be excited as easily as a glass tube, so as to act like one in every respect; that even the first stroke would make it strongly electrical †.

---

* Phil. Tranf. abridged, Vol. xlvii. p. 239.
† Ibid. Vol. xlviii. pt. ii. p. 784.

BUT

BUT the greateſt improvement which Mr. Canton diſcovered for increaſing the power of electricity, was by rubbing on the cuſhion of the globe, or on the oiled ſilk rubber of the tube, a ſmall quantity of an amalgam of mercury and tin, with a very little chalk or whiting. By this means, a globe or tube may be excited to a very great degree with very little friction, eſpecially if the rubber be made more damp or dry as occaſion may require *.

MR. WILCKE ſays, that a glaſs tube excited with a woollen cloth, on which ſome white wax or oil has been put, will throw out flames with a great noiſe in the dark †. Theſe flames, he ſays, he never knew to be thrown from a globe, except ſometimes when they were firſt uſed ‡.

OUR electrical apparatus has been much augmented within this period by the diſcovery of Father Windelinus Ammerſin of Switzerland, who, in a Latin treatiſe, publiſhed at Lucern, in the year 1754, has ſhewn us, that wood properly dried, till it becomes very brown, is a non-conductor of electricity. He recommends boiling the wood in linſeed oil, or covering it over with varniſh, after being dried, to prevent any return of moiſture into its pores; and adds, that wood, ſo treated, ſeems to afford ſtronger appearances of electricity than even glaſs. He himſelf made uſe of common wooden meaſures, ſuch as are

* Phil. Tranſ. Vol. lii. pt. ii. p. 461.
† Wilcke, p. 124.   ‡ Ibid. p. 126.

ufually found in granaries, firft boiled in oil, and afterwards mounted, fo as to be turned by a wheel *.

It appears from the Philofophical Tranf-actions, fays Mr. Wilfon, fo early as the year 1747, that Dr. Watfon having occafion to fupport a long wire, in an experiment made near Shooter's Hill, with a view to determine the velocity of electric fluid, ufed ftakes of dry wood, which he told him, were baked, to prevent the electric fluid from efcaping in-to the ground †.

A more extraordinary method of procur-ing electricity than by baked wood, was one that Signior Beccaria made ufe of. He put a dry and warm cat's fkin upon his glafs globe, and rubbing it with his hand, excited a very powerful electrity ‡.

These wooden cylinders electrify pofitive-ly or negatively as the rubber is filk or flannel, but much more powerfully when negative than when pofitive, owing to the rough-nefs which there generally is upon their fur-faces, and therefore make an agreeable va-riety in an electrical apparatus. But the oldeft and moft ufual method of procuring negative electricity was by globes of fulphur. Thefe Mr. Le Roi made by putting a coating of fulphur upon a globe of glafs, and then fmoothing it with an hot iron; but Mr. Nol-let preferred melting the fulphur in the infide

* Phil. Tranf. Vol. lii. pt. i. p. 342.
+ Ibid. Vol. li. pt. ii. p. 896.
‡ Lettere dell' Elettricifmo, p. 58.

of

of the glafs globe, and then breaking the glafs
from off it, becaufe this method made a much
finer polifh *.

ONE globe he made of a mixture of fulphur and pounded glafs, but he found that it
had the fame effect as if it had been all of
fulphur. He fays that, when one part of
this globe was excited, the whole furface became electrical †.

BUT fince Mr. Canton's difcovery of the
negative power of rough glafs, fome philofophers have made ufe of glafs globes made
rough by emery; and the ufual method of
taking off their polifh was by rubbing them
as they turned upon their axis; but Mr.
Speedler, a mathematical inftrument maker at
Copenhagen, obferves, in his letters upon
the fubject of electricity, that glafs globes,
made rough by drawing the ftone, or emery,
from pole to pole, have a much greater virtue; this method of taking off the polifh giving them a greater roughnefs with refpect to
the rubber ‡.

BUT a better, and a readier method than
all thefe of producing negative electricity, is
by infulating the rubber of a fmooth globe,
and connecting it with an infulated prime conductor, while the common conductor hath a
communication with the ground. The rubber,
if well infulated, is fure to produce a negative electricity, equal in power to the pofitive
of the fame globe. Mr. Dalibard directs a

* Nollet's Letters, Vol. ii. p. 121.
† Ibid. p. 125, 127.   ‡ Wilcke, p. 57.

great

great number of precautions, in order to electrify well at the rubber, and to prevent it
from receiving any electric fire in its state of
infulation *.

Mr. Bergman of Upfal, fays, that very
often, when his glafs globes could not be excited to a fufficient degree of ftrength, he
lined them with a thin coating of fulphur,
and that then they gave a much ftronger pofitive electricity than before †.

In Italy, and other places, Mr. Nollet informs us, it is the cuftom of electricians to
put a coating of pitch, or other refinous matter on the infide of their globes, which they
pretend, makes them always work well ‡.

We are obliged to the Abbé Nollet for
fome obfervations on the electrical powers of
different kinds of glafs, in the fixth volume
of his *Leçons de phyfique* printed in the year
1764.

It is not every fort of glafs, fays he, that
is equally electrizable. There are fome forts
which are not fo at all, or hardly at all; fuch,
for example, is that of which they make plates
of glafs at St. Gobin in Picardy. I have tried
it, fays he, an hundred times, in the form of
plates, tubes, and globes, and in all kinds of
weather, but have fcarce been ever able to
draw from it the leaft fenfible fign of
electricity.

* Dalibard's Franklin, p. 110.
† Phil. Tranf. Vol. lii. pr. ii. p. 485.
‡ Lettres, Vol. ii. p. 122.

The

The glafs of which panes for windows are made, and which is alfo ufed for drinking-glaffes, when it is newly manufactured, is excited with great difficulty. I have often, fays he, repeatedly rubbed tubes, and other pieces, even in the glafs-houfe where they were made, but without fuccefs; and it has not been till after fome months, and fometimes years, that I could bring them to act.

It is certain, and he fays he has conftantly obferved, that glafs becomes more fit for electrical experiments by force of rubbing and that fometimes it has required fome months to bring globes and tubes to act well.

He did not think that thefe facts could be accounted for either by the different degrees of tranfparency, or the different colours of glafs. This, indeed, was evident from fome globes acquiring electricity from ufe which had it not originally. The glafs of which bottles are made at Severs ferved him very well, whereas globes of white glafs did not become tolerable till after having been ufed a certain time.

He could not tell pofitively why certain kinds of glafs were electrizable or not by rubbing, but he fufpected, that it was principally owing to the degree of its hardnefs and vitrification. He was induced to think fo, becaufe he found that the glafs at the French manufactory at St. Gobin, and at Cherbourg (the hardeft, the moft compact, and the beft vitrified of all the kinds of glafs in France)

was

was the moſt difficult to be electrized; whereas the cryſtal glaſs of England, that of Bohemia, &c. which are much ſofter, were
the beſt of all for experiments in electricity.
He ſays, moreover, that he had procured
imperfect glaſſes, which had not been long
enough in the furnace to be clear; and that,
though they were of the ſame compoſition as
plates of glaſs, which, he obſerved before,
were not eaſily electrized, yet that theſe were
excited very ſenſibly.

He ſays that a globe of ten or twelve
inches diameter, and which makes about four
revolutions in a ſecond of time, will receive a
convenient rubbing; but that we muſt not
expect that if the globe be one half, or one
fourth part greater or leſs, the effects will be
increaſed or diminiſhed in proportion *.

Upon the ſubject of inſulating bodies, he
obſerves, that when the cakes of ſulphur,
reſin, ſealing-wax, and bees-wax are made
uſe of for this purpoſe, they ought to be well
cooled before they are uſed : for, he ſays, he
has conſtantly obſerved, that when they are
newly made, they are not ſo proper to inſu-
late bodies, as they generally are at the end
of ſome months †.

It will be proper, under this head, to acquaint young electricians, that globes have
been ſeveral times known to burſt during the
act of excitation, and that the fragments have
been thrown with great violence in every di-

* Leçons de Phyſique, Vol. vi. p. 273—276.
† Ibid. p. 299.

rection, fo as to be very dangerous for the by-ftanders. This accident happened to Mr. Sabatelli in Italy, Mr. Nollet in France, Mr. Beraud at Lyons, Mr. Boze at Wittemburgh, Mr. Le Cat at Rouen, and Mr. Robein at Rennes.

THE air in the infide of Mr. Sabatelli's globe had no communication with the externul air, but that of the Abbé Nollet had. This laft, which was of Englifh flint, which had been ufed two years, and which was more than a line thick, burft like a bomb in the hands of a fervant who was rubbing it; and the frag-ments (the largeft of which were not more than an inch in diameter) were difperfed on all fides, to a confiderable diftance. The Abbé fays, that all the globes which were burft in that manner exploded after five or fix turns of the wheel; and he afcribes this effect to the action of the electric matter, making the particles of the glafs vibrate in a manner he could not conceive *.

WHEN Mr. Beraud's globe burft (and he was the firft to whom this accident was ever known to happen) he was making fome ex-periments in the dark, on the 8th of Febru-ary 1750; when a noife was firft heard, as of fomething rending to pieces; then follow-ed the explofion, and when the lights were brought in, it was obferved, that thofe places of the floor which were oppofite to the equa-torial diameter of the globe were ftrewed with

* Nollet's Letters, Vol. i. p. 19.

fmaller

fmaller pieces, and in greater numbers than thofe which were oppofite to other parts of it. This globe had been cracked, but it had been in conftant ufe in that ftate above a year, and the crack had extended itfelf from the pole to the equator. The proprietor afcribed the accident to the vibration of the particles of the glafs, and thought that the crack had fome way impeded thofe vibrations *.

WHEN Mr. Boze's globe broke, he fays that the whole of it appeared in the act of breaking, like a flaming coal; a circumftance which we fhall fee accounted for hereafter by Mr. Wilcke †.

MR. BOULANGER fays, that glafs globes have fometimes burft like bombs, and have wounded many perfons, and that their fragments have even penetrated feveral inches into a wall ‡. He alfo fays, that if globes burft in whirling by the gun-barrel's touching them, they burft with the fame violence, the fplinters often entering into the wall §.

THE Abbé Nollet had a globe of fulphur which alfo burft, as he was rubbing it with his naked hands, after two or three turns of the wheel, having firft cracked inwardly. It broke into very fmall pieces, which flew to a great diftance; and into a fine duft, of which part flew againft his naked breaft; where it entered the fkin fo deep, that it could not be got off without the edge of a knife ‖.

* Hiftoire, p. 87.   † Wilcke, p. 124.
‡ Boulanger, p. 23.   § Ibid. p. 144.
‖ Nollet's Letters, Vol. ii. p. 220.

SECTION

SECTION II.

Observations on the condcuting Power of various substances, and particularly Mr. CANTON's experiments on air; and Signior BECCARIA's on air, and water.

ONE of the principal *desiderata* in the science of electricity, is to ascertain wherein consists the distinction between those bodies which are conductors, and those which are non-conductors of the electric fluid. All that has been done relating to this question, till the present time, amounts to nothing more than observations, how near these two classes of bodies approach one another; and before the period of which I am now treating, these observations were few, general, and superficial. But I shall now present my reader with several very curious and accurate experiments, which, though they do not give us intire satisfaction with respect to the great *desideratum* above mentioned; yet throw some light upon the subject. They show that substances which had been considered as perfect conductors, or non-conductors, are so only to a certain degree; and that, probably, all the known parts of nature have, in some measure, the properties of both.

THESE experiments were made by two persons, whom, in the style of history, I

R   may

may juftly call two of the greateft *heroes* of this part of my work, viz. Mr. CANTON, whofe difcoveries in electricity are far more numerous, and more confiderable than thofe of any other perfon, within this period, in England; and Signior BECCARIA, one of the moft eminent of all the electricians a-broad.

THAT air was capable of receiving electricity by communication, and of retaining it when received, had not been difcovered by any perfon before Mr. Canton; but, by the help of one of his exquifite contrivances, he was able to afcertain that delicate circumftance, and even meafure the degree of it, if it was in the leaft confiderable.

HE got a pair of balls, turned in a lathe, out of the dry pith of elder. Thefe he put into a narrow box, with a fliding cover, fo difpofed that the threads (which were of the fineft linen) were kept ftraight in the box. Holding this box by the extremity of the cover, the balls would hang freely from a pin in the infide. Thefe balls hung at a fufficient diftance from buildings, trees, &c. eafily fhow the electricity of the atmofphere. They alfo determine whether the electricity of the clouds and the air be pofitive, by the decreafe; or negative, by the increafe of their repulfion, at the approach of excited amber or fealing-wax.

BY the help of this inftrument, he obferved, that it was poffible to electrify the air of a room near the apparatus; and even
the

the air of the whole room in which it was, to a confiderable degree, and he was able to do it both pofitively and negatively.

In a paper read at the Royal Society, December the 6th, 1753, he obferves, that the common air of a room might be electrified to a confiderable degree, fo as not to part with its electricity for fome time. Having rendered the air of his room very dry, by means of a fire, he electrified a tin tube (with a pair of balls fufpended at one of its extremities) to a great degree; when it appeared, that the neighbouring air was likewife electrified. For, having touched the tube with his finger, or any other conductor, the balls, notwithftanding, continued to repel one another, though not at fo great a diftance as before *. But he obferves that their repulfion would decreafe as they were moved towards the floor, wainfcot, or any of the furniture; and that they would touch each other when brought within a fmall diftance of any conductor. Some degree of this electric power, he has known to continue in the air above an hour after the rubbing of the tube, when the weather had been very dry.

To electrify the air, or the moifture contained in it, negatively, Mr. Canton fupported, by filk ftretched between two chairs (placed back to back, at the diftance of about three feet), a tin tube with a fine fewing needle at

* Phil. Tranf. Vol. xlix. pt. i. p. 300.

one

one end of it; and rubbed fulphur, fealing-wax, or a rough glafs tube as near as he could to the other end, for three or four minutes; after which he found the air to be negatively electrical, and that it would continue fo a confiderable time after the apparatus was removed into another room *.

In a paper dated November the 11th, 1754, he fays, that dry air, at a great diftance from the earth, if in an electric ftate, will continue fo till it meets with fome conductor, is probable from the following experiment. An excited glafs tube, with its natural polifh, being placed upright in the middle of a room (by putting one end of it into an hole, made for that purpofe, in a block of wood) would, generally, lofe its electricity in lefs than five minutes, by attracting to it a fufficient quantity of moifture, to conduct the electric fluid from all parts of its furface to the floor; but if, immediately after it was excited, it was placed, in the fame manner, before a good fire, at the diftance of about two feet, where no moifture would adhere to its furface, it would continue electrical a whole day, and how much longer he knew not †.

Since the publication of the firft edition of this work, Mr. Canton has hit upon another, much readier, and more powerful method of communicating electricity to the air than that defcribed above. This he gives me

* Phil. Tranf. Vol. xlviii. pt. ii. p. 784.   † Ibid.

leave

leave to publish, and it appears to me to be
of such a nature, as that it may very possibly
lead to farther discoveries concerning the
electricity of the atmosphere, and the phenomena depending upon it. " Take," says he,
" a charged phial in one hand, and a lighted
" candle, insulated, in the other; and, going
" into any room, bring the wire of the phial
" very near to the flame of the candle, and
" hold it there about half a minute: then
" carry the phial and candle out of the room,
" and return with the pith balls, suspended,
" and held at arm's length. The balls will
" begin to separate on entering the room,
" and will stand an inch and half, or two
" inches a part, when brought near the
" middle of it."

SIGNIOR BECCARIA, who had no knowledge of what Mr. Canton had done, made
the same discovery of the communication of
electricity to the air, and diversified the experiment in a much more pleasing and satisfactory manner. He proves, that the air,
which is contiguous to an electrified body,
acquires, by degrees, the same electricity;
that this electricity of the air counteracts that
of the body, and lessens its effects, and that
as the air acquires, so it also parts with this
electricity very slowly.

HE began his experiments by hanging
linen threads upon an electrified chain, and
observing, that they diverged the most after
a few turns of his globe. After that, they
came nearer together, notwithstanding he

R 3   kept

kept turning the globe and the excitation was as powerful as ever *.

WHEN he had kept the chain electrified a considerable time, and then discontinued the friction, the threads collapsed by degrees, till they hung parallel. After this, they began to diverge again, without any fresh electrification; and, if the air was still, this second divergence would continue an hour, or more.

THIS divergence was lessened by the electrification of the chain. For if the globe was turned again, the threads would first become parallel, and then begin to diverge again as before. Thus the second divergence of the threads took place, when the chain was deprived of its electricity, and when that which the air had acquired began to show itself.

WHILE the threads were beginning to diverge with the electricity of the air, if he touched the chain, and thereby took off what remained of its electricity, the threads would separate farther. Thus the more the electricity of the chain was lessened, the more did the electricity of the air appear.

WHILE the threads were in their second divergence, he hung two other threads, shorter than the former, by another silk thread to the chain; and when all the electricity of the chain was taken quite away, they would separate, like the former threads.

* Lettere dell' Elettricifmo, p. 87.

IF

IF he prefented other threads to the former, in their fecond divergence, they would all avoid one another *.

IN this complete and elegant manner did Signior Beccaria demonftrate, that air actually receives electricity by communication, and lofes it by degrees; and that the electricity of the air counteracts that of the body which conveys electricity to it.

SIGNIOR BECCARIA alfo made a variety of other experiments, which demonftrate other mutual affections of the air and the electric fluid; particularly fome that prove their mutual repulfion; and that the electric fluid, in paffing through any portion of air, makes a temporary vacuum.

HE brought the ends of two wires within a fmall diftance of one another, in a glafs tube, one end of which was clofed, and the other immerged in water; and obferved, that the water funk in the tube, every time that a fpark paffed from the one to the other, the electric fluid having repelled the air †.

HE made the electric explofion a great number of times, in the fame air, inclofed in a glafs tube, in order to afcertain whether the elafticity of the air was affected by it; but he could not find any alteration. After the operation, he broke the tube under water, but neither did any air make its efcape, nor any water force its way into the tube. The expe-

---

* Lettere dell' Elettricifmo, p. 90.
† Elettricifmo artificiale e naturale, p. 110.

riment

riment was made with all the precaution, with
refpect to heat and cold, that the nature of
the cafe required *.

S·GNIOR BECCARIA's experiments on *water*, fhowing its imperfection as a conductor,
are more furprifing than thofe he made upon
air, fhowing its imperfection in the contrary
refpect. They prove that water conducts
electricity according to its quantity, and that
a fmall quantity of water makes a very
great refiftance to the paffage of the electric
fluid.

HE made tubes, full of water, part of the
electric circuit, and obferved, that when they
were very fmall, they would not tranfmit a
fhock, but that the fhock increafed as wider
tubes were ufed †.

BUT what aftonifhes us moft in Signior
Beccaria's experiments with water, is his
making the electric fpark vifible in it, notwithftanding its being a real conductor of electricity. Nothing, however, can prove more
clearly how imperfect a conductor it is.

HE inferted wires, fo as nearly to meet, in
fmall tubes filled with water; and, difcharging fhocks through them, the electric fpark
was vifible between their points, as if no water had been in the place. The tubes were
generally broken to pieces, and the fragments driven to a confiderable diftance. This
was evidently occafioned by the repulfion of
the water, and its incompreffibility, it not

---

* Elettricifmo artificiale e naturale, p. 81.
† Ibid, p. 113.

being

being able to give way far enough within itfelf, and the force with which it was repelled being very great *.

THE force with which fmall quantities of
water are thus repelled by the electric fluid,
he fays, is prodigious. By means of a charge
of four hundred fquare inches, he broke a
glafs tube two lines thick, when the pieces
were driven to the diftance of twenty feet.
Nay he fometimes broke tubes eight or ten
lines thick, and the fragments were driven to
greater diftances in proportion †.

HE found the effect of the electric fpark
upon water greater than the effect of a fpark
of common fire on gunpowder; and fays he
does not doubt, but that, if a method could
be found of managing them equally well, a
cannon charged with water would be more
dreadful than one charged with gunpowder.
He actually charged a glafs tube with water,
and put a fmall ball into it, when it was difcharged with great force, fo as to bury itfelf in fome clay which he placed to receive it ‡.

THIS refiftance which fmall quantities of
water make to the electric matter, he imagined, was greater than the refiftance made
to it by air §. And yet he thought it was

---

* Elettricifmo artificiale e naturale, p. 114.

† Lettre dell' elettricifmo, p. 74.

‡ Ibid. p. 75, 76. Mr. LULLIN fays, he produced much
greater effects than thefe, by making the electric fpark vifible
in *oil* inftead of water. Oil being a much worfe conductor, the
fpark in it would be larger. Differtatio Phyfica, p. 26.

§ Elettricifmo artificiale, &c. p. 115.

poffible, that, in this cafe, the electric matter might not act upon the water immediately, but upon the fixed air that was in it. For
when the tubes were not broken, he obferved
that a great number of air bubbles were let
loofe, through the whole mafs of the water,
rofe to the top, and mixed with the common
atmofphere *.

HE alfo imagined that the electric fluid
acted upon the fixed air in all bodies, though
no experiment could make it fenfible †.

ON the contrary, he fuppofed that the action of the electric matter tended to fix elaftic
air, by exciting a fulphureous matter, which
Dr. Hales fhows to have that property ‡. But
the experiment above-mentioned, of the electric fpark taken in a clofed tube, doth not
favour this fuppofition.

WHEN a fmall drop of water was put between the points of two wires, and a large
fhock paffed through them, the water was
equally difperfed on the infide of a glafs
fphere, in which they were all inclofed. In
the fame manner, he conjectures, that the action of the electric matter promotes the evaporation of water §.

DISCHARGING a fhock through a quantity
of water, poured on a flat furface, where fome
parts of the circuit were purpofely left almoft
dry; thofe parts became quite dry fooner than
they would have been, if no fhock had paffed
through them ‖.

* Elettricifmo artificiale, &c. p. 116.   † Ibid. p. 83.
‡ Ibid.   § Ibid. p. 117.   ‖ Ibid. p. 121.

UPON

Upon this principle he accounts for the ſuppoſed burſting of the blood veſſels in ſmall birds killed by the electric ſhock *. And when a muſcle contracts by the ſhock, he ſuppoſes it is owing to the dilatation of the fluids their fibres contain, as the electric matter paſſes through them.

So imperfect a conductor of electricity is mere water, that, he thought, a green leaf conducted a ſhock better than an equal thickneſs of water †. If this be true, and vegetable fluids conduct electricity better than water, it will confirm a conjecture which Dr. Franklin told me he had drawn from ſome experiments that he had not properly purſued, viz. that animal fluids conducted electricity better than water. He tried milk many years ago; and Mr. Kinnerſley, and others in America, have ſince tried blood and urine, and alſo the ſinews of animals newly killed; and they were all found to be exceedingly good conductors, remarkably better than water.

Signior Beccaria alſo found, that even *metal* was not a perfect conductor of electricity, but made ſome reſiſtance to the paſſage of the electric fluid. This he aſcertained, by meaſuring the time that it was retarded, in its paſſing through long and ſmall wires, notwithſtanding the experiments which had been made before, that ſeemed to prove the contrary.

---

* Elettriciſmo artificiale, &c. p. 128.   † Ibid. p. 135.

He

HE fufpended a wire of five hundred Paris feet, in a large building, and, by means of a pendulum which vibrated half feconds, obferved, that light bodies placed under a ball of gilt paper, at one end, did not move, till, at leaft, one vibration of this pendulum, after he had applied the wire of a charged phial to the other.

TRYING the fame with a hempen cord, he could count fix, or more vibrations before they would ftir; but when he had wetted the cord, they were moved after two or three vibrations *. He does not, however, abfolutely fay that, the electric fluid muft have taken up all this time in its progrefs, as it might require a certain quantity of the fluid, before it could raife the light bodies. But he did imagine, that it moved with more velocity, in proportion as the bodies into which it paffed had more or lefs of the fluid before †. And he was confirmed in this opinion by feveral phenomena of the atmofphere, which will be related in their proper place, particularly by feeing, very evidently, the progrefs of a quantity of electric matter in the air, as it advanced to ftrike his kite.

To thefe experiments of Signior Beccaria on the conducting powers of air and water, I fhall fubjoin another curious fet of the fame author, fhowing the manner in which the fmoke of rofin and of colophonia is affected by the approach of an electrified

---

* Elettricifmo artificiale, &c. p. 51.   † Ibid.

body,

body, as they have a very near affinity to this fubject.

REPEATING Dr. Franklin's experiments to make electric atmofpheres vifible with the fume of colophonia, which he preferred, for this purpofe, to rofin; he obferved feveral curious circumftances, which had efcaped the notice of that ingenious philofopher.

HE heated the colophonia on a coal, which he held in a fpoon under an electrified cube of metal; and obferved, that when part of the fmoke afcended to the cube, another part covered the handle of the fpoon, and fpread to his hand *.

THE fmoke lay higher on the flat parts of the cube than on the edges, and corners.

IF a fpark was taken from the conductor, the fmoke was thrown into an agitation, but prefently refumed its former fituation.

THE cube with its atmofphere gave larger, and longer fparks, than a cube not furround-ed with one.

A LARGER fpark might be taken from it by the fpoon, than by any other body.

HAVING infulated the fpoon, he obferved, that hardly any of the fmoke went to the cube; and that what happened to go near it was not affected by it, any more than it would have been by any other body. He put his finger to the fpoon, and the former phenomena returned. Taking it off again,

* Elettricifmo artificiale, p. 72.

the

the fmoke that had fettled on the cube foon difperfed *.

UNDER this head of the electricity of various fubftances, it will not be improper to mention an experiment made by Mr. Henry Eeles of Lifmore in Ireland, which, he thought, proved that fteam, and exhalations of all kinds, are electrical. The paper containing this account was read at the Royal Society, April the 23d, 1755.

HE electrified a piece of down, fufpended on the middle of a long filk ftring, and made fteam and fmoke of feveral kinds pafs under it, and through it; and obferved, that its electricity was not in the leaft diminifhed, as he thought it would have been, if the vapour had been non-electric, and confequently had taken away with it part of the electric matter with which the down was loaded. He obferved that the effect was the fame, whether the down was electrified with glafs or wax, which he thought was not eafy to be accounted for †.

To this experiment Dr. Darwin of Litchfield, in a letter addreffed to the Royal Society, and read May the 5th, 1757, anfwers; that many electrified bodies, and particularly all light, dry, animal, and vegetable fubftances, will not eafily part with their electricity, though they be touched, for a confiderable time, with conductors. He touched

---

* Elettricifmo artificiale, p. 73, 74.
† Phil. Tranf. Vol. xlix. pt. i. p. 153.

a feather,

a feather, electrified like that of Mr. Eeles, nine times with his finger, and still found it electrified. A cork ball was touched seven times in ten seconds before it was exhausted*.

MR. KINNERSLEY of Philadelphia, in a letter dated March 1761, informs his friend and correspondent Dr. Franklin, then in England, that he could not electrify any thing by means of *steam* from electrified boiling water; from whence he concluded, that, contrary to what had been before supposed by himself and his friend, steam was so far from rising electrified, that it left its share of common electricity behind †.

To try the effects of electricity upon air, Mr. Kinnersley contrived an excellent instrument, which he calls *an electrical air thermometer*. It consisted of a glass tube, about eleven inches long, and one inch in diameter, made air tight, closed with brass caps at each end, and a small tube, open at both ends, let down through the upper plate, into some water at the bottom of the wider tube. Within this vessel he placed two wires, one descending from the brass cap at the upper end, and the other ascending from the brass cap at the lower end; through which he could discharge a jar, or transmit a spark, &c. and at the same time see the expansion of the air in the vessel, by the rise of the water, in the small tube. With this instrument he made the following experiments, related in a let-

* Phil. T anf Vol. l. pt. i. p. 252.
† Ibid. Vol liii. pt. i. p. 84.

ter to Dr. Franklin, dated March the 12th, 1761.

H E set the thermometer on an electric stand, with the chain fixed to the prime conductor, and kept it well electrified a considerable time; but this produced no considerable effect: from whence he inferred, that the electric fire, when in a state of rest, had no more heat than the air, and other matter wherein it resides.

W H E N the two wires within the vessel were in contact, a large charge of electricity, from above thirty square feet of coated glass, produced no rarefaction in the air; which showed, that the wires were not heated by the fire passing through them.

W H E N the wires were about two inches asunder, the charge of a three pint bottle, darting from one to the other, rarefied the air very evidently; which shewed, that the electric fire produced heat in itself, as Mr. Kinnersley says, as well as in the air, by its rapid motion.

T H E charge of a jar which contained about five gallons and a half, darting from wire to wire, would cause a prodigious expansion in the air; and the charge of his battery of thirty square feet of coated glass would raise the water in the small tube quite to the top. Upon the coalescing of the air, the column of water, by its gravity, instantly subsided, till it was in equilibrio with the rarified air. It then gradually descended, as the air cooled, and settled where it stood before. By carefully

fully obferving at what height the defcending water firft ftopped, the degree of rarefaction, he fays, might be difcovered, which, in great explofions, was very confiderable.

IT is obvious to remark, that the firft fudden rife of the water of Mr. Kinnerfley's thermometer, upon an explofion being made in the veffel which contained it, is not to be afcribed to the rarefaction of the air by heat, but to the quantity of air actually difplaced by the electrical flafh. It is only when that firft fudden rife is fubfided, as Mr. Kinnerfley himfelf obferves, that the degree of its rarefaction by the heat can be eftimated, viz. by the height at which the water then ftands above the common level.

DR. FRANLKIN had faid, that *ice* failed to conduct a fhock of electricity, and Mr. Bergman, in a letter to Mr. Wilfon, read at the Royal Society November the 20th, 1760, fhows (what Signior Beccaria had done before) that a fmall quantity of water failed as much as the ice had done with Dr. Franklin, who feems to have made ufe of an icicle which, Mr. Bergman thought, was not large enough for the purpofe. From hence he fufpected, that large quantities of ice would tranfmit a fhock of electricity as perfectly as a large quantity of water *.

HOWEVER, he feems, afterwards, to have changed his fentiments with refpect to ice: for, in a fubfequent paper, read at the Royal

* Phil. Tranf. Vol. li. pt. ii. p. 908.

S

Society March the 18th, 1762, when he had remarked that fnow would not conduct the electric fhock, he fays, he believes, if he could procure plates of ice of a proper thicknefs, he could charge them in the fame manner as glafs *.

JOHANNES FRANCISCUS CIGNA was fo fully perfuaded of the non-conducting power of ice, that he made ufe of it in an experiment, defigned to afcertain whether electric fubftances did, according to Dr. Franklin's hypothefis, contain more of the electric matter than other bodies. He inclofed a quantity of ice in a glafs veffel, and when he thought he had converted it from an electric to a non-electric by melting; he tried whether it was electrified; but, though he found no appearance of its having acquired any more of the fluid than it ought to have in its new ftate, he does not feem to have given up his opinion †.

IN the laft part of this work the reader will find fome experiments, which, it is imagined, will afcertain the clafs of bodies in which ice ought to be ranked, by proving its conducting power to be, at leaft, nearly equal to that of water.

---

* Phil. Tranf. Vol lii. pt. ii. p. 485.
† Memoirs of the Academy at Turin, for the year 1765, p. 47.

SECTION

SECTION III.

MR. CANTON's EXPERIMENTS AND DIS-
COVERIES RELATING TO THE SURFACES
OF ELECTRIC BODIES, AND OTHERS MADE
IN PURSUANCE OF THEM, OR RELATING
TO THE SAME SUBJECT; ALL TENDING
TO ASCERTAIN THE DISTINCTION BE-
TWEEN THE TWO ELECTRICITIES.

TILL this laft period of the hiftory, the
same electricity had always been produced by the fame electric. The friction of
glafs had always produced a pofitive, and the
friction of fealing-wax, &c. had always produced a negative electricity. Thefe were
thought to be effential, and unchangeable
properties of thofe fubftances; and hence the
one was by many called the vitreous, and
the other the refinous electricity; and to electrify negatively, that is produce a refinous electricity, by means of glafs; or to electrify pofitively, that is, produce a vitreous electricity,
by means of fealing-wax, &c. would have
been thought as great a paradox, as to electrify at all by the friction of brafs or iron.
For though it was not known why the electric matter fhould flow from the rubber to
the excited glafs, or to the rubber from excited fealing-wax, the fact had been invariable; and nothing is even mentioned to
have happened, in the courfe of any experi-

S 2   ments,

ments, that could lead a perfon to fufpect the poffibility of the contrary.

WHAT then muft have been the furprife of electricians, to find that thefe different powers of glafs and fulphur were fo far from being invariable, that they were even interchange-able; and that the fame glafs tube could be made to affume the powers of both! And what muft have been their fatisfaction to find the circumftance' on which the convertibility of thofe oppofite powers depended, complete-ly afcertained. This furprife and pleafure was given them by Mr. Canton, who fhowed that it depended only on the rubber, and the furface of the glafs, whether it electrified po-fitively or negatively.

IN what manner, by what train of thought, or by what accident he was led to this difco-very, this excellent philofopher has not been pleafed to inform us; but it is certainly a dif-covery which, in an eminent manner, diftin-guifhes this period of my hiftory. It throws great light upon the doctrine of pofitive and negative electricity, and led the way to other difcoveries which throw ftill more light up-on it.

THIS fubject of the two electricities feems to have engaged the attention of electricians in a more particular manner, in the whole courfe of this period, and ever fince the dif-covery of Dr. Franklin, that the electricity of the two furfaces of charged glafs are always contrary to one another. Accordingly, the reader will find feveral fections in this period

8   of

of the hiftory relating to it; but he will find that though much has been done, much yet remains to be done; ·and that we are ftill far from thoroughly underftanding the nature of the two electricities, with their dependence upon and relation to one another.

Previous to the communication of the difcovery itfelf, Mr. Canton obferves, that fealing-wax might have pofitive electricity fuperinduced upon it. He excited a ftick of fealing-wax about two feet and a half in length, and an inch in diameter; and, holding it by the middle, he drew an excited glafs tube feveral times over one part of it, without touching the other. The confequence was, that that half which had been expofed to the action of the excited glafs was pofitive, and the other half negative: for the former half deftroyed the repelling power of balls electrified by glafs, while the other half increafed it *.

The experiments, which prove that the appearances of pofitive and negative electricity depend upon the furface of the electrics, and that of the rubber, were made in the latter end of December 1753.

Having rubbed a glafs tube with a piece of thin fheet lead, and flour of emery mixed with water, till its tranfparency was intirely deftroyed, he excited it (when it was made perfectly clean and dry) with new flannel, and found it act in all refpects like excited

* Phil. Tranf. Vol. xlviii. pt. i. p. 356.

fulphur

fulphur or fealing-wax. The electric fire feemed to iffue from the knuckle, or end of the finger, and to fpread itfelf on the furface of the tube, in a very beautiful manner.

IF this rough or unpolifhed tube was excited by a piece of dry oiled filk, efpecially when rubbed over with a little chalk or whiting, it would act like a glafs tube with its natural polifh. In this cafe the electric fire appeared only at the knuckle, or the end of the finger, where it feemed to be very much condenfed, before it entered.

BUT if the rough tube was greafed all over with tallow from a candle, and as much as poffible of it wiped off with a napkin, then the oiled filk would receive a kind of polifh by rubbing it; and, after a few ftrokes, would make the tube act in the fame manner as when excited at firft by flannel.

THE oiled filk, when covered with chalk or whiting, would make the greafed rough tube act again like a polifhed one; but if the friction was continued till the rubber became fmooth, the electric power would be changed to that of fulphur, fealing-wax, &c.

THUS, fays he, may the pofitive and negative powers of electricity be produced at pleafure, by altering the furfaces of the tube and rubber, according as the one or the other is moft affected by the friction between them. For if the polifh be taken off one half of a tube, the different powers may be excited with the fame rubber at a fingle ftroke; and, he adds, the rubber is found to move much

2   eafier

eafier over the rough, than over the polifhed part of it.

THAT polifhed glafs electrified pofitively, and rough glafs rubbed with flannel negatively, feemed plain from the appearance of the light between the knuckle, or end of the finger, and the refpective tubes. But this, Mr. Canton thought, was farther confirmed by obferving, that a polifhed glafs tube, when excited by fmooth oiled filk, if the hand was kept three inches, at leaft, from the top of the rubber, would, at every ftroke, appear to throw out a great number of diverging pencils of electric fire; but that none were ever feen to accompany the rubbing of fulphur, fealing-wax, &c. nor was he ever able to make any fenfible alteration in the air of a room merely by the friction of thofe bodies; whereas the glafs tube, when excited fo as to emit pencils, would, in a few minutes, electrify the air, to fuch a degree, that, after the tube was carried away, a pair of balls, about the fize of the fmalleft peas, turned out of cork, or the pith of elder, and hung to a·wire by linen threads of fix inches long, would repel each other to the diftance of an inch and an half, when held at arm's length in the middle of the room *.

AFTER thefe experiments of Mr. Canton, Mr. Wilfon made feveral, which throw a little more light upon this curious fubject; but it is difficult to draw any general conclu-

* Phil. Tranf. Vol. xlviii. pt. ii. p. 782.

fion

fion from them, and his own is not fufficiently determinate. It is, that two electrics being rubbed together, the body whofe fubftance is hardeft, and electric power ftrongeft,
will always be *plus*, and the fofteft and
weakeft *minus* *. Rubbing the tourmalin and
amber together, he produced a *plus* electricity
on both fides of the ftone, and a *minus* on the
amber; but rubbing the tourmalin and diamond together, both fides of the tourmalin
were electrified *minus*, and the diamond *plus*.

These experiments, which, he thought,
proved this propofition, encouraged him to
try what would be the effect of rubbing or
forcing air againft different electrics, and the
effects were very confiderable. In thefe experiments he only made ufe of a common pair
of bellows, and his firft experiment was upon the tourmalin. This fubftance he brought
near the end of the pipe, and found, that after it had received about twenty blafts, it was
electrified *plus* on both fides. Air, therefore, feemed to be lefs electric than the tourmalin.

Into the place of the tourmalin, he brought
a pane of glafs, and blew againft it the fame
number of times as in the former experiment;
and when he had examined both fides, he
found that they were electrified *plus* alfo, but
lefs than the tourmalin.

Amber, treated in the fame manner, was
electrified lefs than the glafs.

* Phil. Tranf. Vol. li. pt. i. p. 331.

He

HE next had recourſe to a ſmith's bellows. The difference which theſe occaſioned was only a much ſtronger electricity in the tourmalin. Amber was ſtill weaker than the glaſs; and the glaſs weaker than the tourmalin.

HAVING in view the medium (which, I have obſerved, he laid great ſtreſs upon, as conſtituting the difference between electrics and non-electrics) he conſidered that heat would rarify it on the ſurfaces of the particles of air; by which means, air, having its reſiſtance leſſened, would more readily part with the electric fluid, and, of conſequence, electrify more powerfully.

THE pipe of the bellows being made red hot, he blew againſt the tourmalin, twelve times only, which was eight times leſs than in the former experiment with cold air. In this experiment the tourmalin was electrified *plus* on both ſides, but to a conſiderable degree more than was done in the former experiments. The hot air had the ſame effect upon glaſs, but electrified it leſs than the tourmalin; and amber, though, like the other bodies, it received an increaſe of power by the ſame treatment, was electrified the leaſt of all.

FROM the air electrifying more powerfully when it was hot than when it was cold, and the tourmalin being electrified more than glaſs, and glaſs more than amber, as appeared by the laſt experiments, we ſeem, ſays Mr. Wilſon, to have obtained a proof, that the

the whole atmosphere is constantly promoting a flow of the electric fluid, by the alternate changes of heat and cold; and farther,
that air is not only less electric than the tourmalin, but less than glass, or even amber *.

In another paper, read at the Royal Society November the 13th, 1760, Mr. Wilson
recites some curious experiments, which, he
says, shew that a *plus* electricity may be produced by means of a *minus* electricity.

Having electrified the inside of a large
Leyden bottle *plus*, by means of a conducting
wire from an excited glass globe; he set it on
a stand of prepared wood, and took away the
conducting wire, after which the mouth of
the bottle was closed with a stopple of glass.
Then the pointed end of an ivory conductor
was brought opposite to the middle of the
bottle, and about two inches from it. Upon
doing this, the balls were electrified *minus*;
and the more so as the ivory was moved nearer
the bottle, in an horizontal direction.

But, on removing the ivory to a greater
distance, the *minus* electricity decreased; and,
at a certain distance, there was not any sign
of it remaining; but when the distance was
increased to about eighteen inches from the
bottle, a *plus* electricity appeared, which continued even after the ivory was removed entirely away †.

With a cylinder of baked wood he electrified the balls hanging to the ivory *minus*, at

* Phil. Transf. Vol. li. pt. i. p. 332, &c.
† Ibid. pt. ii. p. 899, &c.

the

the diftance of four feet or more, by holding the cylinder over the middle of the ivory, and continuing it there; and, on moving it nearer, they were more ftrongly electrified *minus*; but the fame cylinder, on removing it back again to the diftance of two or three feet, or more, electrified the balls *plus*.

WHEN another conductor of metal, without edges or points, was ufed, inftead of the ivory, and without any thing hanging from it, the fame cylinder held over the metal (as was done in the laft experiment over the ivory, at the diftance of two feet) produced a *plus* electricity; and this was rendered weaker as the cylinder was moved nearer; but by leffening the diftance to about one foot, the *minus* electricity took place. In thefe cafes Mr. Wilfon thought, that the *plus* appearance arofe from the earth, air, or other neighbouring bodies.

WHEN the preceding experiments were firft made, he was a little embaraffed, by the uncertain appearances of a *plus* electricity at one time, and a *minus* at another, in the fame experiment; but, by repeated trials and obfervations, he found, that a *plus* or *minus* electricity may be produced at pleafure, by carefully attending to the three following circumftances; viz. the form of the bodies, their fudden or gradual removal, and the degrees of electrifying.

MR. WILSON, after this, proceeds to mention fome other circumftances of a very nice nature, where, the flighteft and almoft imperceptible

perceptible differences in the pofition or in
the courfe of the friction of two bodies produce, in either of them, the *plus* electricity at
one time, and the *minus* at another.   Such,
fays he, are the effects of this fubtle and active fluid, when the experiments are carefully
made ; and therefore they require the moft
fcrupulous attention to trace out the caufes
which occafion them.

SEALING-WAX and filver were the bodies
ufed in the two firft experiments, but many
other fubftances feemed to perform as well.
The fealing-wax was clean, and undifturbed
by any friction whatever, but that of the air
furrounding it, and had been fo for fome
hours.   The filver was fixed to a piece of
prepared wood, which was alfo preferved
from friction for the fame length of time.
Then, taking one of thofe fubftances in each
hand, the filver being at the end of the wood
the fartheft from the hand, he laid the
fmootheft part of the filver upon the fealing-
wax, and moved it along the furface gently,
once only, and with a very flight preffure,
after which the filver was electrified *plus*, and
the wax *minus*.

ON repeating the experiment with equal
care, and in the fame manner, except that
the fmooth fide of the filver was a little inclined, fo that the edge of it preffed againft
the wax; the filver, after moving it as before, was electrified *minus*, and the wax *plus*,
contrary to what was obferved in the laft experiment.

THESE

These oppofite effects, occafioned by the different applications of the *flatted part* or *edge* of the filver, feemed to arife from an alteration made in the furface of the wax, by deftroying the polifh in one cafe, and not in the other; and in this refpect refembled the polifhed and rough glafs mentioned before.

Upon making ufe of prepared wood inftead of wax, and employing different degrees of preffure in the friction, with the fame edge of the filver, he produced the like appearances; the leaft preffure caufing a *plus*, and the greateft preffure a *minus* appearance in the filver.

A flat piece of fteel well polifhed, and the edges rounded off, afforded the fame appearances, by only applying the flat furface to the wood, but it required more preffing to produce the *minus* effect in this cafe than it did in the former, where the edge was concerned.

Whether the reafon offered above for explaining thefe laft curious appearances be true or not, Mr. Wilfon did not venture to affirm, for want of farther experiments; but thus much he thought might be fafely advanced, that we have learned to produce at pleafure a *plus* or *minus* electricity from the fame bodies, by attending to the manner of their application and friction *.

Mr. Bergman, in a letter to Mr. Wilfon, read at the Royal Society February the 23d,

---

* Phil. Tranf. Vol. li. pt. ii. p. 899, &c.

1764, gives an account of fome curious experiments of his, which, in conjunction with thofe of Mr. Canton above mentioned, concerning furfaces, may throw confiderable light upon the doctrine of pofitive and negative electricity.

THE experiments were made with two ribbons of filk, one of which was extended in a frame, while Mr. Bergman held the other in his hand. He obferved, that if the two ribbons were the fame with refpect to texture, colour, fuperficies, and in every thing elfe, as far as could be judged; and if he drew the whole length of the ribbon which he held in his hand over one part of that which was extended in the frame, that in his hand contracted the pofitive electricity, and that in the frame a negative. If he drew one part of that which he held in his hand over the whole length of the other, the effects were reverfed.

IF the ribbon in his hand was of a different colour from that in the frame (provided it was not black) the event was the fame.

IF the ribbon in his hand was black, it was always negative, which ever way it was rubbed, except that in the frame was black too; for then, if the whole length of it was rubbed, it was electrified pofitively.

IN endeavouring to account for thefe effects, he obferves, that the ribbon which was moft rubbed was made *fmoother*, and *warmer* than the other; and was of opinion, that though fmoothnefs did difpofe bodies to be excited
pofitively,

pofitively, yet that other circumftances were
alfo to be taken into confideration; having
found that when he held in his hand a ribbon,
which, by much friction, was made very
fmooth, and drew it over one part of another
ribbon, which was rough, and had never
been ufed before, that the rough ribbon was,
neverthelefs, pofitive. From this experiment
he concluded, that this effect was, in fome
meafure, owing to the colour; and, in purfuing this thought farther, he was led to the following experiments.

If the ribbon in his hand was well warmed, though it was drawn over one part of
that in the frame, it became electrified negatively, and that in the frame pofitively. He
made thefe experiments with the fame fuccefs
upon ribbons of filk of various colours, blue,
green, red, white, &c.

If the ribbon in the frame was black, it
never contracted a pofitive electricity, though
that in his hand had been much heated, except this were black too. From thefe experiments, he thought he might fafely conclude,
that heat did difpofe fome fubftances, at leaft, to
a negative ftate; and he thought that the want
of attention to this circumftance might have
occafioned miftakes in the event of fome experiments, efpecially thofe concerning ifland
cryftal.

From the whole he concludes, that there
is a certain fixed order with refpect to negative and pofitive electricity, in which all
bodies may be placed, while other circumftances

ftances remain the fame. Let A, B, C, D, E, be certain fubftances, each of which, when rubbed with one which is antecedent to it, is negative, but with a fubfequent pofitive. In this cafe, the lefs diftance there is between the bodies that are rubbed, the weaker, *cæt. par.* will be the electricity; wherefore it will be ftronger between A and E, than it will be between A and B. Heat, he fays, difpofes bodies to a negative electricity, but if the diftance above-mentioned be confiderable, it may not be able to *overcome*, though it may *weaken* that electricity, as is evident from the ribbon of black filk. When a glafs globe grows warm in whirling, we are fenfible that its electric power is diminifhed. Is it not owing, fays he, to this circumftance, that by heat it is more difpofed to negative electricity, by which means the diftance above-mentioned between the glafs and the rubber is leffened * ?

Upon the fubject of this fection, I muft introduce to the acquaintance of my reader two eminent electricians whofe difcoveries will give him the greateft fatisfaction; I mean Mr. WILCKE, and Mr. ÆPINUS, the former of Roftock in Lower Saxony, and the latter of Peterfburgh: a circumftance which gives me an occafion of congratulating all the lovers of the fciences, and particularly of electricity, on the extenfive fpread of their ftudies. What joy would it have given Mr.

---

* Phil. Tranf. Vol. liv. p. 86.

Haukfbee,

Haukſbee, or Mr. Grey, to have foreſeen that two ſuch admirable treatiſes on the ſubject of electricity, as thoſe of the perſons abovementioned, would come from countries ſo remote from the place of its riſe !

MR. WILCKE relates many curious experiments concerning the generation of what he calls *ſpontaneous electricity*, produced by the liquefaction of electric ſubſtances, which, compared with thoſe of Mr. Canton, throw great light upon the doctrine of poſitive and negative electricity.

HE melted ſulphur in an earthen veſſel, which he placed upon conductors ; then, letting them cool, he took out the ſulphur, and found it ſtrongly electrical; but it was not ſo when it had ſtood to cool upon electric ſubſtances.

HE melted ſulphur in glaſs veſſels, whereby they both acquired a ſtrong electricity in the circumſtances above mentioned, whether they were placed upon electrics or not; but a ſtronger in the former caſe than in the latter; and they acquired a ſtronger virtue ſtill, if the glaſs veſſel into which they were poured was coated with metal. In theſe caſes, the glaſs was always poſitive, and the ſulphur negative. It was particularly remarkable, that the ſulphur acquired no electricity till it began to cool and contract, and was the ſtrongeſt when in the ſtate of greateſt contraction ; whereas the electricity of the glaſs was, at the ſame time, the weakeſt; and was the ſtrongeſt of all when the ſulphur was ſhaken

T   out,

out, before it began to contract, and acquired
any negative electricity.

PURSUING thefe experiments, he found
that melted fealing-wax, poured into glafs, acquired a negative electricity, but poured into
fulphur it acquired a pofitive electricity, and
left the fulphur negative. Sulphur poured into baked wood became negative. Sealing-
wax alfo poured into wood was negative, and
the wood confequently pofitive; but fulphur
poured into fulphur, or into rough glafs, acquired no electricity at all *.

EXPERIMENTS fimilar to thefe were alfo
made by Mr. Æpinus. He poured melted
fulphur into metal cups, and obferved that
when the fulphur was cold, the cup and the
fulphur together fhowed no figns of electricity, but fhowed very ftrong figns of it the
moment they were feparated. The electricity always difappeared when the fulphur was
replaced in the cup, and revived upon being
taken out again. The cup had acquired a negative, and the fulphur a pofitive electricity;
but if the electricity of either of them had
been taken off while they were feparate, they
would both, when united, fhow figns of that
electricity which had not been taken off. This
electricity, he obferves, was only on the furface of the fulphur †.

MR. WILCKE has, likewife, recited feveral
curious experiments, which he made on the
friction of various fubftances, which like-

* Wilcke, p. 44, &c.   † Æpini Tentamen, p. 66. 70.

wife throw confiderable light on the fame fubject.

SULPHUR and glafs rubbed together produced a ftrong electricity, pofitive in the glafs, and negative in the fulphur.

SULPHUR and fealing-wax being rubbed together, the wax became pofitive, and the fulphur negative.

WOOD rubbed with cloth was always negative.

WOOD rubbed againft fmooth glafs became negative, but againft rough glafs pofitive.

SULPHUR rubbed againft metals was always pofitive, and this was the only cafe in which it was fo; but being rubbed againft lead it became negative, and the metal pofitive; lead appearing, thereby, to be not fo good a conductor as the other metals.

AFTER thefe experiments, Mr. Wilcke gives the following catalogue of the principal fubftances with which electrical experiments are made, in the order in which they are difpofed to acquire pofitive or negative electricity; any of the fubftances becoming pofitively electrical when rubbed with any that follow it in the lift, and negative when rubbed with any that precede it.

Smooth glafs.	White wax,
Woollen cloth.	Rough glafs.
Quills.	Lead.
Wood.	Sulphur,
Paper.	Other metals *,
Sealing-wax.	

* Wilcke, p. 54, &c,

IN

IN all experiments made to determine the order of thefe fubftances, Mr. Wilcke fays, that great care is neceffary, to diftinguifh original electricity from that which is communicated, or the confequence of friction *.

MR. WILCKE fays that fmooth glafs is in all cafes pofitive, and thence infers that it attracts the electric fluid the moft of all known fubftances; but Mr. Canton tells me he has found, that the fmootheft glafs will acquire a negative electricity by being drawn over the back of a cat.

OF the fame nature with thefe experiments of Mr. Wilcke are the following of Æpinus. He preffed clofe together two pieces of looking-glafs, each containing fome fquare inches; and obferved, that when they were feparated, and not fuffered to communicate with any conductor, they each acquired a ftrong electricity, the one pofitive, and the other negative. When they were put together again, the electricity of both difappeared, but not if either of them had been deprived of their electricity when they were afunder; for in that cafe, the two when united, had the electricity of the other. The fame experiment, he fays, may be made with glafs and fulphur, or with any other electrics, or with any electric and a piece of metal †.

* Wilcke, p. 69.   † Æpini Tentamen, p. 65.

SECTION

SECTION IV.

Mr. DELAVAL's EXPERIMENTS RELATING TO THE TWO ELECTRICITIES, AND HIS CONTROVERSY WITH Mr. CANTON UPON THAT SUBJECT,

MR. CANTON, in the courfe of experiments related in the preceding fection, clearly proved, that the production of either of the two electricities depends intirely upon the furface of the excited electric with refpect to the rubber, and fhowed, that the very fame glafs tube would produce either of them at pleafure; yet, notwithftanding this demonftration, Mr. Delaval, feveral years afterwards, propofed another theory of the two electricities, which feems to be more ingenious than folid; as it goes upon the old fuppofition of the different powers depending intirely upon the different fubftances themfelves. The account of this theory was read at the Royal Society, March the 22d, 1759. It necefſarily occafioned fome controverfy with Mr. Canton, in the courfe of which fome new experiments were made, and fome new facts difcovered; on account of which I fhall, with the utmoft impartiality, report all that was advanced on both fides.

Mr. DELAVAL obferved, that there are two of the pure chymical principles of bodies, viz. *earth* and *fulphur*, which are each poſ-

T 3 ſeſſed

feffed of a different kind of electricity; one
of which we might call a *plus* electricity, the
other a *minus*; and thought that it might be
expected, that, in a body compounded of
both, the oppofite powers of thofe ingredi-
ents would counterbalance, and deftroy the
effect of each other ; and therefore, that
bodies in which the negative and pofitive
powers were equal, would be neutral, or
non-electrics. Such a fubftance he took metal to be, confifting of calx and fulphur ; metals not being calcinable without a degree of
heat fufficient to diffipate all their fulphur; as
is evident from their not being reducible again
to their metallic form, without the admix-
ture of fome unctuous matter. The fame
diffipation of fulphur, he fays, muft take
place in animal and vegetable fubftances, before they become white afhes. Tranfparent
ftones he confidered as little more than pure
earth, free from the leaft mixture of oil;
judging of others by the chymical refolution
of cryftal.

To confirm this theory, Mr. Delaval made
experiments with dry powders of calcined
metals, viz. cerufs, lead afhes, minium, calx
of antimony, &c. inclofing them in long
glafs tubes, and endeavouring to tranfmit the
electric virtue through them, and always finding it impoffible. Animal and vegetable fubftances, when reduced to afhes, were alike
impermeable to electricity, as alfo the ruft of
metals.

He

He was firſt led to theſe experiments, and to this hypotheſis, by finding that dry mould would not conduct electricity. This he alſo tried with dry Portland ſtone, ſome of which he had cut into plates nearly as thin as window glaſs. Theſe he heated to a proper degree, and coated them on both ſides with metal, in order to make the Leyden experiment. When the ſtone was hot enough to ſinge paper, it conducted as perfectly as when cold; but on cooling a little, it began not to conduct, and afforded ſmall ſhocks; which gradually increaſed in ſtrength for about ten minutes, at which time it was about its moſt perfect ſtate, and remained ſo near a quarter of an hour. After that time, the ſhocks gradually decreaſed, as the ſtone grew cooler; till, at laſt, they ceaſed, and the ſtone returned to its conducting ſtate again, but this ſtate appeared before the ſtone was quite cold.

Experiments of this kind ſucceeded with all bodies abounding with calx, or earth, as ſtones, earth, dry clay, wood when rotten, or burned in the fire till the ſurface becomes black. Among other ſubſtances he tried a common tobacco-pipe, part of which, near the middle, he heated to a proper degree, and then applied one end of it to an electrical bar, while the other was held in the hand; and he obſerved, that the electric fluid paſſed no farther along the pipe than to the heated part *.

* Phil. Tranſ. Vol. li. pt. i. p. 83.

From

From thefe experiments Mr. Delaval inferred, that ftones and other earthy fubftances were convertible, by feveral methods, and particularly by different degrees of heat, from non-electrics to electrics. But finding, afterwards, that it was the opinion of fome perfons (Mr. Canton was the perfon chiefly hinted at) that this change did not immediately, but only confequentially depend on heat, by evaporating the moifture, which would return again when the fubftance cooled; he obferves, in a paper read at the Royal Society, December the 17th, 1761, that the tobacco-pipe loft its electricity before it was cold, and therefore before it could have imbibed moifture fufficient to deftroy its electricity; and befides, that the fubftance employed in the experiment was not of that kind of bodies which is apt fuddenly to draw moifture from the air.

To account for Mr. Delaval's experiments, Mr. Canton fuppofes, in a paper read to the Royal Society, February 4th, 1762, that ftone, tobacco-pipe, wood, &c. will conduct when cold by the moifture they contain in that ftate; that when their moifture is evaporated by heat they become non-conductors; and that when they are made very hot, the hot air at, or near their furfaces will conduct, and the bodies will appear to be conductors again. Hot air, he fays, may eafily be proved to be a conductor of electricity, by bringing a red hot-iron poker, but for a moment, within three or four inches of a fmall electrified

fied

fied body ; when it would be perceived, that its electric power would be almost, if not intirely destroyed; and by bringing excited amber within an inch of the flame of a candle, when it would lose its electricity before it had acquired any sensible degree of heat.

To confirm this, he mentions his having observed, that the tourmalin, Brasil topaz, and Brasil emerald, would give much stronger signs of electricity when cooling, after they had been held about a minute within two inches of an almost surrounding fire, where the air is a conductor, then they ever will after heating them in boiling water. He adds, that if both sides of those stones be equally heated, in a less degree than will make the surrounding air a conductor, the electricity of each side, whether *plus* or *minus*, would continue so all the time the stone was both heating and cooling, but would increase while it was heating, and decrease while it was cooling; whereas, if the heat was sufficient to make the surrounding air conduct the electric fluid from the positive side of the stone to the negative side of it, while it was heating, the electricity of each side would increase while the stone was cooling, and be contrary to what it was while the stone was heating.

As to the tobacco-pipe, Mr. Canton says, that it not only attracts the moisture of the air, but absorbs it. Hence a tobacco-pipe, after it begins to cool, will become a conductor again sooner than wood. And that it imbibes moisture faster than wood, he says, is

evident,

evident, becaufe when wetted, it will not continue wet fo long as wood, imbibing the moifture prefently.

THAT tobacco-pipe does not become a
conductor by a particular degree of heat,
without evaporating its moifture, is evident,
he fays, from the following experiments.

IF three or four inches of one end of a tobacco-pipe, of more than a foot in length, be
made red hot, without fenfibly heating the
other end, this pipe will prove a ready conductor, through the hot air furrounding one
part of it, and the moifture contained in the
other; although fome part of it muft have the
degree of heat of a non-conductor. But if
the whole pipe be made red hot, and fuffered
to cool till it has only fuperficial moifture
enough to make it a good conductor, and then
three or four inches of one end be again made
hot, it will become a non-conductor.

IF a nail be placed at, or near each end of
a longifh folid piece of any of the abforbent
bodies above-mentioned, fo as the point of
each nail may be about half the thicknefs of
the body within its furface; this body, by
heat, may be made a non-conductor exter-
nally or fuperficially, while it remains a good
conductor internally. For the electric fluid
will readily pafs from one nail to the other,
through the middle of the body, when it will
not pafs on its furface, and even when the internal parts of the body are in an equal degree of heat with the external, as they muft
foon be after it begins to cool. But if the
                                        fame

fame body be expofed, for a fhort time, to a greater degree of heat than before, or if it be kept longer in the fame heat, it will become a non-conductor intirely *.

Mr. DELAVAL, in confirmation of particular bodies requiring particular degrees of heat to render them electric or non-electric, independent of moifture, mentions a fubftance which, he fays, is affected by heat in an oppofite manner to the former inftances; fince the degrees of heat, neceffary to render the other fubftances electric, makes this non-electric.

THE fubftance was *ifland cryftal* (which is well known for its fingular property of a double refraction) on a piece of which he made the following obfervations. 1. After this piece of cryftal had been rubbed, when the heat of the air was moderate, it fhowed figns of electricity, though not very ftrong ones. 2. If the heat was increafed, fo as to be a little greater than that of the hand, it deftroyed its electric power intirely. 3. By cooling the ftone again, the electric power was reftored.

HE immerfed this piece of cryftal into a veffel filled with quickfilver, and furrounded with ice, where it remained near two hours, when the weather was very cold; and obferved, that, upon taking it out with a pair of tongs (that it might not be altered by the

Phil. Tranf. Vol. lii. pt. ii. p. 459.

heat

heat of his hands) and rubbing it again, it was more ftrongly electric then he had at any other time experienced; but that, on placing it a few minutes upon the hearth, at fome diftance from the fire, its electric property was again deftroyed, for that rubbing would not occafion any figns of it.

THUS, fays he, we fee two different kinds of fixed bodies, the one of which acquires an electric property with the fame heat with which another lofes it; while a third fet of fubftances, as glafs, &c. retain their electricity through both the degrees of heat neceffary to the other two.

SOME pieces of ifland cryftal, which he had procured from different places, had not the property of lofing their electricity by a moderate heat. He had, in particular, a piece of that cryftal, one part of which, when greatly heated, became non-electric, while the other part, with the fame heat, or even with a much greater one, remained perfectly electric.

HE found feveral other earthy fubftances, whofe electricity was deftroyed by different degrees of heat.

FROM confidering that the degree of heat, at which the ifland cryftal firft mentioned was in its moft perfect electric ftate, was lefs than the ufual heat of the air, and that a fmall increafe of that heat rendered it non-electric; he did not think it improbable, that many fubftances, which are not known to be electric,

tric, might prove fo, if expofed to a greater degree of cold then they have been hitherto examined in *.

To thefe obfervations Mr. Canton replies, that having formerly obferved that the friction between mercury and glafs in vacuo would not only produce the light of electricity, as in the luminous barometer, or within an evacuated glafs ball, but would alfo electrify the glafs on the outfide, he immerged a piece of dry glafs in a bafon of mercury; and found, that by taking it out, the mercury was electrified *minus*, and the glafs *plus*, to a confiderable degree. He alfo found, that amber, fealing-wax, and ifland cryftal, when taken out of mercury, were all electrified pofitively. How then, fays he, does it appear, that the electricity which was obferved in rubbing the laft mentioned fubftance, after it was taken out of mercury furrounded by ice, was owing to cold, and not to the friction between it and the mercury in taking it out. Ifland cryftal when warm is a non-conductor, and all non-conductors may be excited with proper rubbers †.

M . Bergman of Upfal, in a letter to Mr. Wilfon, read at the Royal Society, April the 14th, 1761, fays, that he had tried the experiments of Mr. Delaval with ifland cryftal, but that the event had always been contrary to

* Phil. Tranf. Vol. lii. pt. i. p. 354, &c.
† Ibid. pt. ii, p. 461.

what

what Mr. Delaval had reported. Trying
different pieces of cryſtal, he found one which
inſtead of having its virtue increaſed by cooling, was ſenſibly increaſed by heating. Afterwards trying all the reſt which he had by
him, whether Swediſh cryſtal, or iſland, he
found the effect to be the ſame. From this
he inferred, that the cryſtals which he had
were of a quite different kind from that of
Mr. Delaval *.

SECTION V.

MR. CANTON'S EXPERIMENTS AND DIS-
COVERIES RELATING TO BODIES IMMERG-
ED IN ELECTRIC ATMOSPHERES, WITH
THE DISCOVERIES OF OTHERS, MADE BY
PURSUING THEM.

IN this ſection I ſhall preſent my reader
with the fineſt ſeries of experiments that
the whole hiſtory of electricity can exhibit,
and in which we ſhall ſee diſplayed the genius and addreſs of four of the moſt eminent
electricians in this whole period; viz. Mr.
Canton and Dr. Franklin, Engliſhmen; and
Meſſrs. Wilcke and Æpinus, foreigners. Mr.
Canton had the honour to take the lead, and he
made all the eſſential experiments. Doctor
Franklin profeſſedly purſued them; and
though *all his ſtrength he put not forth* on

* Phil. Tranſ. Vol. liii. pt. i. p. 98.

this

this occasion, he diverfified the experiments, and made fome improvement in the method of accounting for them. But Meffrs. Wilcke and Æpinus in conjunction carried the experiments vaftly farther, and completed the difcovery; which is, certainly, one of the greateft that has been made fince the time of Dr. Franklin. I fay the time of Dr. Franklin, though he himfelf be one of the perfons concerned; for by the *time of Dr. Franklin* will always be underftood the time in which he made his capital difcoveries in America. This will always be a diftinguifhed epocha in the hiftory of electricity, from which all his own future difcoveries will be dated.

THE original experiments in this fection, when Mr. Canton firft publifhed them, in his ufual concife, though perfpicuous manner, without any preamble, to inform us how he was led to them, exhibit fuch a variety of attractions and repulfions of electrified bodies in different circumftances, as looked like the power of magic; and were they conducted with a little art, I do not know any electrical experiments (made without light, or noife) more proper for a deception of this kind. But when they are attentively confidered, they demonftrate a remarkable property of all electrified bodies, which has often been referred to in the courfe of this hiftory, but which had not been attended to before; nor indeed do I apprehend that it was fully underftood, till it was explained in all its extent by Mr. Wilcke and Æpinus. It is,

7   that

that the electric fluid, when there is a redundancy of it in any body, repels the electric
fluid, in any other body, when they are
brought within the sphere of each other's influence, and drives it into the remote parts of
the body; or quite out of it, if there be any
outlet for that purpose. In other words,
bodies immerged in electric atmospheres always become possessed of the electricity, contrary to that of the body, in whose atmosphere
they are immerged. This principle pursued
led them to the method of charging a plate of
air, like a plate of glass, and to make the
most perfect imitation of the phenomena of
thunder and lightning.

THE paper, containing an account of Mr.
Canton's experiments, was read at the Royal
Society, December the 6th, 1753.

MR. CANTON suspended cork balls, one
pair by linen threads, and another pair by
silk; then holding the excited tube at a considerable distance from the balls with the linen
thread, they separated; and, upon drawing
it away, they immediately came together:
but he was obliged to bring the excited tube
much nearer to the balls hanging by silk
threads, before they would separate; though
when the tube was withdrawn, they continued separate for some time.

As the balls in the former of these experiments were not insulated, Mr. Canton observes, that they could not properly be said to
be electrified; but that when they hung within the atmosphere of the excited tube, they
might

might attract and condenfe the electric fluid round about them, and be feparated by the repulfion of its particles. He conjectures alfo, that the balls, at this time, contain lefs than their common fhare of the electric fluid, on account of the repelling power of that which furrounds them, though fome may be continually entering and paffing through the threads. And if that be the cafe, he fays, the reafon is plain why the balls hung by filk in the fecond experiment muft be in a much more denfe part of the atmofphere of the tube before they will repel each other. He adds, that at the approach of an excited ftick of wax to the balls, in the firft experiment, the electric fire is fuppofed to come through the threads into the balls, and to be condenfed there, in its paffage towards the wax; fince, according to Dr. Franklin, excited glafs emits the electric fluid, and excited wax receives it.

WHEN two balls, fufpended by linen threads upon an infulated tin tube, were electrified pofitively, and had feparated; he obferved, that the approach of the excited tube would make them come nearer together; if brought to a certain diftance, they would touch; and if brought nearer, they would feparate again.

IN the return of the tube, they would approach each other, till they touched, and then repel as at firft. If the tin tube was electrified by wax, or the wire of a charged phial; the balls would be affected in the fame manner

U ner

ner at the approach of excited wax, or the
wire of the phial. If the cork balls were electrified by glafs, their replufion would be increafed at the approach of an excited ftick of
wax. And the effect would be the fame, if
the excited glafs was brought towards them,
when they had been electrified by wax.

THE bringing the excited glafs to the end,
or edge of the tin tube, in the former of thefe
experiments, is by Mr. Canton fuppofed to
electrify it pofitively, or to add to the electric
fire it before contained; and therefore fome
will be running off through the balls, and
they will repel each other. But at the approach of excited glafs, which likewife emits
the electric fluid, the difcharge of it from the
balls will be diminifhed, or part will be driven
back, by a force acting in a contrary direction, and they will come nearer together. If
the tube be held at fuch a diftance from the
balls, that the excefs of the denfity of the
fluid round about them above the common
quantity in air, be equal to the excefs of the
denfity of that within them above the common quantity contained in cork, their repulfion will be quite deftroyed. But if the tube
be brought nearer, the fluid without being
more denfe than that within the balls, it will
be attracted by them, and they will recede
from each other again.

MR. CANTON farther obferves, that when
the apparatus has loft part of its natural
ftore of this fluid, by the approach of excited
wax to one end of it, or is electrified negatively,

ly, the electric fire is attracted and imbibed
by the balls, to supply the deficiency; and
that more plentifully at the approach of excited glafs, or a body positively electrified,
than before; whence the diftance between the
balls will be increafed, as the fluid furrounding them is augmented. And, in general,
whether by the approach or recefs of any
body, if the difference between the denfity of
the internal and external fluid be increafed,
or diminifhed; the repulfion of the balls will
be increafed, or diminifhed accordingly.

He obferved, that when the infulated tin
tube was not electrified, if the excited glafs
was brought towards the middle of it, the
balls hanging at the end would repel each
other, and the more fo as the excited tube
was brought nearer. . When it had been held
a few feconds, at the diftance of about fix
inches, and withdrawn, the balls would approach each other till they touched; and, feparating again, as the tube was removed farther, would continue to repel when the tube
was taken quite away. This laft repulfion
would be increafed by the approach of excited glafs, and diminifhed by that of excited
wax; juft as if the apparatus had been electrified by wax, after the manner defcribed in
the laft experiment.

He infulated two tin tubes, which may be
diftinguifhed by calling them A and B, fo as
to be in a line with each other, and half an
inch afunder, and at the remote end of each
fufpended a pair of cork balls. Then, upon
bring-

bringing the excited glafs tube towards the
middle of A, and holding it a fhort time at
the diftance of a few inches, he obferved each
pair of balls to feparate. Upon withdrawing
the tube, the balls of A would come together,
and then repel each other again, but thofe of
B would hardly be affected. By the approach of excited glafs the repulfion of the
balls of A would be increafed, and thofe of
B diminifhed *.

IN the former of thefe experiments, Mr.
Canton fuppofes the common ftock of electric
matter in the tin tube to be attenuated about
the middle, and to be condenfed at the ends,
by the repelling power of the atmofphere of
the excited glafs tube, when held near it. And
perhaps, he fays, the tin tube may lofe fome
of its natural quantity of the electric fluid before it receives any from the glafs, as that
fluid will more readily run off from the ends
or edges of it than enter at the middle; and
accordingly, when the glafs tube is withdrawn, and the fluid is again equally diffufed
through the apparatus, it is found to be electrified negatively; fince excited glafs brought
under the balls will increafe their repulfion.

IN the latter of the experiments, Mr. Canton fuppofes that part of the fluid driven out
of one tin tube enters the other, which is
found to be electrified pofitively, by the de-
creafing of the repulfion of its balls at the approach of excited glafs.

* Phil. Tranf. Vol. xlviii. pt. i. p. 350.

IT

IT will readily be feen that, at the time thefe experiments were made, Mr. Canton retained the common idea of electric atmofpheres; whereas it will appear by the experiments of Meffrs. Wilcke and Æpinus (which in fact contain nothing more than thofe of Mr. Canton) that they tend to refute the common opinion, and are much eafier explained upon the fuppofition, that the portion of fluid belonging to any electrified body is conftantly held in contact, or very nearly in contact, with the body; but acts upon the electricity of other bodies at a certain diftance.

DR. FRANKLIN purfued, or rather diverfified the experiments of Mr. Canton, but retaining, likewife, the common opinion of electric atmofpheres, he thought that the phenomena were more eafily explained upon the fuppofition, that thefe atmofpheres, being brought near each other, did not eafily mix, and unite into one atmofphere, but remained feparate, and repelled each other ; and moreover, that an electric atmofphere, would not only repel another electric atmofphere, but alfo the electric fluid contained in the fubftance of a body approaching it, and, without joining or mixing with it, force it into the other parts of the body that contained it.

THOUGH it muft be difficult to affign a reafon why the particles of one atmofphere fhould repel the particles of another atmofphere, or of the fluid contained in another body with more force than they repel one another, or the particles of the fluid contained

in

in the body to which they belong, since the matter is the same in both; yet this idea of the mutual repulsion of electric atmospheres, could it once be supposed, will certainly and clearly account for all the facts; and the theory pleases on account of its simplicity. But the same appearances will be accounted for, in a manner as simple and intelligible, upon the supposition, that the portion of electric fluid belonging to each body, being strongly attracted by the body, is held in close contact with it; but that it acts by repulsion upon the electric fluid belonging to other bodies, at a distance from them; and that the electric fluid doth not actually pass out of one body into another, till it have first repelled the fluid out of the other body, and then be more strongly attracted by the other body, than by its own; which has already got more than its natural share.

THE paper containing an account of these experiments of Dr. Franklin was read at the Royal Society, December the 18th, 1755. His apparatus was different from that of Mr. Canton, but still he exhibited the same effects proceeding from the same cause. He fixed a tassel of fifteen or twenty threads, each three inches long, at one end of his prime conductor, which was five feet long and four inches in diameter, supported by silk lines. The threads were a little damp, but not wet.

IN these circumstances, an excited tube brought near the end of the prime conductor, opposite to the threads, so as to give it

some

some sparks, made the threads diverge, each thread having thereby acquired its separate electric atmosphere.

In this state, the approach of the excited tube, without giving any sparks, made the threads diverge more; but, being withdrawn, they closed as much; the atmosphere of the conductor being driven by that of the tube into the threads, and returning again upon withdrawing the tube, which had then left no part of its atmosphere behind it.

The excited tube brought under the diverging threads made them close a little, having driven part of their atmospheres into the conductor. Upon being withdrawn, they diverged as much; that portion of their atmospheres which they had lost returning again from the conductor, and the tube having left no part of its own.

The excited tube, held at the distance of five or six inches from the end of the conductor opposite to the threads, made them separate, and, upon being withdrawn, they came together again: but if, in their state of separation, a spark was taken from the conductor near them, they would close; and, upon removing the tube, would separate. The tube, in both cases, left no part of its atmosphere behind it. It only drove the natural quantity of electricity contained in the conductor towards the threads; and part of that being taken away by the spark, the tube would leave the conductor and threads negative, in

U 4

which

which cafe, they would repel one another, as if they had been electrified pofitively.

In this fituation, if the excited tube was brought near the conductor, they would clofe again; the atmofphere of the tube forcing that of the conductor into the threads, to fupply the place of what they had loft : but, upon withdrawing the tube, they would open again; the tube, as before, taking its whole atmofphere away with it. When the excited tube was brought under the threads, diverging with negative electricity, they diverged more; the atmofphere of the tube driving away more of the atmofpheres of the threads, and giving them none in its place.

Lastly the Doctor brought the excited tube near the prime conductor, when it was not electrified; and when the threads were, thereby, made to diverge, he brought his finger near them, and obferved, that they receded from it. This appearance had been taken notice of by Mr. Haukfbee, and others. Dr. Franklin accounts for it by fuppofing, that when his finger was plunged into the atmofphere of the glafs tube, part of its natural electricity was driven back, through his hand and body, fo as to leave the finger negatively electrified, as well as the threads; in which cafe they muft neceffarily repel one another. To confirm this hypothefis, he held a flender lock of cotton, two or three inches long, near the prime conductor, electrified by excited glafs, which made the cotton ftretch itself towards

wards the conductor; and obferved, that, in this ftate, it would recede from the finger of his other hand, at the fame time that it was attracted by a wire of a bottle charged pofitively *.

THESE experiments of Dr. Franklin, made in purfuance of thofe of Mr. Canton, were confirmed, as I obferved before, and carried much farther by Meffrs. Wilcke and Æpinus.

MR. WILCKE obferves, that a fmall body immerged in any electric atmofphere, if it be touched by no other body, and be withdrawn before it be repelled, fcarce ever fhows any fign of electricity; if any, it is of the fame kind with that of the body into whofe atmofphere it was plunged †. If any body, communicating with the ground, he brought to this light body, while it remains immerged in the atmofphere of the electrified body, it is firft attracted, and then repelled by it. If a point be prefented to this light body, and afterwards withdrawn, it will be found to have acquired an electricity oppofite to that of the electrified body. From this he concludes, that parts of non-electric bodies, plunged in electric atmofpheres, acquire an electricity oppofite to that of the atmofphere in which they are plunged ‡.

HE placed two large infulated conductors with their ends oppofite to one another, and a cork ball fufpended on filk between them; and obferved, that, upon the application of

---

* Phil. Tranf. Vol. xlix. pt. i. p. 300.
† Wilcke, p. 73.   ‡ Ibid. p. 77.

the excited glafs tube to one end of either
of them, the cork ball would play between
them very faft; and if the tube were held
a while at the fame diftance, would be at
reft. Upon withdrawing the tube, the motion of the cork ball began again, and, at
length, ceafed gradually as before. If the
conductors were removed from one another,
while they were within the atmofphere of the
tube, they would, upon being brought together again, give a fpark. This experiment
confirmed the demonftration, that the part of
a body which is immerged in the atmofphere
of an electrified body acquires the contrary
electricity *.

But the moft complete demonftration of
this general maxim is an experiment of Mr.
Æpinus. He placed a fmall weight upon one
end of a large metallic conductor, and, by
means of a filk ftring, removed it from the
conductor, while the end on which it refted
was immerged in the atmofphere of an electrified body; and found that it had actually
acquired a different electricity from that of the
atmofphere. If the end of the conductor,
oppofite to that on which the moveable weight
was placed, was made to communicate with
the earth, ftill that part of it which was near
the excited electric was affected with the oppofite electricity. Placing the moveable weight
on the oppofite end of the conductor, when it
was infulated, he found that it had fometimes

* Wilcke, p. 78.

acquired

acquired an electricity contrary to that of the excited electric, sometimes the same electricity, though weak, and sometimes no electricity at all *.

THE same ingenious philosopher considered that the same principle must extend to glass, and all other electrics; since they, as well as conductors, contain a certain quantity of the electric fluid, in their natural state. To verify this, he took a glass tube, and electrified one end of it positively. The consequence was, that four or five inches of that end were positive ; but beyond that there were two inches negative ; and beyond that the tube was again positive, though weakly so. This experiment he repeated very often with the same success; as also when, instead of glass, he used a solid stick of sulphur. To account for this fact, he supposed, that the electricity communicated to the end of the tube repelled the natural quantity of the fluid in the glass to some distance. This natural quantity retiring from its former situation, he supposes to become condensed, and consequently to repel another quantity of the fluid natural to the glass from its place; and that thus the whole rod would be alternately positive and negative. The author asserts, that it was from theory only that he was led to this curious experiment, the fact exactly corresponding to what he had before deduced, as the necessary consequence of Dr. Franklin's

* Æpini Tentamen, p. 129.

principles

principles of negative and positive electricity *.

THE hint of these experiments Mr. Æpinus received from those above mentioned of Mr. Wilcke; and these gentlemen, residing at the same time at Berlin, pursued these curious experiments jointly, till they were led by them to discover a method of charging a plate of air in the same manner as plates of glass had usually been charged, and to throw still more light upon the theory of the famous Leyden experiment.

IN the above mentioned experiments, these gentlemen observed, that the negative state of one of the bodies depended on the opposite state of the other, which was known to be exactly the case of the two sides of a charged pane of glass; and the reason of the non-communication of the same electricity was evidently the impermeability of the glass to the electric fluid in the one case, and the impermeability of the air in the other. Upon this hint they made several attempts to give the electric shock by means of air; and at length succeeded, by suspending large boards of wood covered with tin, with the flat sides parallel to one another, and at some inches asunder. For they found, that upon electrifying one of the boards positively, the other was always negative, agreeable to the former experiment : but the discovery was made complete and indisputable by a person's touch-

* Æpini Tentamen, p. 192.

ing

ing one of the plates with one hand, and
bringing his other hand to the other plate;
for he then received a fhock through his
body, exactly like that of the Leyden experiment *.

WITH this plate of air, as we may call it,
they made a variety of curious experiments.
The two metal plates, being in oppofite ftates,
ftrongly attracted one another, and would
have rufhed together, if they had not, been
kept afunder by ftrings. Sometimes the electricity of both would be difcharged by a
ftrong fpark between them, as when a pane
of glafs burfts with too great a charge. A
finger put between them promoted the difcharge, and felt the fhock. If an eminence
was made on either of the plates, the felf-dif-
charge would always be made through it, and
a pointed body fixed upon either of them prevented their being charged at all.

THE ftate of thefe two plates, they excellently obferve, juftly reprefents the ftate of
the clouds and the earth during a thunder
ftorm; the clouds being always in one ftate,
and the earth in the oppofite; while the body
of air between them anfwers the fame purpofe as the fmall plate of air between the
boards, or the plate of glafs between the two
metallic coatings in the Leyden experiment.
The phenomenon of lightning is the burfting of the plate of air by a fpontaneous difcharge, which is always made through emi-

* Wilcke, p. 97.

nences, and the bodies through which the discharge is made are violently shocked *.

THIS principle, they likewise thought, would explain an observation of the Abbé Nollet, that electricity was often observed to be peculiarly strong, when the room was full of company, and more particularly, when numbers of them drew near together, to see the experiments. The conductor was then in one state, and the company in another; so that, constituting a large surface, when any of them took a spark, as he thereby discharged the electricity of all the company, he would feel it more sensibly than if he had stood single †.

THIS discovery, of the method of giving the electric shock by means of a plate of air, may be reckoned one of the greatest discoveries in the science of electricity since those of Dr. Franklin. It is beautiful to observe how this fine discovery took its rise from the experiments of Mr. Canton. Mr. Canton's experiments were pursued by Dr. Franklin, and those of Dr. Franklin, pursued by these gentlemen, produced the discovery. It is one and the same principle that, in different circumstances, accounts for this beautiful series of experiments.

THIS experiment of charging a plate of air is likewise related by Mr. Æpinus, who says that he was led to the discovery, by rea-

* Wilcke, p. 161.   † Ibid. p. 96, &c.

soning

foning from the confequences of Dr. Franklin's theory.

FROM thefe experiments he was alfo led to
form a more diftinct idea of the impermeability of glafs to the electric fluid. For fince a
plate of air might be charged as well as a
plate of glafs, that property, whatever it be,
muft be common to them both; and could
not, as Dr. Franklin once fuppofed, be any
thing peculiar to the internal ftructure of glafs.
Impermeability, he, therefore, infers, muft be
common to all electrics; and fince they can
all receive electricity by communication to a
certain degree, it muft confift in the difficulty
and flownefs with which the electric fluid
moves in their pores; whereas, in perfect conductors, it meets with no obftruction at all *.

IT was chiefly this courfe of experiments,
alfo, that led Mr. Æpinus to deny the exiftence of electric atmofpheres, confifting of
effluvia from electrified bodies.

HE feems, however, to confider this as a
bold opinion; fince he herein differs, as he
fays, from all the electricians who had written
before him, and even from Dr. Franklin himfelf. Though the common opinion, he fays,
is by no means countenanced by the general
principles of this theory, which fuppofe the
electric fluid to move with difficulty through
every electric fubftance like the air.

To thofe who might fay, that an electric
atmofphere is a thing obvious to the fenfes,

* Æpini Tentamen, p 82.

and

and no matter of theory; fince it may be felt like a fpider's web upon the hands or face; he replies, that this feeling, together with the fulphureous fmell of electrified bodies, are only fenfations excited by the action of the fluid in the electrified bodies upon the electric fluid in the noftrils, or the hand; or upon thofe parts of the body themfelves in an unelectrified ftate; and that they are not felt by a perfon who is not poffeffed of the fame kind and degree of electricity.

HE, therefore, thinks there never was any fufficient reafon to admit thofe atmofpheres; and declares, that whenever he ufes the word, he means no more by it than the *fphere of action* of the electricity belonging to any body. Or, he fays, the neighbouring air, which is electrified by it, may be fo called.

BUT that thefe atmofpheres have little effect in electrical experiments, he fays, is evident from this circumftance; that if it be blown upon with a pair of bellows, the electricity of the body which it furrounds is not fenfibly diminifhed. The electric fluid, he fuppofes, to refide wholly in the electrified body, and from thence to exert its attraction or repulfion to a certain diftance *.

THE fubject of electric atmofpheres had not efcaped the attention of the accurate Signior Beccaria, who was probably prior to Mr. Æpinus in fuppofing, that electrified bodies have no other atmofphere than the electricity commu-

* Æpini Tentamen, p. 257.

nicated

ticated to the neighbouring air, and which goes with the air, and not with the electrified bodies, agreeable to that curious difcovery of his mentioned above.

HE alfo mentions an experiment, which, he thinks, directly proves, that all the electricity communicated to any body adheres to its furface, and does not fpread into the air. He electrified a large conductor of gilt paper, in which the gilding was, in feveral places, taken off quite round; and obferved that whenever he difcharged it, by taking a fpark at the end, other fparks were vifible at all the interruptions; the charge of the more remote parts having come off through the fubftance of the metal, and not along the air; as the greateft part of it, at leaft, might have done, if it had lodged there *.

IT is now alfo Mr. Canton's opinion, that electric atmofpheres are not made of effluvia from excited or electrified bodies, but that they are only an alteration of the ftate of the electric fluid contained in, or belonging to the air furrounding them, to a certain diftance; that excited glafs, for inftance, repels the electric fluid from it, and confequently, beyond that diftance makes it more denfe; whereas excited wax attracts the electric fluid exifting in the air nearer to it, making it rarer than it was before.

THIS will be beft underftood by a figure. Let A (Pl. I. fig. 1.) reprefent unexcited glafs

* Elettricifmo artificiale, p. 54.

X or

or wax. B excited glafs, and C excited wax; and let the dots on each fide of A reprefent a line of particles of the electric fluid at their proper diftance in a natural ftate.

Let B and C be carried about where you will in the air, B will make an atmofphere equally denfe, and C an atmofphere equally rare, while the quantity of the electric fluid each of them contains is the fame as at firft. When any part of a conductor comes within the atmofphere of B, the electric fluid it naturally contains will be repelled by the denfe atmofphere, and will recede from it. But if any part of a conductor be brought within the atmofphere of C, the electric fluid it naturally contains will be attracted by the rare atmofphere, and move towards it. And thus may the electric fluid contained in any body be condenfed or rarefied; and if the body be a conductor, it may be condenfed or rarified in any part of it, and fome may be eafily drawn out of, or an additional quantity put into it.

It was obferved before, that an experiment of Dr. Franklin, which he thought proves that electric atmofpheres did not exclude the air, might juftly make us fufpect the exiftence of thofe atmofpheres, fince the electric matter is known to repel the air. Another experiment of the fame nature was made by Dr. Darwin of Litchfield, who fent an account of it to the Royal Society, which was read May the 5th, 1757. He got a glafs tube, open at one end, and having a ball at the other. This ball and half of the tube he coated; and when he had

inverted

inverted it, and dipped a confiderable part of it into a veffel containing oil of turpentine, he introduced a wire into it, and charged it; and obferved, that the oil did not at all appear to fubfide. From this he concluded, that the electric atmofphere, flowing round the wire and the coating the tube, above the oil, did not difplace the air, but exifted in its pores *.

An experiment fimilar to that of Dr. Franklin and that of Dr. Darwin was made by Signior Beccaria. He took a coated phial, and when he had inferted into it a fmall glafs tube, bent horizontally when it came out of the phial; he clofed it with cement, and prefented light afhes to the extremity of the tube, the orifice of which was very fine; and always found, that the afhes were blown off, when a fpark was taken into the phial, but they returned towards the end of the tube afterwards †. It is probable, that the metal not being fufficiently in contact with the infide coating, a fpark was made in the infide, which expelled the air, and caufed the motion in the afhes. The faireft method of trying it would be with a phial, in which the metal that received the fire from the conductor, fhould be a production of the inward coating.

* Phil. Tranf. Vol. l. pt. i. p. 351.
† Lettere dell' elettricifmo, p. 79.

SECTION VI.

Mr. SYMMER's EXPERIMENTS RELATING
TO THE TWO ELECTRICITIES, AND THOSE
MADE BY JOHANNES FRANCISCUS
CIGNA IN PURSUANCE OF THEM.

IT had hitherto been univerfally fuppofed,
that all the phenomena of electricity were
produced by the action of one electric fluid.
Even Mr. Du Fay, at the time that he. imagined he had difcovered another electric fluid,
diftinct from that of glafs, and peculiar to
rofin, &c. thought, however, that it was quite
independent of the other, and that their operations were never combined. Dr. Watfon,
and Dr. Franklin thought it was very evident,
that the difference between the two electricities confifted in the one being a redundancy,
and the other a deficiency of the fame matter.
And. all the experiments that had been made
concerning the two electricities feemed to confirm this hypothefis. At length, however,
Mr. Symmer produces a great number of curious experiments, relating to the fame fubject; and infers from them the probable
exiftence of *two electric fluids*, not independent, but always co-exiftent, and counteracting one another.

THE firft fet of his experiments are very
remarkable, but he does little more than relate naked facts. They were diverfified, and

2   purfued

purſued much farther by Mr. Cigna, of Turin, who has alſo explained them upon the principles of Dr. Franklin's theory; though he was of opinion, that no experiments that had yet been made were deciſive in favour of either of the two hypotheſes. Few hiſtories of experiments are more entertaining than the firſt of theſe of Mr. Symmer; the ſubſequent experiments are leſs ſatisfactory. The papers relating to them all were read at the Royal Society in the year 1759 [*].

THIS gentleman had for ſome time obſerved, that upon putting off his ſtockings, in an evening, they made a crackling or ſnapping noiſe, and that, in the dark, he could perceive them to emit ſparks of fire. He had no doubt but that this proceeded from the principle of electricity, and, after a great number of obſervations, to determine on what circumſtances thoſe ſtrong electrical appearances depended, he found, at length, that it was the combination of white and black that produced the electricity; and that the appearances were the ſtrongeſt when he wore a white and black ſilk ſtocking upon the ſame leg [†]. Theſe, however, diſcovered no ſign of electricity while they were upon the

---

[*] Phil. Tranſ. Vol. li. pt. i. p. 340.

[†] The Abbé Nollet, in repeating theſe experiments of Mr. Symmer, found, that it was not abſolutely neceſſary, that one of the ſtockings ſhould be black, for that, if one of them was only dipped in a decoction of gall-nuts, which doth not dye them black, but is only a preparative to it, it would have the ſame effect. Nollet's Lettres, Vol. iii. p. 42.

leg,

ieg, or hand (for he found that his hand was
fufficient) though they were drawn backwards and forwards upon it feveral times.
Nor when taken from the hand, and prefented to an electrometer (i. e. Mr. Canton's balls)
did they appear to have acquired any more
than a very fmall degree of electricity; but
the moment they were feparated, they were
found, both of them, to be highly electrified, the white pofitively, and the black negatively.

BOTH the ftockings, when held at a diftance
from one another, appeared inflated to fuch
a degree, that, when highly electrified, they
exhibited the intire fhape of the leg; and
when two black, or two white ftockings were
held together, they would repel one another,
fo as to form an angle, feemingly, of thirty or
thirty-five degrees.

WHEN a white and black ftocking were
prefented to each other; they would be mutually attracted; and, if permitted, would
rufh together with furprifing violence. In
their approach their inflation gradually fubfided, and their attraction of foreign objects
diminifhed, but their attraction of one another increafed. When they actually met,
they grew flat, and joined as clofe together,
as if they had been fo many folds of filk.
When they were feparated, their electricity
did not feem to have been in the leaft impaired by the fhock of meeting; for they would
be again inflated, attract, repel, and rufh together as before.

WHEN

When this experiment was performed with two black ſtockings in one hand, and two white ones in the other, it exhibited a curious ſpectacle. The repulſion of thoſe of the ſame colour and the attraction of thoſe of different colours, threw them into an agitation which was not unentertaining, and made them catch each at the oppoſite colour, at a greater diſtance than could have been expected.

When the ſtockings were ſeparated from one another, they would loſe their power very ſoon, much like the excited tube; but when they were together, they would retain it an hour or two, or longer, if the air was favourable to electricity. The ſharpeſt metallic point could not deprive them of it; and when they were one within the other, no means he could think of could procure the leaſt perceivable diſcharge of the electricity. In this reſpect, Mr. Symmer thought there was a conſiderable reſemblance between the black and the white ſtocking, when put within one another, and the Leyden phial.

What was ſtill more remarkable in theſe experiments with the white and black ſtockings, was the power of electrical coheſion which they exhibited. Mr. Symmer perceived that the white and black ſtockings, when electrified, and allowed to come together, not only joined extremely cloſe, but actually ſtuck to each other. By means of a balance, he found, that in order to ſeparate them, it required from one to twelve ounces. Another

X 4

time

time they raifed feventeen ounces, which was twenty times the weight of that ftocking which fupported them, and this in a direc-tion parallel to its furface.

WHEN one of the ftockings was turned in-fide out, and put within the other, it requir-ed twenty ounces to feparate them, though when they were applied to each other exter-nally, ten ounces were fufficient.

GETTING the black ftockings new dyed, and the white ones wafhed, and whitened in the fumes of fulphur; and then putting them one within the other, with their rough fides together, it required three pounds three ounces to feparate them. And he had reafon to think that the fulphur contributed nothing to the experiment.

TRYING this experiment with ftockings of a more fubftantial make, he found the effects more confiderable. When the white ftocking was put within the black one, fo that the out-fide of the white was contiguous to the infide of the black, they raifed nine pounds want-ing a few ounces, which was fifty times the weight of the ftocking. When the white ftocking was turned infide out, and put with-in the black one, fo that their rough furfaces were contiguous, they raifed fifteen pounds one pennyweight and a half, which was nine-ty-two times the weight of the ftocking.

HAVING cut off the ends of the thread, and the tufts of filk, which had been left in the infide of the ftockings, the cohefion was confiderably diminifhed. Preffing them together

gether between his hands contributed much
to ſtrengthen it *.

WHEN the white and black ſtocking were
in coheſion, and another pair, more highly
electrified were ſeparated from one another,
and preſented to the former, their coheſion
would be diſſolved; and each ſtocking of the
ſecond pair would catch hold of, and carry
away with it, that of its oppoſite colour. If
the degree of electricity of both pairs were
equal, the coheſion of the former pair would
be weakened, but not diſſolved; and all the
four would cohere, forming one maſs. If the
ſecond pair were but weakly electrified, the
coheſion of the firſt pair would be but little
impaired, and the coheſion of the whole maſs
would be ſmall in proportion.

MR. SYMMER alſo obſerved, that white and
black ſilk, when electrified, not only cohered
with each other, but would alſo adhere to
bodies with broad, and even with poliſhed
ſurfaces, though thoſe bodies were not electrified. This he diſcovered accidentally, having, without deſign, thrown a ſtocking out
of his hand, which ſtuck to the paper hang-
ings of the room. He repeated the experiment, and found it would continue hanging
near an hour.

HAVING ſtuck up the black and white
ſtockings in this manner, he came with another pair of ſtockings highly electrified; and
applying the white to the black, and the

* Phil. Tranſ. Vol. li. pt. i. p. 393.

black

black to the white, he carried them off from the wall, each of them hanging to that which had been brought to it.

THE same experiments held with the paint-ed boards of the room, and likewife with the looking-glafs, to the fmooth furface of which both the white and the black filk appeared to adhere more tenacioufly than to either of the former *.

A FEW obfervations, fimilar to fome of thefe of Mr. Symmer, were made by Signior *Aleffandro Amadeo Vaudonia*, a friend of Signior Beccaria. He put a beaver fhirt be-tween two others, which he wore in extreme cold weather; and whenever he put off the uppermoft fhirt, which he did every day, he found it adhered to the beaver fhirt, and, on the feparation, electric fparks were vifible be-tween them. Whenever he put off the beaver fhirt, it adhered ftill more to the under fhirt, and when held at a confiderable diftance from it, would rufh to it. Thefe attractions would be repeated many times, but they grew more languid by degrees, till they intirely ceafed. Signior Beccaria, upon hearing of this expe-riment, repeated it with fome variation, and found it to anfwer on himfelf †.

THE cohefion of the two ftockings induced Mr. Symmer to try the force of electrical co-hefion in electrified panes of glafs. For this purpofe, he got two panes of common window glafs, the thinneft and the fmootheft that he

---

* Phil. Tranf. Vol. li. pt. i. p. 366.
† Dell' elettricifmo artificiale, p 197.

could

could find, and coated one of the fides of each
with tinfoil, leaving a fpace uncovered near
the edges. He then put the uncovered fides
together, and charging them both as one
pane, he found, as he expected, that their
cohefion was confiderably ftrong : but he had
no apparatus to meafure the ftrength of it.
He then turned the plates upfide down, and
found that the fame operation which had before charged them, did now uncharge them,
according to the analogy of the Leyden
phial.

PLACING two panes of glafs, each of them
coated on both fides, one upon the other, he
found that they were both charged feparately, and that there was no cohefion between
them.

IN purfuance of thefe laft mentioned experiments of Mr. Symmer, and another made
at Pekin (which will be recited prefently) Signior Beccaria made the following, which are
very curious; but which, after the example
of the author, I fhall relate without attempting an explanation.

HAVING charged a coated plate of glafs, he
flipped the coating from off the negative fide,
and applied another, uncoated and uncharged
plate of glafs clofe to it. After this, putting
a coating upon the uncharged glafs (fo that
the whole refembled one coated plate, confifting of two *laminæ*) he formed a communication between the coatings. The confequence
was an explofion, and a cohefion of the
plates.

IF

IF he feparated the plates before the explofion, after they had been in conjunction fome
time, the charged plate was pofitive on both
fides, and the uncharged plate negative on
both fides.   But if he feparated them after the
explofion, the charged plate was negative on
both fides, and the uncharged plate pofitive
on both fides.

IF after the explofion he feparated and
joined them again alternately, a fmall circle of
paper, placed under the uncharged plate, adhered to it upon every feparation, and was
thrown off again upon every conjunction.
This he could repeat even five hundred times,
with once charging the plate.   This was the
experiment that he fays was made by fome
Jefuits at Pekin, in the year 1755, and being fent to the Academy of Sciences at Peterfburgh, was publifhed in their Memoirs, vol.
viii. p. 276.

IF, in thefe experiments, the charged plate
was inverted, and the pofitive fide applied to
the uncharged plate, all the effects were
exactly the reverfe of the former.   If it was
inverted ever fo often, after remaining fome
time in contact with the uncharged glafs, it
would produce a change in the electricity.   In
the dark, a light was always feen upon the
feparation of thefe plates.

LAYING the two plates together, like one
plate, and coating the outfides of them, he
charged them both together, and, at the diftance of about four feet, he diftinguifhed fix
of the *coloured rings*, which Newton defcribes
in his book of Optics, all parallel to one another,

other, and nearly parallel to the edge of the coating. At the angles of the coatings the rings fpread to a greater diftance; where the coatings did not quite touch the glafs, the rings bent inwards; and where the coatings adhered very clofe, they retired farther from them. Upon difcharging thefe two plates, the coloured rings vanifhed, and the electric cohefion (which Mr. Symmer had obferved in this cafe) ceafed with them.

UPON feparating thefe plates before the explofion, that which had received the pofitive electricity was pofitive on both fides, and the other negative on both fides. If they were feparated after the explofion, each of them (as in the former experiment) was affected in a manner juft the reverfe of this. Upon inverting thefe plates, that which was the thinner appeared to be poffeffed of the ftronger electricity, and (like the charged plate in the former experiment) brought the other to correfpond to it.

CHARGING the two plates feparately, and taking off two of the coatings, fo as to place the two pofitive or the two negative fides together, there was no cohefion or explofion. But joining a pofitive and a negative fide, they cohered, and a communication being formed on the outfide, there was an explofion, which increafed the cohefion. Making the above-mentioned experiments with thefe plates, he fays, they acted juft as the two that were charged at the fame time *.

* Phil. Tranf. Vol. lvii. p. 458.

Mr.

MR. SYMMER concludes his account of thefe experiments with declaring it be his opinion,' that there are two electric fluids, or emanations of two diftinct electric powers, effentially different from each other; that electricity does not confift in the afflux and efflux of thefe fluids, but in the accumulation of the one or the other of them in bodies electrified ; or, in other words, it confifts in the poffeffion of a larger portion of one or the other power, than is requifite to maintain an even balance within the body; and laftly, that, according as the one or the other power prevails, the body is electrified in the one or the other manner. Nor will this principle, fays he, of two diftinct electrical powers be found, upon due confideration, to difagree with the general fyftem of nature. It is one of the fundamental laws of nature, that action and reaction are infeparable and equal ; and, when we look round, we find that every power which is exerted in the material world meets with a counteracting power, which controuls and regulates its effects, fo as to anfwer the wife purpofes of providence *.

MR. SYMMER alfo alledges, in proof of his two diftinct powers of electricity, the experiment which Dr. Franklin has related, of piercing a quire of paper with an electric fhock. He thought that the bur which was raifed on both fides of the paper was produced by two fluids, moving in two different direc-

* Phil. Tranf. Vol. li. pt. i. p. 389.

tions.

tions. To fhow the manner in which this ftroke was made more evidently, he mentions two other fimilar experiments, in which the circumftances of the ftroke were a little varied.

A PIECE of paper, covered on one fide with Dutch gilding, and which had been left accidentally between two leaves, in a quire of paper in which the former experiment had been made, was found to have the impreffion of two ftrokes upon it, about a quarter of an inch from each other; the gilding being ftripped off, and the paper left bare for a little fpace in both places. In the center of one of thefe places was a little round hole, in the other only an indenture or impreffion, fuch as might have been made with the point of a bodkin.

THESE obfervations Mr. Symmer communicated to Dr. Franklin, who, notwithftanding Mr. Symmer was endeavouring to eftablifh a theory of electricity contrary to his own, with the generofity natural to him, affifted him with his apparatus in making another experiment in purfuance of that mentioned above.

IN the middle of a paper book, of the thicknefs of a quire, Mr. Symmer put a flip of tinfoil; and in another, of the fame thicknefs, he put two flips of the fame fort of foil, including the two middle leaves of the book between them. Upon ftriking the two different books, the effects were anfwerable to what he expected. In the firft, the leaves on

each

each fide of the foil were pierced, while the foil itfelf remained unpierced; but, at the fame time, he could perceive an impreffion had been made on each of its furfaces, at a little diftance from one another; and fuch impreffions were ftill more vifible on the paper, and might be traced, as pointing different ways. In the fecond, all the leaves of the book were pierced, excepting the two that were between the flips of foil; and in thefe two, inftead of holes, the two impreffions in contrary directions were vifible.

MR. SYMMER afterwards got an electrical apparatus of his own, formed on the model of that of Dr. Franklin, with which he frequently repeated the experiments above-mentioned, the refult of all which he comprifes in the three following obfervations.

1. WHEN a quire of paper, without any thing between the leaves, is pierced with a ftroke of electricity, the two different powers keep in the fame track, and make but one hole in their paffage through the paper: not but that the power from above, or that from below, fometimes darts into the paper at two or more different points, making fo many holes, which, however, generally unite before they go through the paper. They feem to pafs each other about the middle of the quire, for there the edges are moft vifibly bent different ways; whereas, in the leaves near the outfide of the quire, the holes very often carry more the appearance of the paffage of a power iffuing out, and ex-
ploding

ploding into the air, than of one darting into the paper.

2. WHEN any thin metallic fubftance, fuch as gilt leaf, or tinfoil, is put between the leaves of the quire, and the whole is ftruck, in that cafe, the counteracting powers deviate from the direct tract, and leaving the path which they would in common have taken through the paper, only make their way in different lines to the metallic body, and ftrike it in two different points, diftant from one another about a quarter of an inch, more or lefs; the diftance appearing to be the leaft when the power is greateft: and whether they pierce it, or only make impreffions upon it, in either cafe they leave evident marks of motion from two different parts, and in two contrary directions. It is this deviation from a common courfe, and the feparation of the lines of direction confequent upon it, fays he, that affords a proof of the exertion of two diftinct and counteracting powers.

3. WHEN two flips of tinfoil are put into the middle of the quire, including two or more leaves between them, if the electricity be moderately ftrong, the counteracting powers only ftrike againft the flips, and leave their impreffion there. When it is ftronger, one of the flips is generally pierced, but feldom both; and from what he had obferved in fuch cafes, he fays it fhould feem, as if the power which iffued from the outfide of the phial acted more ftrongly than that which proceeded from within, for the lower flip was moft com-

monly

monly pierced. But this, he adds, may be owing to the greater fpace which the power from within has to move through before it ftrikes the paper *.

In the fame paper, Mr. Symmer furnifhes a remarkable inftance of the power of an hypothefis in drawing facts to itfelf, in making proofs out of facts which are very ambiguous, and in making a perfon overlook thofe circumftances in an experiment which are unfavourable to his views.

When a phial is electrified but a little, Mr. Symmer fays, if we touch the coating of it with a finger of one hand, and, at the fame time, bring a finger of the other hand to the wire, we fhall receive a pretty fmart blow upon the tip of each of the fingers, the fenfation of which reaches no farther. If the phial be electrified a degree higher, we fhall feel a ftronger blow, reaching to the wrifts, but no farther. When, again, it is electrified to a ftill higher degree, a feverer blow will be received, but will not be felt beyond the elbows. Laftly, when the phial is ftrongly charged, the ftroke may be perceived in the wrifts, and elbows; but the principal fhock is felt in the breaft, as if a blow from each fide met there. This plain and fimple experiment, fays Mr. Symmer, feems obvioufly to fuggeft to obfervation the exiftence of two diftinct powers, acting in contrary directions; and, I believe, fays he, it would be held as a

* Phil. Tranf. Vol. li. pt. i. p. 377, &c.

fufficient

fufficient proof by any perfon, who fhould try the experiment, with a view to determine the queftion fimply from his own perceptions *.

It is a fufficient anfwer to this remark of Mr. Symmer, that if twenty people join hands, they may all be made to feel the fhock in their wrifts, or their elbows, without having their breafts affected in the leaft. And can it be fuppofed, that the two currents of electric fire could come at all their wrifts or elbows, without paffing through their breafts? According to Mr. Symmer's hypothefis, it fhould feem, that, in a large circle, thofe perfons only who ftood near the phial, on either hand, fhould feel *a fmall fhock*; that a few perfons more, at each extremity of the circle, fhould feel one fomething ftronger; and that it could only be a very ftrong fhock, which could at all affect the perfon who ftood in the middle; and that then he fhould be affected the leaft of any perfon in the company. But all thefe confequences are contrary to fact.

This hypothefis of Mr. Symmer, notwithftanding he has failed in his application of it' to the experiments above mentioned, has attracted the notice of feveral electricians, both at home and abroad; and fome perfons feem inclined to adopt it, in preference to Dr. Franklin's theory. I fhall therefore confider it more at large, when I come to treat of *theories*

* Phil. Tranf. Vol. li. pt. i. p. 373, &c.

profeffed-

profeffedly; till which time, I take leave of
this ingenious philofopher, and his two electric fluids.

THE experiments of Mr. Symmer excited
the attention of Mr. Cigna, and led him
to a courfe of experiments, which throws ftill
more light, both upon the doctrine of the
two electricities and the Leyden phial. They
are alfo a farther illuftration of the difcovery
of Mr. Canton, improved by Meffrs. Wilcke
and Æpinus, of the mutual repellency of fimilar electric atmofpheres.

HE took two white filk ribbons, juft dried
at the fire, and having extended them upon a
fmooth plain, either a conductor or a non-
conductor, he drew over them the fharp edge
of an ivory ruler, and found, that both the
ribbons had acquired electricity enough to adhere to the plain; though, while they remained upon the plain, they fhewed no other
fign of it. If they were both taken off from
the plain together, they attracted one another,
the upper having acquired the refinous and
more powerful, and the lower the vitreous
and weaker electricity. If they were taken
up feparately, they repelled one another,
having both acquired the refinous electricity *.

IN this feparation of both the ribbons from
the plain, as alfo in their feparation, afterwards, from one another, electric fparks
were vifible between them; but if they were

* Memoirs of the Academy at Turin for the year 1765,
P 31.

again

again put upon the plain, or joined together, no light appeared upon their second separation, without another friction of the ruler. Also, when, by being taken off separately, they had been made to repel one another, if they were laid on the plain again, and taken off together, they would not attract; and if, by being taken off together, they had first been made to attract one another, and were laid on the plain a second time, and then taken off separately, they would not repel, without another friction.

WHEN, by the operation above mentioned, they had acquired the same electricity, if they were placed, not upon the smooth body on which they had been rubbed, but on a rough one, and a conductor, as hemp or cotton, not very dry; they would, upon being separated, show contrary electricities; which, when they were joined together, would disappear as before *.

IF they had been made to repel one another, and were afterwards placed one upon the other, on the rough surface above mentioned, they would, in a few minutes, attract one another; the lower of the two ribbons having changed its resinous into a vitreous electricity.

IF the two white ribbons received their friction upon the rough surface, they always acquired contrary electricities; the upper of the two having the resinous, and the lower

* Memoirs of the Academy at Turin for the year 1765, p. 33.

Y 3

the vitreous, in whatever manner they were taken off.

THE fame thing that was done by a rough furface was done by any pointed conductor. If two ribbons, for inftance, were made to repel, and hang parallel to one another; and the point of a needle were drawn oppofite to one of them, along its whole length, they would prefently rufh together; the electricity of that ribbon to which the needle was prefented being changed into the contrary *.

IN the fame manner in which one of the ribbons changed its electricity, a ribbon not electrified would acquire electricity, viz. by putting it upon a rough furface, and laying an electrified ribbon upon it; or by holding it parallel to an electrified ribbon, and prefenting a pointed conductor to it.

HE placed a ribbon not quite dry under another that was well dried at the fire, upon a fmooth plain; and when he had given them the ufual friction with his ruler, he found that, in what manner foever they were removed from the plain, the upper of them had acquired the refinous, and the lower the vitreous electricity †.

IF both the ribbons were black, all the above mentioned experiments fucceeded, in the fame manner as if they had been white ‡.

* Memoirs of the Academy at Turin for the year 1765, p. 34.　　　† Ibid, p. 35.　　　‡ Ibid.

IF,

IF, inſtead of his ivory ruler, he made uſe of any ſkin, or of a piece of ſmooth glaſs, the event was the ſame; but if he made uſe of a ſtick of ſulphur, the electricities were, in all caſes, the reverſe of what they were before; the ribbon which was rubbed having always acquired the vitreous electricity.

WHEN he made uſe of paper, either gilt or not gilt, the reſults were uncertain.

WHEN the ribbons were wrapped in paper, gilt or not gilt, and the friction was made upon the paper, laid upon the plain above mentioned, the ribbons acquired, both of them, the reſinous electricity *.

IF the ribbons were one black, and the other white, which ever of them was laid uppermoſt, and in whatever manner the friction was made, the black generally acquired the reſinous, and the white the vitreous electricity †.

HE obſerved, however, the following conſtant event; that whenever the texture of the upper piece of ſilk was looſe, yielding, and retiform, like that of a ſtocking, ſo that it could move, and be rubbed againſt the lower, and the rubber was of ſuch a nature as to impart but little electricity to glaſs; the electricity which the upper piece of ſilk acquired, did not depend upon the rubber, but upon the body it was laid upon; in which caſe the black was always reſinous, and the white vi-

---

* Memoirs of the Academy at Turin for the year 1765, p. 36. † Ibid. p. 38.

treous.

treous. But when the filk was of a clofe
texture, hard and rigid, and when the rubber
was fuch as imparted a great degree of electricity to glafs, the electricity of the upper
piece did not depend upon the lower, but
upon the rubber. Thus a white filk ftocking, rubbed with gilt paper upon glafs, became refinous, and the glafs vitreous; but if
a piece of filk, of a firmer texture, was laid
upon a plate of glafs, it always acquired the
vitreous electricity, and the glafs the refinous,
if it was rubbed with fulphur; and for the
moft part, if it was rubbed with gilt paper *.
So that the filk that was rubbed received its
electricity, fometimes from the rubber, and
fometimes from the fubftance placed under it;
according as it received greater friction from
the one or the other, or in proportion as one
or the other was more proper to give electricity to glafs.

ANOTHER fet of experiments, which the
fame Mr. Cigna made, illuftrate the adhefion
of Mr. Symmer's electrical ftockings to bodies
with fmooth furfaces. He infulated a plate
of lead, and bringing an electrified ribbon
near it, obferved that it was attracted very
feebly. Bringing his finger to the lead, a
fpark iffued out of it, upon which it attracted the ribbon vigoroufly, and both together
fhewed no figns of electricity. Upon the feparation of the ribbon, they again both ap-

* Memoirs of the Academy at Turin, for the year 1765,
p. 40.

peared

peared to be electrified, and a spark was perceived between the plate and the finger *.

LAYING two plates of glass upon a smooth conductor communicating with the ground, and rubbing them in the same manner as the ribbons had been rubbed, they likewise acquired electricity, and adhered firmly, both to one another, and to the conductor. If it were a plate of lead, not very thick, it would be supported by the attraction. When they were together, they showed no other signs of electricity †.

WHEN the two plates of glass were separated from the conductor, and kept together, they showed, on both sides, a vitreous electricity; and the conductor, if it had been insulated, was seen to have contracted a resinous electricity.

THE two plates of glass themselves, when separated, were possessed of the two electricities; the upper of the vitreous and stronger, and the lower of the resinous and weaker.

WITH a rough conductor, whether they were originally rubbed upon it, or brought to it, after they had been rubbed upon a smooth one, they scarce contracted any electricity; though, when they were separated from one another, they were affected as before.

UPON this principle, Mr. Cigna endeavours to account for the non-excitation of a globe

* Memoirs of the Academy at Turin, for the year 1765,
P. 43.   † Ibid. p. 52.

or tube from which the air is exhaufted, or
which is lined with conducting fubftances.
In this cafe, he fays, the vitreous electricity
on the external furface of the glafs is balanced
by the refinous in the inward coating, or in
the vacuum which ferves inftead of a coating; and therefore it is in the fituation of
the plates of glafs while they lie upon the
conductor above-mentioned : but when the
inward coating is taken away, the electricity
appears on the outfide, without any frefh
excitation, as when the plates were removed
from the conductor *.

WHEN he laid a number of ribbons of the
fame colour upon the fmooth conductor, and
drew his ruler over them ; he found, that
when he took them up fingly, they all gave
fparks, at the place where they were feparated, as the laft ribbon did with the fmooth
plate, and had all acquired the refinous electricity †.

IF they were all taken from the plate together, they cohered in one mafs, which, on
both fides, appeared to be refinous. If they
were laid upon the rough conductor, in the
fame order (whereby the oppofite electricities
were brought to an equilibrium) and they
were all feparated fingly, beginning with the
loweft, fparks appeared as before; but all
the ribbons had acquired the vitreous electricity, except the uppermoft, which retained

---

* Memoirs of the Academy at Turin, for the year 1765,
p. 54.   † Ibid. p. 61.

the

the refinous electricity it had received from the friction *.

IF they received the friction upon the rough conductor, and were all taken up at once (in order to have a bundle in which the oppofite electricities were balanced) all the intermediate ribbons acquired the electricity, either of the higheft or the loweft ribbon, according as the feparation was begun with the higheft, or the loweft.

IF two ribbons were feparated from the bundle at the fame time, they clung together; and, in that ftate, fhowed no fign of electricity, as one of them alone would have done. When they were feparated, and the different electricities were manifeft, the electricity was obferved to refide in the outermoft, and was oppofite to that by which they had both adhered to the bundle, but much weaker †.

HE placed a number of ribbons upon a plate of metal, which received electricity from the globe, while he held a pointed body to the other fide of the ribbons. The confequence was, that all the ribbons became poffeffed of the electricity oppofite to that of the plate, or of the fame, according as they were taken off; except the moft remote, which always kept an electricity oppofite to that of the plate.

FROM thefe experiments he infers, that as electricity is propagated from the outermoft

* Memoirs of the Academy at Turin, for the year 1765, p. 61.   † Ibid.

ribbon

ribbon to thofe underneath it, or elfe from
the plate below to thofe next above it, when
they are feparated, fo likewife when the coating is feparated from a charged pane of glafs,
it likewife depofits its electricity upon the fuperficies of the glafs, the phenomena being
the fame in both. For when he put metal
coatings on the fide of a plate of glafs, without any cement, they adhered firmly to the
glafs when it was charged, and a light appeared upon their being feparated from it, as in
the cafe of the ribbons *.

WHEN he coated a number of ribbons in
the fame manner, and charged them, the
coatings adhered firmly to the ribbons; but
he could never feparate one of them, but (in
confequence of the loofe texture of the filk) a
fpark would go to the oppofite coating, which
immediately fell off, the whole being then
difcharged †.

BUT he thought the coatings did not depo-
fite all their electricity on the plate, when they
were taken off; for though, when both were
taken off, the electricities of the two fides ftill
balanced one another (becaufe each retained
the fame diminifhed quantity) yet, when one
fuperficies of the glafs, or of the ribbons, received its electricity from friction, and the
other only from the oppofite coating, he obferved, that the electricities which balanced
one another while the coating was on, were
no longer balanced when it was taken off;

* Memoirs of the Academy at Turin, for the year 1765,
p. 63.   † Ibid. p. 64.

the

the electricity of the furface which was rubbed then prevailing, becaufe the conducting coating had, upon its feparation, taken part of its electricity along with it *.

To confirm this, he adds another experiment. He charged a pane of glafs, coated on one fide, while the other received electricity by a pointed conductor from the machine: he likewife inverted the plate, and made the coated fide communicate with the prime conductor, while a pointed piece of metal was prefented to the oppofite fide; and, in both cafes, found, that while the coating remained, the two electricities balanced one another ; but that when the coating was flipped off, the electricity of the oppofite fide prevailed, fo as to be apparent on both fides of the plate †.

* Memoirs of the Academy at Turin for the year 1765, p. 65.　　　　† Ibid.

SECTION

SECTION VII.

THE HISTORY OF THE LEYDEN PHIAL
CONTINUED.

GREAT as were the difcoveries of Dr.
Franklin concerning the Leyden phial,
he left fome curious particulars for this period of the hiftory of electricity; and the
fubject is by no means exhaufted. Many of
the properties of this *wonderful bottle*, as the
Doctor calls it, are ftill unexplained. But as
more and more light is perpetually thrown
upon it, let us hope that, at length, we fhall
thoroughly underftand this great experiment.
The greateft difcovery concerning the properties of the Leyden phial, in this period, hath
already been related in the account of Meffrs.
Wilcke's and Æpinus's method of giving the
fhock by means of a plate of air ; and other
obfervations have, likewife, been occafionally
mentioned, in places where their connection
required them to be inferted. This fection,
however, will contain feveral experiments
of a mifcellaneous nature, which are well
worth notice.

IMMEDIATELY upon the difcovery of the
fhock given by glafs, all electricians attempted to charge other electric fubftances, but
none of them fucceeded before Signior Beccaria. He found that a very fmooth plate of
fealing-wax, made by pouring that fubftance,

when

when melted, upon an oiled marble table, would receive a confiderable charge *.

AFTER trying feveral other electrics, in the fame manner, he found that a mixture of pitch and colophonia was charged lefs than fealing-wax, but more than fulphur, and a great deal more than pitch alone †.

BUT the moft curious experiment of this philofopher, relating to this fubject, was made with a view to afcertain the real direction of the electric fluid in a difcharge. He fufpended a coated plate of glafs by a filk thread, and having charged it, and kept it perfectly ftill; he obferved that no motion was given to it, when the difcharge was made by a crooked wire approaching both the fides at the fame time. The experiment, in fact, proved the re-action of the glafs upon the electric matter; whereby the plate were kept ftill, notwithftanding the fluid rufhed with great violence from one fide to the other. He compares the glafs to an ivory ball placed between two others, which keeps its place, when, by an impulfe given to one of them, the oppofite ball flies off ‡.

MR. HARTMAN of Hanover has publifhed an account of a curious experiment, which feems to fhow the progreffive motion of the electrical explofion. He paffes a fhock through a great number of cannon balls, fometimes to the number of forty, placed near one another, upon fmall drinking-glaffes;

* Lettere dell' elettricifmo, p. 64. † Ibid. p. 66.
‡ Ibid. p. 72.

when

when all the fparks are feen at the fame moment of time, and all the fnappings make
but one report. But when he fubftitutes eggs
inftead of the balls of metal, the progrefs of
the explofion is vifible, every two giving a
fnap and a flafh feparately. This experiment
requires weather very favourable to electricity, and, he fays has generally fucceeded
the beft with only ten or twelve eggs *. This
author has not exprefsly faid in which direction the fparks ran; but as he adopts Dr.
Franklin's hypothefis, it may be prefumed,
that he imagined them to go from the pofitive to the negative fide of the charged
glafs.

A VERY ingenious experiment has alfo
been made by Mr. Amadeus Lullin of Geneva, in order to afcertain the direction of the
electric fluid in explofions, and which he
thinks comes nearer to the *experimentum crucis*
than any other. He placed a common card
in the circuit of the electrical explofion, while
the wire which communicated with the pofitive fide of the jar lay on one fide of it, and
that which communicated with the negative
fide lay on the other, their extremities not
being placed oppofite to one another, but at
fome diftance. Things being thus circum-
ftanced, he obferved, that upon making the
difcharge, the card was conftantly pierced
clofe to the extremity of the wire which communicated with the negative fide of the jar,

* Abhandlung, p. 58, &c.

as

as if the electric fluid, rushing from the positive side of the jar into the wire which communicated with it, and issuing from the extremity of it, was driven by its own impulse along the surface of the card, and did not pierce it, till it came opposite to the extremity of the other wire, which communicated with the negative side, by which it was strongly attracted *.

A very curious and elegant experiment on the Leyden phial was màde by professor Richman of Peterſburgh, whoſe unfortunate death will be related in this hiſtory.

He coated both sides of a pane of glaſs, within two or three inches of the edge, and faſtened linen threads to the upper part of the coating, on both sides; which, when the plate was not charged, hung down in contact with the coating; but ſetting the plate upright, and charging it, he obſerved, that when neither of the sides was touched by is nger, or any other conductor communicating with the earth, both the threads were repelled from the coating, and ſtood at an equal diſtance from it; but when he brought his finger, or any other conductor, to one of the sides, the thread hanging to that ſide fell nearer to the coating, while the thread on the oppoſite side receded as much; and that when his finger was brought into contact with one of the sides, the thread on that side fell into contact with it likewiſe, while the

* Diſſertatio Phyſica, p. 24.

Z   thread

thread on the oppofite fide receded to twice
the diftance at which it hung originally; fo
that the two threads always hung fo as to
make the fame angle with one another *.

ÆPINUS fhows, that it is not ftrictly true,
that an infulated perfon, difcharging the Leyden phial through his own body, contracts no
electricity. Electrifying a large plate of air,
he obferved, that if the nearer plate, (by
which I fuppofe he means that which he firft
touched) was electrfiied pofitively, he acquired a pofitive electricity by the difcharge; but
if it were negative, he acquired a negative
electricity. He fuppofes that the reafon why
the experiment did not fucceed with Dr.
Franklin, was, that the furfaces with which
he tried the experiment were not large enough
to make the effect fenfible; and that the diftance of the metal plates was, likewife, too
fmall, as it neceffarily muft be in charging of
glafs †.

MR. CIGNA has invented a new method of
charging a phial, upon the principle difcovered by Mr. Canton and Mr. Wilcke, viz. that
the electricity of one body repels that of another, efpecially if it have a flat furface, and
gives it the contrary electricity.

HE infulates a fmooth plate of lead, and
while he brings an electrified body, as a
ftocking, to it, he takes a fpark with the wire
of a phial from the oppofite fide; and removing the ftocking, he takes another fpark with

---

* Æpini Tentamen, p. 335.   † Ibid. p. 27.

his

his finger, or any conductor communicating with the ground. Bringing the ftocking nearer the plate a fecond time, he takes a fecond fpark, with the wire of the phial, as before; and, removing it again, takes another, in the fame manner, with his finger. This operation he continues, till the phial is charged; which, in favourable weather, may be done with very little diminution of the electricity of the ftocking *.

IF, inftead of taking a fecond fpark with his finger, he had taken it with the wire of another phial, that would have been charged likewife, with no additional labour, and with an electricity oppofite to that of the other phial. If the fecond fpark were taken with the coating of the fame phial, the charging would be accelerated, but the operation would be troublefome to manage.

The theory of this new method of charging a phial is very eafy, upon the principle referred to above. The approach of the electricity in the ftocking, not being able to enter the broad fmooth furface of the metal, drives the electric fluid out of that part of the plate which is oppofite to it, to the other 'fide, which, being thereby overcharged, will part with its fuperfluity to the wire of the phial. The ftocking being taken away, the plate will have lefs than its natural fhare of the electric fluid, and will therefore readily take

* Memoirs of the Academy at Turin for the year 1765, p. 49.

a fpark

a fpark, either from the finger, or the wire of another phial *.

THE fame ingenious philofopher makes a confiderable difference between the electric fluid which gives the fhock, and that on which fome other phenomena of coated glafs depend. The former, which is far the greateft quantity, he fuppofes to refide, either in the coating itfelf, or on the furface of the glafs; whereas the other, he imagines, to have entered the pores, and affected the fubftance of the glafs itfelf.

HE laid two plates of glafs, well dried, one upon the other, as one piece; the lower of them being coated on the outfide; and, when they were infulated, he alternately rubbed the uppermoft plate with one hand, and took a fpark from the coating of the lower with the other, till they were charged; when the coating, and both the plates adhered firmly together. Giving a coating to the other fide, and making a communication between that and the other coating, the ufual explofion was made. But the plates, though thus difcharged, ftill cohered; and though, while they were in this ftate, they fhowed no other fign of electricity; yet, when they were feparated, they were each of them found to be poffeffed of an electricity oppofite to that of the other.

IF the two plates were feparated before they were difcharged, and the coating of

* Memoirs of the Academy at Turin for the year 1765, P. 51.

each

each were touched, a fpark came from each; and when put together, they would cohere as before, but were incapacitated for giving a fhock *.

HE, therefore, compares the electricity which gives the fhock to the electricity of the metal plate in the former experiment; which is loft with taking one fpark, as the filk is removed from it, and is different from the electricity by which the two plates of glafs cohere. The one is difperfed at once, but the other flowly; the one exifting, as he fuppofes, in the conductors, or upon the furfaces of the electrics, and the other in the fubftance itfelf †.

AMONG experiments relating to the electric fhock, we ought to mention what has been obferved within this period of its amazing force in melting wires, and producing other furprifing effects.

THAT even artificial electricity, fays Dr. Watfon, in a paper read at the Royal Society June 28th, 1764, when in too great a quantity, and hurried on too faft, through a fine iron wire, has a remarkable effect upon the wire, appears from a very curious experiment of Mr. Kinnerfley. This gentleman, in the prefence of Dr. Franklin, made a large cafe of bottles explode at once through a fine iron wire. The wire at firft appeared red hot, and then fell into drops, which burned

* Memoirs of the Academy at Turin for the year 1765, p. 55. † Ibid. p. 56.

them

themfelves into the furface of his table or floor. Thefe drops cooled in a fpherical figure like very fmall fhot, of which Dr. Franklin tranfmitted fome to Mr. Canton, who repeated the experiment. This proves the fufion to have been very complete; as nothing lefs than the moft perfect fluidity could give this figure to melted iron.

MR. CANTON, in a note fubfcribed to the fame paper, obferves, that the diameter of a piece of Mr. Kinnerfley's wire, which he received from Dr. Franklin, was one part in 182 of an inch. He adds, that artificial lightning, from a cafe of thirty-five bottles, would entirely deftroy brafs wire, of one part in 330 of an inch. At the time of the ftroke, he fays, a great number of fparks, like thofe from a flint and fteel, would fly upwards, and laterally, from the place where the wire was laid, and lofe their light, in the day-time, at the diftance of about two or three inches. After the explofion, a mark appeared on the table, the whole length of the wire, and fome very round particles of brafs were difcovered by a magnifier near the mark, but no part of the wire itfelf could be found *.

SIGNIOR BECCARIA was able to melt fmall flips of metal, without inclofing, or covering them with pieces of glafs. But he thought that the fame colour was impreffed upon glafs by all the metals; and imagined that this

*Phil. Tranf. Vol. liv. p. 208.

circum-

circumftance was a trace of the fundamental principles being the fame in them all *.

MR. DALIBARD obferved, that, when a large pane of glafs difcharged itfelf, the polifh was taken off at the place of the difcharge, and that the track it left behind it was ufually, as he expreffes it, in the *zig zag* form. With the piece of glafs with which he made thefe difcharges he pierced 160 leaves of paper. It contained 1200 fquare inches †.

MR. WILCKE fays, that, if a fmall piece of metal be hung in a fmall filken ftring, oppofite to a part of a glafs jar, made thin for the purpofe; upon the fpontaneous difcharge through that place, the piece of metal will be driven off to the diftance of five or fix inches ‡.

MR. WINKLER fired the feeds of clubmofs (lycopodium) by difcharging a phial through a quantity of them. He alfo fired the *aurum fulminans* placed upon a piece of parchment, which was torn to pieces by the explofion §.

BY the electric fhock, Signior Beccaria could melt borax and glafs. But the moft remarkable of his experiments with the electric fhock are thofe by which he *revivified metals*. This he did by making the explofion between two pieces of the calces. In this manner he

---

* Elettricifmo artificiale, &c. p. 134, 135.
† Hiftoire abrigée, p. 84.
‡ Remarks on Franklin's Letters, p. 266.
§ Phil. Tranf. Vol. xxxviii. pt. ii. p. 773.

revivified

revivified several of the metals, and among others, zink. He even produced real quick-silver from cinnabar *. In this case of revivi-fication, he always observed streaks of black beyond the coloured metallic stains, owing, as he imagined, to the phlogiston driven thither from the parts that were vitrified, when the other part revivified the calx †.

ANOTHER curious experiment he made with the electric shock, by discharging it through some brass dust, sprinkled between two plates of sealing-wax. The whole was perfectly luminous and transparent ‡. An experiment which throws some light upon one of Mr. Haukfbee's.

WITH the electric shock he also made that capital experiment, on which he lays so much stress in his theory of thunder storms, and by which he proves, that the electric matter forces into its passage all light con-ducting substances; by means of which it is enabled to pass through a quantity of resist-ing medium, which it could not otherwise do. He put a narrow piece of leaf silver be-tween two plates of wax, laying it across the plates, but so as not quite to reach one of the sides. The discharge being made through this strip of metal, by bringing a wire oppo-site to the silver, at the place where it was discontinued; the silver was found melted, and part of it dispersed all along the track that the electric matter took, between the plates

* Lettere dell' elettricifmo, p. 282.   † Ibid. p. 255.
‡ Ibid. p. 257.

of wax, from the filver to the wire *. An accident gave him occasion to obferve another fact of a similar nature. He once, inadvertently, received the charge of a fmall jar, through fome fmoke of fpirit of nitre; when a hole was made in his thumb, where the fire entered; and which he thought could only have been made by the nitre, which was carried along with the electric fluid †.

VIOLENTLY as the electric explofion generally affects the human body, we have accounts of fome perfons who could not be made to feel it; particularly three or four mentioned by Mr. Mufchenbroeck, among whom was a young woman ‡. I have alfo been told, that this was the cafe with a perfon near Leeds, who was at the fame time a little paralytic.

I SHALL clofe the hiftory of the Leyden phial for this period with the accounts of fome extremely curious facts, which Mr. Canton gives me leave to publifh relating to this fubject. They certainly deferve the utmoft attention of philofophers, and may probably throw fome light upon the electricity of the tourmalin.

HE procured fome thin glafs balls, of about an inch and a half in diameter, with ftems or tubes of eight or nine inches in length, and electrified them, fome pofitively on the infide, and others negatively, after the manner of charging the Leyden phial,

---

* Lettere dell' elettricifmo, p. 248.   † Ibid. p. 249.
‡ Monthly Review, October 1767, p. 250.

and

and then fealed them hermetically. Soon after, he applied the naked balls to his electrometer, and could not difcover the leaft fign of their being electrical : but holding them to the fire, at the diftance of five or fix inches, they became ftrongly electrical, in a very fhort time, and more fo when they were cooling. Thefe balls would, every time they were heated, give the electric fire to, or take it from other bodies, according to the *plus* or *minus* ftate of it within them. Heating them frequently, he found, would fenfibly diminifh their power ; but keeping one of them under water a week did not appear in the leaft to impair it. That which he kept under water was charged the 22d of September 1760, was feveral times heated before it was kept in water, and had been heated frequently afterwards; and yet it ftill retained its virtue to a confiderable degree, on the 31ft of October following, when he fent an account of it to Dr. Franklin. The breaking two of his balls accidentally gave him an opportunity of meafuring their thicknefs, which he found to be between feven and eight parts in 1000 of an inch.

THE balls mention in the account above, which was written fix years ago, ftill * retain their virtue, but in a lefs degree.

MR. LULLIN alfo found, that a glafs tube charged, and hermetically fealed, would fhow figns of electricity when it was heated †.

* In 1769. † Differtatio Phyfica, p. 32.

SECTION VIII.

EXPERIMENTS AND OBSERVATIONS CONCERING ELECTRIC LIGHT.

MY reader has been informed of the necessity I was under of dividing the business of this period of my history into several parts. He has already seen titles which he could not have expected from the divisions of the preceding periods, but he would perhaps least of all expect a distinct section upon electric light; and yet the experiments and observations which have been made, immediately relating to this subject, are so many, that they deserve a place by themselves. And I would rather err by making too many subdivisions, than too few; because, above all things, I would wish to preserve perspicuity, which is chiefly injured by crowding together things dissimilar.

MANY experiments had been made very early, by Mr. Haukfbee and others, on electricity, and particularly electric light, in vacuo; but so little was, at that time, known of the nature of electricity in general, that, comparatively, little use could be made of those experiments. Very fortunately, Dr. Watson happened to turn his thoughts that way, after the great discovery of the accumulation of electricity in the Leyden phial; and by this means he discovered, that our atmosphere,

when

when dry, is the agent by which, with the
affiftance of other electrics per fe, we were
enabled to accumulate electricity upon non-
electrics (he might have added electrics too),
that is, to communicate to them a greater
quantity of electricity than thofe bodies naturally have. That upon the removal of the
air, the electric fluid pervaded the vacuum to
a confiderable diftance, and manifefted its
effects upon any non-electric fubftances by
which it was terminated.

THIS he demonftrated by one of the moft
beautiful experiments which the whole compafs of electricity yet exhibits. He exhaufted a glafs cylinder, three feet in length, and
three inches in diameter, with a contrivance
to let down a brafs plate, as far as he pleafed, into it; in order to make it approach
another plate, fixed near the bottom of the
veffel.

THIS cylinder, thus prepared, he infulated, and obferved, that when the upper plate
was electrified, the electric matter would pafs
from one plate to another, at the greateft diftance to which the brafs plates could be drawn;
and that the brafs plate at the bottom of the cylinder was ftrongly electrified, as if a wire had
connected it with the prime conductor. It
was a moft delightful fpectacle, he fays,
when the room was darkened, to fee the electric matter in its paffage through this vacuum;
to obferve, not as in the open air, fmall
brufhes or pencils of rays, an inch or two in
length, but corufcations of the whole length

of

of the tube, and of a bright filver hue. Thefe
did not immediately diverge, as in the open
air, but frequently, from a bafe apparently
flat, divided themfelves into lefs and lefs ramifications, and refembled very much the
moft lively corufcations of the aurora borealis.

SOMETIMES he obferved, that when the
tube had been exhaufted in the moft perfect
manner, the electric fluid was feen to pafs
between the brafs plates in one continued
ftream, of the fame dimenfions throughout
its whole length; which he thought demonftrated, that the caufe of that very powerful
mutual repulfion of the particles of electric
fire, which is feen in the open air, is more
owing to the refiftance of the air, than to any
natural tendency of the electricity itfelf. For,
in the open air we obferve that thefe brufhes,
when the electricity is ftrong, diverge fo
much, as to form almoft a fpherical figure *.

HE made this vacuum part of a circuit neceffary to make the difcharge of a phial; and,
at the inftant of the explofion, there was feen
a mafs of very bright embodied fire, jump-
ing from one of the brafs plates in the tube
to the other. But this did not take place
when one of the plates was farther diftant
from the other than ten inches. If the diftance was greater, the fire began to diverge,
and lofe part of its force : and this force
diminifhed in proportion to its divergency,

* Phil. Tranf. Vol. xlvii. p. 367.

which

which was nearly as the diſtance of the two plates.

To find a more perfect vacuum for the paſ-ſage of the electric fluid, he had recourſe to an excellent invention of Lord Charles Ca-vendiſh; who, by means of a long bent tube of glaſs, filled with mercury, and inverted, made all the bended part of it (which was above the mercury) the moſt perfect vacuum that can be made. This vacuum Dr. Watſon inſulated, and one of the baſons of the mer-cury being made to communicate with the con-ductor, when ſome non-electric ſubſtance touched the other, the electric matter pervad-ed the vacuum in a continued arch of lambent flame, and, as far as the eye could follow it, without the leaſt divergency.

CONNECTING one of the baſons with the machine, which was inſulated, the fire was ſeen pervading the vacuum in a contrary di-rection. And this he conſidered as the *expe-rimentum crucis* of two principles which he had advanced before, viz. that electricity is furniſhed to the conductor, not by the excit-ed electric, but from the non-electrics in con-tact with the rubber; and that we are able to take from, or add to that quantity of elec-tricity, which is naturally inherent in bodies.

HE alſo obſerved, that if, in the fore-mentioned circumſtances, the hand of a per-ſon ſtanding upon the floor was brought near the ſide of the glaſs, the coruſcations would dart themſelves that way in a great variety of forms, extremely curious to behold.

BUT

But the Doctor found, that even this vacuum did not conduct so perfectly as metals, or water; because a person standing upon the floor, and applying his finger to the upper brass plate, received a smart stroke. This he conceived to arise from the electricity of the brass being so much more rarefied than that of the body of the man who applied his finger *.

Mr. Wilson engaged Mr. Smeaton, the inventor of a new and more perfect kind of air-pump, to make some electrical experiments in vacuo. The following is the account of them that he transmitted to Mr. Wilson. They are, in several respects, similar to those made by Dr. Watson, and yet are attended with a considerable variety of new circumstances.

A glass vessel, about one foot in length, and eight inches in its greatest diameter, open at both ends, had one of its ends closed by a brass ferule, which constituted one of the centers on which it turned; the other end was closed with a metal plate. In the center of this plate was a square stem, which was applied to the arbor of a lath, by which the glass was turned round. On one side of this last plate was fixed a cork, by means of which the glass was screwed upon the air-pump.

Upon rarefying the air within the glass about 500 times, and afterwards turning the

* Phil. Transf. Vol. xlvii. p. 373.

glafs in the lath, whilft, at the fame time, it was rubbed with his hand; a confiderable quantity of lambent flame, variegated with all the colours of the rainbow, appeared within the glafs, under the hand. This light was pretty fteady in every refpect, except that every part of it was perpetually changing colour.

WHEN a little air was let into the glafs, the light appeared more vivid, and in a greater quantity, but was not fo fteady : for it would frequently break out into a kind of corufcations, like lightning, and fly all about within the glafs. When a little more air was let in, the flaſhing was continual, and ftreams of blueifh light feemed to iffue from under his hand, within the glafs, in a thoufand forms, with great rapidity ; and appeared like a cafcade of fire. Sometimes it feemed to fhoot out into the forms of trees, mofs, &c.

WHEN more air was let in, the quantity of light was diminifhed, and the ftreams compofing the flaſhes narrower. The glafs now required a greater velocity, and harder friction. Thefe circumftances increafed as more air was let in; fo that, by fuch time as the glafs was one third full of air, thefe corufcations quite vanifhed, and a much fmaller quantity of light appeared partly within, and partly without the glafs. And when all the air was let in, the light appeared wholly without the glafs; and much lefs in quantity than when the glafs was in part exhaufted *.

* Wilfon's Effay, p. 216.

MR.

Mr. Canton, in repeating Dr. Watfon's experiment with the Torricellian vacuum, obferved one circumftance attending it, which throws great light upon the Leyden phial. He obferved, that when the excited tube was brought near one of the bafons of this machine (infulated) a light was feen through more than half of the vacuum; which foon vanifhed, if the tube was not brought nearer, but which appeared again as it moved farther off; and that this appearance might be repeated feveral times, without exciting the tube afrefh.

This experiment he confidered as a kind of ocular demonftration of the truth of Dr. Franklin's hypothefis, that when the electric fluid was condenfed on one fide of the glafs, it was repelled from the other, if it met with no refiftance. Thus, at the approach of the excited tube, he fuppofed the fire to be repelled from the infide of the glafs furrounding the vacuum, and to be carried off through the columns of mercury, but to return again as the tube was withdrawn *.

This curious experiment Mr. Canton, as he informed me, fhowed and explained to Mr. Wilfon; who afterwards expatiated upon it, in a book publifhed by him and Dr. Hoadley in conjunction, intitled *Obfervations*

---

* Phil. Tranf. Vol. xlviii. pt. i. p. 356. It has been feen p. 95, that this obfervation, of the return of the electric light *in vacuo*, was made before the difcovery of the Leyden phial by Mr. Grummert of Biala in Poland ; but this was unknown both to Dr. Watfon and Mr. Canton.

en

on a Series of Electrical Experiments; in a note of which, p. 28, he says, " Mr. Can-
" ton has taken notice of this vanishing and
" returning of the light."

Mr. CANTON has since diversified this beautiful experiment, by bringing the excited tube to another glass tube, exhausted, and hermetically sealed; by which means he exhibits the perfect appearance of an aurora borealis. The flame from one of its extremities, which is in a manner coated by the hand which holds it, will dart to the other extremity, at uncertain intervals of time, for near a quarter of an hour together, without repeating the application of the excited tube.

WHEN it was generally agreed among electricians, that what had been called vitreous and resinous electricity were in reality a redundancy of the electric fluid in one case, and a deficiency in the other; and when, in consequence of this supposition, the one was called positive, and the other negative electricity; there still remained some doubt which of the two was positive, and which negative. Mr. Wilson, in a paper read at the Royal Society, December the 6th, 1759, recites an experiment which, he thought, put the matter beyond all dispute, and absolutely determined, that what had been called vitreous was really positive, and what had been called resinous was negative; as, indeed, had generally been supposed, though, as Mr. Wilson thought, without sufficient reason, notwithstanding what had been advanced by Dr.
Franklin,

Franklin, and Mr. Canton upon that fubject.

REPEATING the beautiful experiment mentioned before, as firft contrived by Lord Charles Cavendifh, he fays he attended to a circumftance which feemed to have been overlooked by Dr. Watfon, who publifhed the account of it. This was a fingular appearance of light upon one of the furfaces of the quickfilver. To obferve this remarkable appearance to more advantage, Mr. Wilfon let a fmall quantity of air into the tube, by which means four columns of quickfilver were obtained, and confequently fix vifible furfaces, in one of the legs of the inverted tube. He then electrified the mercury in the other leg, while the mercury on the oppofite fide had a communication with the earth, when, the room being dark, the ftream of electric light was vifible through the whole length of the vacuum, and its general appearance was of a feeming uniform denfity; except at the upper furfaces of each column, where about one tenth of an inch above the furface, the light was always confiderably brighter; whereas the under furfaces exhibited no fuch appearance, the light being rather lefs bright in thofe places than in the general appearance of the whole illuminated vacuum.

THIS luminous appearance Mr. Wilfon afcribed to the refiftance the fluid met with at the upper furface of the quickfilver, in endeavouring to get into it. He therefore inferred that excited glafs electrified bodies po-

fitively,

fitively, or gave them a greater quantity of the electric fluid than they had.

ELECTRIFYING, in the same place, with a cylinder of.rofin, inftead of glafs, the luminous appearances were all on the under furfaces of the columns of quickfilver; from which he inferred, that rofin electrified bodies negatively, depriving them of part of the electric fluid which they naturally had; or, as he expreffes it, occafioning a current of electric fluid to fet the contrary way.

THESE luminous appearances, Mr. Wilfon alfo confidered, as a ftrong confirmation of the exiftence of a *medium,* at or near the furfaces of bodies, which hindered the entrance or exit of the electric fluid. A doctrine which Mr. Wilfon had advanced, and laid great ftrefs upon on feveral other occafions *.

THE arguments which to Mr. Wilfon appeared conclufive, in proof of what is commonly fuppofed, that glafs electrifies *plus,* and fulphur, &c. *minus,* did not appear fo to Mr. Æpinus; though he acknowledges that the knobs of light in the vacuum did, in common with many other appearances, prove a real difference between the two electricities; and thought that it was very eafy to conceive, that when an elaftic fluid iffues from a body, it fhould be denfer near the furface from whence it iffues, than where it finds more liberty to expand itfelf. He might have added, that this might have been expected, from

* Phil. Tranf, Vol. li. pt. i. p. 308.

the

the mutual attraction which is fuppofed to fubfift between the electric fluid, and other bodies. But Æpinus did not exprefsly mention this circumftance. Mr. Wilfon, therefore, makes light of the objection; and adds, that when he related the experiment with the bent tube, in his letter to Dr. Heberden, he omitted fome phenomena attending the fact, which greatly favoured the doctrine he advanced. If, fays he, when glafs is electrified, and applied to the firft column, we fuffer the electric fluid to pafs along the tube in fmall quantities only, and at fhort intervals, little luminous ftreams will be feen to move from the firft to the fecond column of quickfilver, and confequently from the glafs. The like appearances happen, but in a contrary direction, when rofin or amber is made ufe of, and applied to the fame column. Glafs, therefore, he concludes, electrifies *plus*, or fills bodies with more of this fluid than belongs to them naturally, and rofin, &c. *minus* *.

This controverfy took its rife, in fome meafure, from a deception: for Mr. Canton informs me, and gives me leave to inform the public, that the light which Mr. Wilfon takes notice of, as appearing on one furface of the mercury in the double barometer of Lord Charles Cavendifh, and which Mr. Wilfon takes to be a proof of the exiftence of a medium on the furface of bodies, which hinders the entrance or exit of the electric fluid to

* Phil. Tranf. Vol. liii. p. 438. p. 441.

fome

some degree, he found to be caused by nothing but common air. For if the Torricellian vacuum be properly made, no difference of light can be seen on the surfaces of the columns of mercury; but if as much air be let into the vacuum, as will make each column of mercury a quarter of an inch shorter than that of a good barometer, the light will appear as Mr. Wilson has described it. When Mr. Wilson supposed that Dr. Watson, when he made the experiment of the Torricellian vacuum, did not attend to the singular appearance of light on one of the surfaces of the mercury, he little suspected that if the vacuum Dr. Watson made was free from air, there was no such singular appearance of light to be attended to. Air, Mr. Canton adds, must be condensed near the surface of all bodies that attract it; and will, therefore, be some hindrance to the exit, or entrance of the electric fluid, except the bodies be very sharply pointed.

SOME curious observations relating to electric light were made by Mr. Wilcke. Rubbing two pieces of glass together in the dark, he observed a vivid phosphoreal light: which, however, threw out no rays, but adhered to the place where it was excited. It was attended with a strong phosphoreal smell, but with no attraction or repulsion. From this experiment he inferred, that friction alone would not excite electricity, so as to be accumulated upon any body; and that to produce this effect, the bodies rubbed together

must

muſt be of different natures, with reſpect to their attracting the electric fluid. He, moreover, imagined, that all examples of phoſphoreal light, without attraction, were owing to the ſame excitation of electricity, without the accumulation of it. Such he imagined to be the caſe of light emitted by the Bolognian ſtone, cadmea fornacum, rotten wood, pounded ſugar, and glaſs of all kinds *.

A TUBE excited with a woollen cloth, on which white wax or oil-had been put, he ſays, threw out flames ; each of which when examined, appeared to riſe out of a little protuberance of fire. The flame was one, and very narrow at the bottom, but farther from the tube it divided into ſeveral ramifications ; which always leaned to thoſe parts of the tube which were the leaſt excited, or to conductors in the neighbourhood †.

HE ſays that, upon preſenting a finger or other non-electric to an excited negative electric, a cone of light is formed ; the baſe of which is at the finger, or other non-electric, and the apex at the electric, on the ſurface of which it ſpreads to a conſiderable diſtance all round ‡.

SOMETIMES, he had ſeen fiery particles thrown laterally from an irregular electric ſpark, which ſhone like ſtars, and were very like thoſe which are produced by the colliſion of flint and ſteel §.

* Wilcke, p. 123, 124. † Ibid. p. 125.
‡ Ibid. p. 127. § Ibid. p. 130.

SUSPEND-

Suspending various balls from his conductor, and presenting others to them, which were sometimes of glass and sometimes of metal, and varying them in every manner possible, he always found (except when two metal balls were used) that the light between them formed a cone, the base of which was always on the body which was positive, and the apex on that which was negative. He says that this criterion is sufficient to distinguish the two electricities from one another.

He observes that, at the apex of a cone issuing from pointed bodies, electrified positively, there is a cylindrical spark, out of which lucid rays, like a river, are darted. These rays, he says, form a lucid cone, the apex of which is turned towards the point from which the fire proceeds. Sometimes from the apex, or at some distance from it, there is a lucid point, which, he says, Haufenius calls *the fire of the second kind*, out of which flew streams of fire. The streams never issue from the electrified body itself, but always from this lucid point. He says, moreover, that this lucid point at the extremity of an electrified body, and which throws out lucid rays, forms the distinctive character of the positive cone *.

A negative cone, he says, is small, consisting of very slender filaments, which immediately adhere to the point at which the light

* Wilcke, p. 132.

enters, or to its fides; and, if accurately examined, feems to form little cones, the bafes
of which reft upon the body.

WHEN he afterwards comes to confider the
caufe of negative cones of light, he owns
himfelf to be at a great lofs how to do it.

MR. WILCKE put Englifh phofphorus upon a pointed body, which, in the dark, rendered the whole vifible; and when he fufpended this pointed body perpendicularly, the
phofphoreal vapours were feen to afcend; but
upon electrifying it, as it hung in the fame
direction, the vapours were carried downwards, and formed a very long cone, extending out of the middle of the cone of electric
light, which was feen perfectly diftinct from
it. When the electrification was difcontinued,
the phofphoreal vapour afcended as at firft.
From this depreffion of the phofphoreal effluvia Mr. Wilcke infers the efflux of the electric fluid from the point, and upon the furface, and not only through the fubftance of
the pointed body. It is pity that he did not
try this curious experiment with pointed bodies electrified negatively. He would certainly have found the fame depreffion of the
phofphoreal effluvia, and would, probably,
have retracted his conclufion concerning this
proof of the efflux *.

MR. WILCKE alfo thought it to be a proof,
that the electric matter did not only flow out
of the fubftance of electrified bodies, but up-

* Wilcke, p. 134.

on

on the furface of them, that a metallic ring, projecting ever fo little beyond the point of a wire
on which it had been put, prevents the appearance of the lucid point.

THE laft obfervation which I fhall recite of
Mr. Wilcke concerning electric light is, that
if a point not electrified be oppofed to a point
electrified pofitively, the cones of light,
which, in other circumftances, would appear
upon both of them, difappear; but that if a
pofitive cone be oppofed to a negative cone,
they both preferve their own characteriftic properties *.

SIGNIOR BECCARIA was of opinion, that
the direction of the electric fluid may be determined from the phenomena of pointed
bodies. The *pencil* (by which he means the
electric fire at a point electrified pofitively) he
fays, contracts as it approaches a flat piece of
metal not electrified; whereas the *ftar* (by
which he means the electric fire at a point
electrified negatively) expands in the fame circumftances, and has a fmall cavity near the
point towards the large fuperficies. The pencil is attended with a fnapping noife, the ftar
makes little or no noife. He hardly gives any
reafon for the firft of thefe phenomena; he
only fays, that fuch is the neceffary confequence of a fluid iffuing out of, or entering
into a point. But the greater noife made by
the pencil, he thought was made by the impulfe given by the electric matter to the air,

* Wilcke, p. 140.

cauſing

cauſing it to vibrate: and this muſt be greater when the fluid is thrown from the point into the air, than when it comes through different portions of the air, and meets in one point *.

WHEN two points are oppoſed to one another, he ſays, the phenomena are much the ſame in both †.

SIGNIOR BECCARIA obſerved that hollow glaſs veſſels, of a certain thinneſs, exhauſted of air, gave a light when they were broken in the dark. By a beautiful train of experiments, he found, at length, that the luminous appearance was not occaſioned by the breaking of the glaſs, but by the daſhing of the external air againſt the inſide, when it was broke. He covered one of theſe exhauſted veſſels with a receiver, and letting the air ſuddenly on the outſide of it, obſerved the very ſame light. This he calls his *new invented phoſphorus* ‡.

THIS excellent philoſopher produced a moſt beautiful appearance of electric light in the following manner. He conveyed poſitive electricity to a braſs ball, ſuſpended by a wire, within an exhauſted receiver, when, upon preſenting to it another ball *in vacuo*, the lower hemiſphere of the former was moſt beautifully illuminated, with a viſible electric atmoſphere. When he conveyed negative electricity to the ball, the ſame beautiful illumination was obſerved on the ball preſented to it. This experiment, he ſays, is a very deli-

* Elettriciſmo artificiale, p. 63.   † Ibid.
‡ Lettere dell' elettriciſmo, p. 365, &c.

cate one, requiring great patience and dexte-
rity, in adjufting the diftances, &c. in order
to make it fucceed perfectly *.

THAT electric light is more fubtle and penetrating, if one may fay fo, than light produced in any other way is manifeft from feveral experiments, particularly the remarkable one of Mr. Haukfbee; but none prove
it fo clearly as fome made by the ingenious
Mr. Lane, who gives me leave to mention
thefe.

WHEN he had, for fome different purpofe,
made the electric fhock pafs over the furface
of a piece of marble, in the dark; he obferved, that the part over which the fire had paffed was luminous, and retained that appearance for fome time. No fuch effect of the
electric fhock having ever been obferved before, he repeated the experiment with a great
variety of circumftances, and found it always
anfwered with all calcarious fubftances, whether
animal or mineral, and efpecially if they had
been burnt into lime. And, as far as he had
tried, many more fubftances would retain this
light than would not do it; among others feveral vegetable fubftances would do it, particularly white paper. Tiles and brick were luminous, but not tobacco-pipe clay, though
well burnt.

THAT gypfeous fubftances, when calcined, were luminous, appeared from bits of

* Phil. Tranf. Vol. lvi. p. 107.

images

images made of plaifter of Paris ; and of this
clafs, he fays, is the famous Bolognian ftone.
But many bodies, he found, were luminous
after the electric ftroke, which were not apparently fo, when expofed to the rays of the
fun.

HE made thefe curious experiments by
placing the chains, or wires that led from the
conductor to the outward coating of his jar,
within one, two, or three inches (according to
the ftrength of the charge) from one another,
on the furface of the body to be tried, and
difcharging a fhock through them. If the
ftone was thin, he found, that if one chain
was placed at the top, and the other at the
bottom, it would appear luminous on both
fides after the explofion.

MR. CANTON, to whom thefe experiments
were communicated, clearly proved, that it
was the *light* only that the fubftances retained, and nothing peculiar to electricity ; and,
moreover, after frequent trials, difcovered a
compofition, which retains both common
light, and that of electricity, much more
ftrongly than either the Bolognian ftone, or
any other known fubftance whatever. With
this new phofphorus he makes a great number of moft beautiful experiments. The flafh
made by the difcharge of a common jar,
within an inch of a circular piece of it, of
about two inches and a half in diameter, will
illuminate it fo much, that the figures on a
watch plate may be eafily diftinguifhed by it

in

in a darkened room, and it will retain the
light half an hour *.

I SHALL clofe this fection of experiments
and obfervations on electric light, with an account of a remarkable appearance which occurred to Mr. Hartman. When he had been
making experiments four or five hours together, in a fmall room, and after going out
of it, returned foon, with a lighted candle in
his hand, walking pretty fwiftly; he perceived a fmall flame to follow him, at the
diftance of about a ftep and a half, but it va-
niſhed when he ftopped to examine it. He
was a good deal alarmed at the appearance at
firft, but afterwards imagined it to be occafioned by the afcenfion of the fulphur, which
had been thrown into the air by the violent
continued electrification †.

* See a particular account of this compofition, and experi-
ments with it, in my *Hiftory of Difcoveries relating to Vifion,
Light, and Colours*, p. 371.
† Abhandlung, p. 135.

SECTION

SECTION IX.

THE ELECTRICITY OF THE TOURMALIN.

THIS period of my hiſtory furniſhes an entirely new ſubjeċt of eleċtrical inquiries ; which, if properly purſued, may throw great light upon the moſt general properties of eleċtricity. This is the *Tourmalin :* though, it muſt be acknowledged, the experiments which have hitherto been made upon this foſſil ſtand like exceptions to all that was before known of the ſubjeċt.

THE tourmalin, as Dr. Watſon ſuppoſes, was known to the antients under the name of the *lyncurium.* All that Theophraſtus ſays concerning the lyncurium agrees with the tourmalin, and with no other foſſil that we are acquainted with. He ſays, that it was uſed for ſeals, that it was very hard, that it was endued with an attraċting power like amber, and that it was ſaid, particularly by Diocles, to attraċt not only ſtraws, and ſmall pieces of wood, but alſo copper and iron, if beaten very thin ; that it was pellucid, of a deep red colour, and required no ſmall labour to poliſh it. The account which paſſed current among the ancients concerning the origin of this ſtone was fabulous, which made Pliny think that all that was ſaid of it was fabulous too.

THIS

This ftone, though not much attended to by European philofophers, till very lately, is common in feveral parts of the Eaft Indies, and more particularly in the ifland of Ceylon, where it is called by the natives *tournamal*. In this ifland the Dutch became acquainted with it, and by them it is called *afchentrikker*, from its property of attracting afhes, when it is thrown into the fire.

THE firft account we have had, of late years, concerning this extraordinary ftone is in the Hiftory of the Royal Academy of Sciences at Paris for the year 1717; where we are told, that Mr. Lemery exhibited a ftone, which was not common, and came from Ceylon. This ftone, he faid, attracted and repelled fmall light bodies, fuch as afhes, filings of iron, bits of paper, &c.

LINNÆUS, in his Flora Zeylonica, mentions this ftone under the name of *lapis electricus*, and takes notice of Mr. Lemery's experiments.

NOTWITHSTANDING this, no farther mention was made of this ftone and its effects till fome years after; when the Duc De Noya, in his letter to Mr. Buffon, prefented to the Royal Society, informed us, that when he was at Naples, in the year 1743, the Count Pichetti, fecretary to the king, affured him, that, during his ftay at Conftantinople, he had feen a fmall ftone called *tourmalin*, which attracted and repelled afhes. This account the Duc De Noya had quite forgotten, but being

in

in Holland in the year 1758, he faw, and purchafed two of thofe ftones. With thefe, in company with Meffrs. Daubenton and Adamfon, he made a great number of experiments, of which he favoured the public with a particular account *.

But prior to the Duc De Noya's experiments, Mr. Lechman had acquainted Mr. Æpinus with the attractive power of the tourmalin, and furnifhed him with two of them, on which he made many experiments; the refult of which he publifhed in the Hiftory of the Academy of Sciences and Belles Lettres at Berlin for the year 1756. The fubftance of the memoir is as follows.

The tourmalin has always, at the fame time, a pofitive and a negative electricity; one of its fides being in one ftate, and the other in the oppofite; and this does not depend on the external form of the ftone. Thefe electricities he could excite in the ftrongeft degree, by plunging the ftone in boiling-water.

If one fide of the tourmalin be heated more than the other (as if it be laid upon a hot cake of metal) each of the fides acquire an electricity oppofite to that which is natural to it; but if left to itfelf, it will return to its natural ftate.

If one of the fides of the tourmalin be rubbed, while the other is in contact with fome conductor communicating with the ground;

* Phil. Tranf. Vol. li. pt. i. p. 396.

the

the rubbed fide is always pofitive, and the other negative. If neither fide be in contact with a conductor, both become pofitive. If, in the former of thefe cafes, the tourmalin be rubbed, fo as to acquire a fenfible heat, and the fide which is naturally pofitive be made negative, it will upon ftanding to cool, return to its natural ftate; but if it have acquired no fenfible heat, it will not return to its natural ftate while any kind of electricity remains. If it be heated, even when it is rubbed and infulated, (in which cafe both fides become pofitive) it will ftill return to its natural ftate upon cooling.

The Duc De Noya mentions thefe experiments of Mr. Æpinus, but does not admit of a *plus* and *minus* electricity belonging to the tourmalin when heated. On the contrary, he fays, that both the fides are electrified *plus*, but one of them more than the other, and that it was the difference between thofe degrees which led Mr. Æpinus into his miftake *.

The tourmalin was introduced to the notice of the Englifh philofophers by Dr. Heberden, who fortunately recollecting to have feen one of them, many years before, in the poffeffion of Dr. Sharp at Cambridge (and it was the only one known in England at that time) procured it for Mr. Wilfon; who, though it was but a fmall one, repeated with it moft of the experiments of Mr. Æpinus, fo far as to

* Phil. Tranf. Vol. lvii. pt. i. p. 315.

fatisfy

satisfy himself that his opinion of its positive and negative power was well founded.

AFTERWARDS, Dr. Heberden, ever desirous of extending the bounds of science, procured some of these stones from Holland, and put them into the hands of those persons who were likely to make the best use of them, particularly Mr. Wilson and Mr. Canton; in whose hands they were not lodged in vain, as will appear by the brief account I shall subjoin of their experiments upon them.

MR. WILSON's observations are too many, and too particular to be all inserted in this work. The result of them was, in the main, the same with that of Mr. Æpinus, establishing the opinion of the two different powers of this stone; but, contrary to Mr. Æpinus, he asserts, that when the sides of the tourmalin are unequally heated, it exhibits that species of electricity which is natural to the hotter side, that is, the tourmalin is *plus* on both sides, when the *plus* side is the hotter; and *minus* on both sides, when the *minus* side is the hotter.

UPON this Mr. Æpinus repeated all his former experiments, and still found the result of them agreeable to his former conclusion, and contrary to that of Mr. Wilson. Mr. Wilson also repeated his, without any variation in the event, and imagined the difference between him and Mr. Æpinus might arise from the different sizes of the tourmalins they made use of, or from their different manner of making the experiments. And it is evident, from

the

the defcription of both their apparatufes, that of Mr. Wilfon was much better calculated for the purpofe of accurate experiments than that of Mr. Æpinus. Mr. Wilfon alfo ufed a greater variety of methods of communicating heat to his tourmalins. He both plunged them in boiling water, held them to the flame of a candle, and expofed them to heated infulated electrics *.

Though the detail of all Mr. Wilfon's experiments would be, as I obferved before, much too long for my purpofe, I cannot help relating one of them, which was made with the laft mentioned method of treating. He heated one end of a glafs tube red-hot, and when he had expofed what both he and Mr. Æpinus call the negative fide of the tourmalin to it; he obferved that about three inches of the heated part of the glafs were electrified *minus*, though the glafs beyond that was electrified *plus*, and continued fo even after the glafs was cold, the electric fluid having paffed from the tourmalin to the glafs; fince thefe were the fame appearances that were produced by prefenting an excited tube to the heated glafs.

He then applied the *plus* fide of the tourmalin to the fame heated glafs, and found that the tube was electrified *minus*, above a foot in length, without the leaft appearance of a *plus* electricity beyond the *minus* one, as in the other experiment; and this *minus* electricity

* Phil. Tranf. Vol. liii. p. 436, &c

appeared

appeared when the tube was nearly cold. In this cafe he judged that the electric fluid had paffed from the glafs to the tourmalin.

MR. WILSON imagined that the tourmalin, as well as glafs, was permeable to the electric fluid, and that the refiftance to its entering the fubftance of it was lefs on what he calls the negative than on the pofitive fide. Thefe conclufions he drew from the two following experiments. Rubbing the pofitive fide of the ftone flightly, he found both fides electrified *plus*, but rubbing the negative fide in the fame manner, both fides were electrified *plus* more ftrongly than before *.

SEVERAL experiments led Mr. Wilfon to conclude that the tourmalin refifted the exit and entrance of the electric fluid confiderably lefs than glafs, or even than amber; and upon the whole he infers, that the tourmalin differs in nothing from other electric bodies but in acquiring electricity by heat †.

EXAMINING a great number of tourmalins, he found that a line drawn from the *plus* part, through the center of the ftone, would always pafs through the *minus* part.

ALMOST all thefe tourmalins he greafed over, and whilft they were warm enough to preferve the greafe liquid, he tried each tourmalin feparately, but found no alteration in the virtue of the ftone, except that it was a little weakened; though it is well known, he fays, that moifture of any fort readily conducts

* Phil. Tranf. Vol. li. pt. i. p. 327.　　† Ibid. p. 329.

the electric fluid. If, therefore, the tourmalin had not a fixed kind of electricity, the
plus and *minus* electricity, obfervable on the
two fides of the ftone, muft, by this treatment, have united and deftroyed each other.
From this circumftance Mr. Wilfon concluded, that the tourmalin fuffered the electric
fluid to pafs through it only in one direction,
and that in this it bore fome analogy to the
loadftone; having, as it were, two electric
poles, which are not eafily deftroyed or altered *. But he was not aware how imperfect
a conductor oil or greafe of any kind is.

THIS induced him to try whether, like the
loadftone, the tourmalin would lofe its virtue after being made red-hot; but, though he
kept two of them in a ftrong fire for half an
hour, he could not perceive the leaft alteration in them: but plunging one in water,
while it was red-hot entirely deftroyed its
virtue, and gave it the appearance of having
been fhivered in many parts without breaking †. He obferves that when a tourmalin,
which he had from Dr. Morton, was held between the eye and the light, and viewed in
the direction through which the electric fluid
is found to pafs, it appears of a darker colour
confiderable than when it is viewed at right
angles to the former direction. This appearance, he fays, obtains in many other tourmalins, efpecially when they happen to be as
conveniently fhaped ‡.

* Phil. Tranf. Vol. li. pt. i. p. 337, 338.
† Ibid. p. 338   ‡ Ibid. Vol. liii. p. 448.

NOT-

NOTWITHSTANDING the attention given to this fubject by Mr. Æpinus and Mr. Wilfon, the moft important difcovery relating to the electricity of the tourmalin was referved for Mr. Canton; who, in a paper read at the Royal Society in the fame month with that above-mentioned of Mr. Wilfon, viz. December 1759, obferves, that the tourmalin emits and abforbs the electric fluid only by the increafe or diminution of its heat. For if the tourmalin, he fays, be placed on a plain piece of heated glafs or metal, fo that each fide of it, by being perpendicular to the furface of the heated body, may be equally heated; it will, while heating, have the electricity of one of its fides pofitive, and that of the other negative. This will, likewife, be the cafe when it is taken out of boiling water and fuffered to cool; but the fide which was pofitive while it was heating will be negative while it is cooling, and the fide which was negative will be pofitive.

IN this paper Mr. Canton refers to the Gentleman's Magazine for the month of September before, in which he had publifhed the refult of fome experiments he had made on a tourmalin which he had procured from Holland. The propofitions he there lays down are fo few, and comprife the principal part of what is known upon this fubject in fo concife and elegant a manner, that I fhall recite them all in this place.

1. WHEN the tourmalin is not electrical or attractive, heating it, without friction, will

B b 4　　　　make

make it fo; and the electricity of one fide
of it (diftinguifhed by A) will be pofitive,
and that of the other fide (B) will be negative.

2. THE tourmalin not being electrical will
become fo by cooling; but with this difference, that the fide A will be negative, and
the fide B pofitive.

3. IF the tourmalin, in a non-electrical
ftate, be heated, and fuffered to cool again,
without either of its fides being touched; A
will be pofitive, and B negative, the whole
time of the increafe and decreafe of its heat.

4. EITHER fide of the tourmalin will be
pofitive by friction, and both may be made fo
at the fame time.

THESE, fays he, are the principal laws of
the electricity of this wonderful ftone; and
he adds, if air be fuppofed to be endued with
fimilar properties, i. e. of becoming electrical by the increafe or diminution of its heat
(as is probable, if its ftate before and after a
thunder ftorm be attended to) thunder clouds
both pofitive and negative, as well as thunder
gufts, may eafily be account for.

THESE capital difcoveries were made before
Mr. Canton had received of Dr. Heberden the
tourmalins above mentioned. When thofe
came to his hands he was enabled to make feveral new and curious experiments, which I
have leave to publifh.

HE put one of the tourmalins, which was
of the common colour into the flame from a
blow-pipe and burnt it white; when he found
that

that its electrical property was intirely destroyed. The electricity of another was only
in part destroyed by the fire. Two other
tourmalins he joined together, when they
were made soft by fire, without destroying
their electrical property. The virtue of another was improved by its being melted at
one end; and he found (contrary to what
Mr. Wilson had observed of another tourmalin, which he treated in the same manner)
that one tourmalin retained its electrical property after it had been frequently made red-
hot, and, in that state, put into cold water.

BUT the most curious of his experiments
were made upon a large irregular tourmalin,
about half an inch in length, which he cut
into three pieces; taking one part from the
positive, and another from the negative end.
Trying these pieces separately, he found the
outer side of the piece which he cut from the
end that was negative when cooling was likewise negative when cooling, and that the
outer side of that piece which was cut from
the end that was positive when cooling was
likewise positive when cooling; the opposite
sides of both pieces being, agreeable to the general law of the electricity of the tourmalin,
in a contrary state.

THE middle part of the same tourmalin was
affected just as it had been when it was intire; the positive end remained positive, and
the negative end continued negative. The
same he had also observed of two other tourmalins,

malins, each about the fize of this, which were alfo cut out of a large one.

On January the 8th, 1762, Mr. Canton took the Doctor's large tourmalin (which Mr. Wilfon has given a defcription of in the fifty-firft volume of the Philofophical Tranfactions, p. 316.) and having placed a fmall tin cup of boiling-water on one end of his electrometer, which was fupported by warm glafs, while the pith balls were fufpended at the other end; he dropped it into the water, and obferved, that during the whole time of its being heated, and alfo while it was cooling in the water, the balls were not at all electrified.

Till the year 1760 it had been fuppofed, that, of all electric fubftances, the tourmalin alone poffeffed the property of being excited by heating and cooling; but in the beginning of that year, Mr. Canton having had an opportunity of examining a variety of gems, by the favour of Mr. Nicolas Crifp a jeweller in Bow Church-yard, firft found the *Brazil topaz* to have the electrical properties of the tourmalin. The largeft he met with he put into the hands of Dr. Heberden, who returned it November the 27th, 1760, and fent with it the tourmalins above mentioned.

In September 1761, Mr. Wilfon (who had been informed of Mr. Canton's difcovery) met with feveral other gems, of different fizes and colours, that refembled the tourmalin with refpect to electrical experiments. The moft beautiful of them were fomething like the ruby,

ruby, others were more pale, and one inclining to an orange colour. In point of hardnefs and luftre, they were nearly the fame with the topaz.

FROM all his experiments upon thefe gems he thought it was abundantly evident, that the direction of the fluid did not depend upon the external figure of the gem, but upon fome particular internal make and conftitution of it. And that there is fome fuch natural difpofition in all gems affording thefe appearances may be collected, he fays, from another curious fpecimen of the tourmalin kind, which is green, and formed of long flender cryftals with feverals fides; many of which are found fticking together, and are brought from South America.

THESE gems, numbers of which were furnifhed him by Mr. Emanuel Mendes Da Cofta, he not only found to be like the tourmalin with refpect to electric appearances; but that the direction of the electric fluid moving therein was always along the grain or fhootings of the cryftals, one end of it being electrified *plus*, and the other end *minus*. And that the fluid is more difpofed to pafs in that direction than in another, he thought, might be farther collected from what has been obferved on the grain of the loadftone by Dr. Knight; who found that though the magnetic poles of the natural loadftone might be varied in any direction, yet that the fame loadftone admitted of being made much more magnetical along the grain than acrofs it.

FROM

From thefe experiments and obfervations Mr. Wilfon inferred by analogy, that the electric fluid, flowing through all thefe ftones and gems, moves in that direction in which the grain happens to lie; and that the reafon of this is, that the refiftance which the fluid meets with in paffing through the gem is lefs in that direction than in any other *.

In a fubfequent paper of Mr. Wilfon's, read at the Royal Society December the 23d, 1763, and March 1764, he recites feveral curious experiments on the effects of removing the tourmalin from one room to another, in which there was fome difference of heat; the refult of which exactly confirms Mr. Canton's difcovery, that the fide which is pofitive when heating is negative when cooling, and *vice verfa*. Upon a very nice examination, and during fome favourable circumftances, Mr. Wilfon fays he has obferved the tourmalin to be feebly electrified, when the thermometer varied up and down only one degree †.

---

* Phil. Tranf. Vol. lii. pt. ii. p. 443.
† Ibid. p. 457.

SECTION

SECTION X.

DISCOVERIES THAT HAVE BEEN MADE SINCE
THOSE OF DR. FRANKLIN, WITH RE-
SPECT TO THE SAMENESS OF LIGHTNING
AND ELECTRICITY.

THE year 1752 makes an æra in electricity no lefs famous than the year
1746, in which the Leyden phial was difcovered. In the year 1752, was verified the
hypothefis of Dr. Franklin, of the identity of
the matter of lightning and of the electric
fluid; and his great project of trying the experiment by real lightning actually brought
down from the clouds, was carried into execution.

THE French philofophers were the firft to
diftinguifh themfelves upon this memorable
occafion, and the moft active perfons in the
fcene were Mr. Dalibard and Delor, both
zealous partifans (as Mr. Nollet calls them) of
Dr. Franklin. The former prepared his apparatus at Marly La Ville, fituated five or fix
leagues from Paris, the other at his own
houfe, on fome of the higheft ground in that
capital. Mr. Dalibard's machine confifted of
an iron rod forty feet long, the lower extremity of which was brought into a centry box,
where the rain could not come; while, on
the outfide, it was faftened to three wooden
pofts by long filken firings defended from the
rain.

rian. This machine happened to be the firſt that was favoured with a viſit from this ethereal fire. The philoſopher himſelf happened not to be at home at that time; but, in his abſence, he entruſted the care of his apparatus to one Coiffier a joiner, a man who had ſerved fourteen years among the dragoons, and on whoſe underſtanding and courage he could depend. This artiſan had all proper inſtructions given him, both how to make obſervations, and alſo to guard himſelf from any harm there might be from them; beſides being expreſsly ordered to get ſome of his neighbours to be preſent, and particularly to ſend for the curate of Marly, whenever there ſhould be any appearance of the approach of a thunder ſtorm. At length the long expected event arrived.

On Wedneſday the 10th of May 1752, between two and three o'clock in the afternoon, Coiffier heard a pretty loud clap of thunder. Immediately he flies to the machine, takes a phial furniſhed with a braſs wire, and preſenting one end of the wire to the rod, he ſees a ſmall bright ſpark iſſue from it, and hears the ſnapping that it made. Taking a ſecond ſpark ſtronger than the former, and attended with a louder report, he calls his neighbours, and ſends for the curate. The curate runs with all his might, and the pariſhioners, ſeeing the precipitation of their ſpiritual guide, imagine that poor Coiffier had been killed with lightning. The alarm ſpreads through the village, and the hail which came on did not prevent

vent the flock from following their shepherd.
The honest ecclesiastic arriving at the machine,
and seeing there was no danger, took the wire
into his own hand, and immediately drew several strong sparks, which were most evidently of an electrical nature, and completed the
discovery for which the machine was
erected.

THE thunder cloud was not more than a
quarter of an hour in passing over the zenith
of the machine, and there was no thunder
heard besides that single clap. As soon as the
storm was over, and no more sparks could be
drawn from the bar, the curate wrote a letter
to Mr. Dalibard, containing an account of this
remarkable experiment, and sent it immediately by the hands of Coiffier himself.

HE says, that he drew sparks from the bar
of a blue colour, an inch and a half in length,
and which smelled strong of sulphur. He repeated the experiment at least six times in the
space of about four minutes, in the presence
of many persons, each experiment taking up
the time, as he, in the stile of a priest expresses himself, of a *pater* and an *ave*. In
the course of these experiments he received
a stroke on his arm, a little above the elbow,
but he could not tell whether it came from the
brass wire inserted into the phial, or from the
iron bar. He did not attend to the stroke at
the time he received it, but, the pain continuing, he uncovered his arm when he went
home, in the presence of Coiffier ; and a mark
was perceived round his arm, such as might
have

have been made by a blow with the wire on his naked skin; and afterwards several persons, who knew nothing of what had happened, said that they perceived a smell of sulphur when he came near them.

COIFFIER told Mr. Dalibard, that for about a quarter of an hour before the curate arrived, he had, in the presence of five or six persons, taken much stronger sparks than those which the curate mentioned *

EIGHT days after, Mr. Delor saw the same thing at his own house, although only a cloud passed over, without either thunder or lightning †.

THE same experiments were afterwards repeated by Mr. Delor, at the request of the king of France, who, it is said, saw them with the greatest satisfaction, and expressed a just sense of the merit of Dr. Franklin. These applauses of the king excited in Mr. De Buffon, Dalibard, and Delor, a desire of verifying Dr. Franklin's hypothesis more completely, and of pursuing his speculations upon the subject.

MR. DELOR's apparatus in Paris consisted of a bar of iron ninety-nine feet high, and answered rather better than that of Mr. Dalibard, which, as was observed before, was only forty feet high. But as the quantity of electricity which they could procure from the clouds, in these first experiments, was but small, they added to this apparatus what they

* Dalibard's Franklin, Vol. ii. p. 109, &c.
† Noilet's Letters, Vol. i. p. 9.

called

called a *magazine* of electricity, confifting of many bars of iron infulated, and communicating with the pointed iron rod. This magazine contained more of the electric matter, and gave a more fenfible fpark, upon the approach of the finger than the pointed bar.

A MAGAZINE of this kind Mr. Mazeas had in an upper room of his houfe, into which he brought the lightning, by means of a wooden pole projecting out of his window, at the extremity of which a glafs tube, filled with rofin, received a pointed iron rod, twelve feet long. But all this while the electrics, which they made ufe of to fupport thefe iron rods, were too much expofed to the open air, and confequently were liable to be wet, which would infallibly defeat their experiments.

THE moft accurate experiments, made with thefe imperfect inftruments, where thofe of Mr. Monnier. He was convinced that the high fituation in which the bar of iron had commonly been placed was not abfolutely neceffary for this purpofe: for he obferved a common fpeaking-trumpet, fufpended upon filk five or fix feet from the ground, to exhibit very evident figns of electricity. He alfo found that a man placed upon cakes of rofin, and holding in his hand a wooden pole, about eighteen feet long, about which an iron wire was twifted, was fo well electrified when it thundered, that very lively fparks were drawn from him; and that another man, ftanding upon non-electrics, in the middle of

C c

a garden, and only holding up one of his hands in the air, attracted, with the other hand, fhavings of wood which were held to him.

He fays, that he obferved a continual diminution of the electricity when the rain came on, though the thunder was ftill very loud, and though the cake of rofin which fupported his conductor was not wet. But he afterwards found, that this was not univerfally true.

He once obferved, that when the conducting wire was furrounded with drops of rain, only fome of them were electrified, as was evident from the conical figure they had, while the reft remained round as before. It was alfo perceived, that the electrified and non-electrified drops generally fucceeded each other alternately; which made Mr. Monnier call to mind a fingular phenomenon, which happened fome years before to five peafants who were paffing through a corn field, near Frankfort upon the Oder, during a thunder ftorm; when the lightning killed the firft, the third, and the fifth of them, without injuring the fecond or the fourth *.

It was not owing to any want of attention to this fubject that the Englifh philofophers were not the firft to verify the theory of Dr. Franklin. They happened to have few opportunities of trying experiments. In the few they had, they were difappointed by

* Phil. Tranf. Vol. xlvii. p. 551.

the

the rain wetting their apparatus, which was not better conftructed than that of the French.

At length fuccefs crowned the affiduity and happier contrivance of Mr. Canton, who, to the lower end of his conducting wire, had had the precaution to faften a tin cover, to keep the rain from the glafs tube which fupported it. By this means, on the 20th of July 1752, he got fparks at the diftance of half an inch, but the whole appearance ceafed in the fpace of two minutes *.

Mr. Wilson, who took great pains in thefe purfuits, as he did in every thing elfe relating to electricity, perceiving feveral electrical fnaps, on the 12th of Auguft following, from no other apparatus than an iron curtain rod; one end of which he put into the neck of a glafs phial, which he held in his hand, while the other was made to point into the air.

Dr. Bevis alfo, at this time, viz. on the 12th of Auguft, obferved nearly the fame appearances that Mr. Canton had done before †.

Mr. Canton afterwards, refuming his obfervations on lightning, with the affiduity and accuracy with which he obferves every thing, found, by a great number of experiments, that fome clouds were in a pofitive, and fome in a negative ftate of electricity. And that, by this means, the electricity of

* Phil. Tranf. Vol. xlvii. p. 568.
† Ibid. p. 569.

his

his conductor would sometimes change from one state to the other five or six times in less than half an hour *.

THIS observation of Mr. Canton, on the different electricity of the clouds was made, and the account of it published in England, before it was known that Dr. Franklin had made the same discovery in America.

WHEN the air was dry, he observed, that the apparatus would continue electrified for ten minutes, or a quarter of an hour after the clouds had passed the zenith, and sometimes till they were more than half way towards the horizon; that rain, especially when the drops were large, generally brought down the electric fire; and hail in summer, he believed, never failed. The last observation he had made before the time of his writing this paper, when his apparatus had been electrified by a fall of thawing snow. This was on the 12th of November 1753, which, he says, was the 26th day, and the sixty-first time, it had been electrified since it was first set up, viz. about the middle of the preceding May.

ONLY two thunder storms had happened at London during that whole summer, and Mr. Canton's apparatus was so strongly electrified by one of them, that the ringing of the bells (which he suspended to his apparatus, to signify when the electrification was begun, and which were frequently rung so loud as to be heard in every room in the

* Phil. Tranf. Vol. xlviii. pt. i. p. 356.

houfe)

houfe) was ftifled by the almoft conftant
ftream of denfe electric fire between each bell
and the brafs ball, which would not fuffer it
to ftrike.

UPON a farther occafion, he obferves, that
in the fucceeding months of January, February, and March, his apparatus was electrified
no lefs than twenty-five times, both pofitively and negatively, by fnow as well as by hail
and rain; and almoft to as great a degree
when Fahrenheit's thermometer was between
twenty-eight and thirty-four, as he had ever
known it in fummer, except in a thunder-
ftorm *.

MR. CANTON concludes his paper with
propofing the two following queries. 1. May
not air fuddenly rarefied give electric fire to,
and air fuddenly condenfed receive electric fire
from clouds and vapours paffing through it?
2. Is not the aurora borealis the flaſhing of
electric fire from pofitive towards negative
clouds at a great diftance, through the upper
part of the atmofphere, where the refiftance is
leaft † ?

MR. CANTON not only obferved the different ftates of pofitive and negative electricity
in the clouds, but alfo noted the proportion
that the one bore to the other for a confiderable time. In the firft period he had obferved
the clouds had been pofitively electrical 83
times, and negative 101. In this period he

* Phil. Tranf. Vol. xlviii. pt. ii. p. 785.
† Ibid. pt. i. p. 358.

had

had punctually set down how often the powers had shifted, and the whole time that the apparatus continued to be electrified, but he had intirely neglected to note the time that each power lasted. But this last circumstance he afterwards carefully attended to for about two months, viz. from the 28th of June to the 23d of August 1754; and found the apparatus to be electrified positively thirty-one times, which taken together lasted three hours thirty-five minutes; and negatively forty-five times, the whole duration of which was ten hours thirty-nine minutes. He also observed that the positive power was generally the stronger. This account he wrote the 31st of August 1754.

These observations, which Mr. Canton gives me leave to make public, are extremely curious, and must have required great attention; but they are hardly sufficient to authorize any general conclusion.

One of the effects of lightning and electricity is the melting of metals. This was first thought to be a cold fusion; but that opinion is refuted, in a very sensible manner, by Dr. Knight, in a paper read at the Royal Society, November 22d, 1759. He observes, that the instances most generally given of cold fusion are two, viz. that of a sword being melted in its scabbard, and that of money being melted in a bag, both the scabbard and the bag remaining unhurt.

A great number of authors, he says, have mentioned both the facts, but without
giving

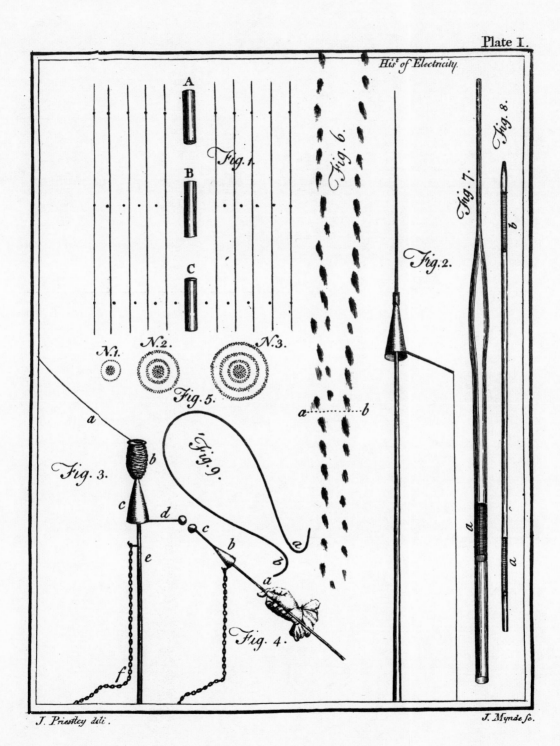

Plate I.

His.ᵗ of Electricity.

Fig. 1.

A

B

C

Fig. 6.

Fig. 7.

Fig. 8.

Fig. 2.

N.1.　N.2.　N.3.

Fig. 5.

Fig. 3.

a

b

c

d

e

f

Fig. 9.

a

b

e

Fig. 4.

a

b

c

d

a

b

a

a

J. Priestley del.ⁱ.　J. Mynde sc.

giving either their own teſtimony, or that of
any one elſe for the truth of them, or deſcrib-
ing any of the other concomitant circumſtances. And it ſeemed to him very poſſible,
that lightning might produce effects ſimilar to
thoſe above mentioned, without our being
obliged to have recourſe to a cold fuſion to
account for them.

IF, ſays he, the edge or external ſurface of
a ſword had been melted, whilſt the main
part of the blade remained entire, it would
have afforded ſufficient ground to aſſert, in
general terms, that the ſword was melted,
and yet the ſcabbard might have remained
unhurt; becauſe either the edge or ſurface of
a ſword might be inſtantly melted by lightning and cooled ſo ſuddenly, as to make no
impreſſion of burning upon the ſcabbard.
Metals, as well as other bodies, he obſerves,
will both heat and cool ſooner in proportion
as they are thin and ſlender; that very ſmall
wire will inſtantly become red hot, and even
melt, and run into a round globule in the
flame of a common candle; though it is no
ſooner removed out of the flame, but it is inſtantly cold He therefore concludes, that the
edge of a ſword, or even its ſurface, might
be inſtantly melted by lightning; and being
in contact with, or rather ſtill united to the
reſt of the blade, which might be cold, it
would part with its heat too ſuddenly to produce any appearance of burning.

HE was confirmed in this reaſoning, by
examining ſome fragments and particles of
wire

wire melted by lightning, which were fent him by Mr. Mountaine. Amongft them appeared globules of various fizes, which had undergone very different degrees of fufion. The largeft of them had not been fluid enough to put on a fperical figure, but they approached nearer to it, in proportion as they were fmaller ; fo that, in the fmalleft granulæ, the fufion was moft perfect, the globules being very round and fmooth. Their fizes continued diminifhing till they became invifible to the naked eye, and fome of them, when viewed with a microfcope, required a third or fourth magnifier to fee them diftinctly.

Some of the bits of wire were rough and fcaly, like burnt iron, and were fwelled in thofe places where they were beginning to melt. Others continued ftraight, and of an equable thicknefs ; but their outward furface feemed to have undergone a perfect fufion, fo that there were two or more pieces adhering together, as if joined by a thin folder.

In the Philofophical Tranfactions, **Dr.** Knight fays, there are two or three relations which feemed at firft to favour a cold fufion, but when duly confidered prove nothing conclufive *.

But that there is really no fuch thing as cold fufion, either by electricity or lightning, was moft clearly demonftrated by Mr. Kinnerfley, in a letter to Dr. Franklin, dated Philadelphia, March 12th, 1761.

* Phil. Tranf. Vol. li. pt. i. p. 294, &c.

HE

HE fufpended a piece of fmall brafs wire, about twenty four inches long, with a pound weight at the lower end; and, by fending through it the charge of a cafe of bottles, containing above thirty feet of coated glafs, he difcovered what he calls a new method of wire-drawing. The wire was red-hot, the whole length well annealed, and above an inch longer than before. A fecond charge melted it fo that it parted near the middle, and meafured, when the ends were put together, four inches longer than at firft.

THIS experiment, he fays, was propofed to him by Dr. Franklin, in order to find whether the electricity, in paffing through the wire, would fo relax the cohefion of its conftituent particles, as that the weight might produce a feparation; but neither of them had the leaft fufpicion that any heat would be produced.

THAT he might have no doubt of the wire being *hot*, as well as *red*, he repeated the experiment on another piece of the fame wire, encompaffed with a goofe quill, filled with loofe grains of gun-powder; which took fire, as readily as if it had been touched with a red-hot poker. Alfo tinder, tied to another piece of the wire, kindled by it; but when he tried a wire about twice as big, he could produce no fuch effects.

HENCE, fays he, it appears, that the electric fire, though it has no fenfible heat, when in a ftate of reft, will, by its violent motion, and the refiftance it meets with, produce heat

in

in other bodies, when paſſing through them, provided they be. ſmall enough. A great quantity will paſs through a large wire, without producing any ſenſible heat; when the ſame quantity, paſſing through a very ſmall one, being there confined to a narrower paſſage, the particles crowding cloſer together, and meeting with a greater reſiſtance, will make it red-hot, and even melt it.

HENCE, he concludes, that lightning does not melt metal by a cold fuſion, as Dr. Franklin and himſelf had formerly ſuppoſed; but that, when it paſſed through the blade of a ſword, if the quantity was not very great, it might heat the point ſo as to melt it, while the broadeſt and the thickeſt part might not be ſenſibly warmer than before.

WHEN trees and houſes are ſet on fire by the dreadful quantity, which a cloud, or ſometimes the earth diſcharges, muſt not the heat, ſays he, by which the wood is firſt kindled, be generated by the lightning's violent motion through the reſiſting combuſtible matter?

IF lightning, by its rapid motion, produced heat in itſelf as well as in other bodies (which Mr. Kinnerſley imagined was evident from ſome experiments made with electrical thermometer, mentioned before) he thought that its ſometimes ſingeing the hair of animals killed by it might eaſily be account for; and that the reaſon of its not always doing ſo might be, that the quantity, though ſufficient to kill a large animal, might not be great

enough

enough, or not have met with refiftance enough, to become by its motion burning-hot.

WE find, fays he, that dwelling-houfes ftruck with lightning, are feldom fet on fire by it; but that when it paffes through barns, with hay or ftraw in them, or ftore-houfes containing large quantities of hemp, or fuch like matter, they feldom, if ever, efcape a conflagration. This, he thought, might be owing to fuch combuftibles being apt to kindle with a lefs degree of heat than was neceffary to kindle wood *.

ALL that was done by the French and Englifh electricians, with refpect to lightning and electricity, fell far fhort of what was done by Signior BECCARIA at Turin. His attention to the various ftates of the atmofphere, his affiduity in making experiments, his apparatus for making them, the extent of his views in making them, the minute exactnefs with which he has recorded them, and his judgment in applying them to a general theory, far exceeded every thing that had been done by philofophers before him, or that has been done by any perfon fince. And though I fhall give confiderable fcope to my account of his experiments and obfervations, I fhall be able to give my reader but a faint idea of the extent, variety, and value of his labours in this great field.

* Phil. Tranf. Vol. liii. p. 92, &c.

HE

HE made ufe both of kites and pointed
rods, and of a great variety of both at the
fame time, and in different places. Some of
the ftrings of his kites had wires in them,
and others had none. Some of them flew to
a prodigious height, and others but low;
and he had a great number of affiftants, to
note the nature, time, and degree of appearances, according as his views required.

To keep his kites conftantly infulated, and
at the fame time to give them more or lefs
ftring, and for many other purpofes, he had
the ftring rolled upon a reel, which was fupported by pillars of glafs; and his conductor
had a communication with the axis of the
reel *.

To diftinguifh the pofitive and negative
ftate of the clouds, when the electricity was
vigorous, with more certainty, and with more
fafety than it could be done by prefenting an
excited ftick of glafs, or fealing-wax to
threads diverging from his conductor ; he inclofed a pointed wire and a flat piece of lead
oppofite to it within a cylindrical glafs veffel,
wrapped in pafteboard, fo that the infide could
have no communication with the external
light. Into this cover, and oppofite to the
point of the wire, he inferted a very long
tube of pafteboard; through which he could
look from a confiderable diftance, and fee the
form of the electric light at the end of the

* Lettere dell' elettricifmo, p. 112.

wire ;

wire; which is the fureft indication of its quality *.

From Signior Beccaria's extremely exact and circumftantial account of the external appearances of thunder clouds, which he prefixes to his obfervations on their probable caufes, I fhall draw a general outline of the moft remarkable particulars, in the ufual progrefs of a thunder ftorm.

The firft appearance of a thunder ftorm (which generally happens when there is little or no wind) is one denfe cloud, or more, increafing very faft in fize, and rifing into the higher regions of the air. The lower furface is black, and nearly level; but the upper finely arched, and well defined. Many of thefe clouds often feem piled one upon another, all arched in the fame manner; but they keep continually uniting, fwelling, and extending their arches.

At the time of the rifing of this cloud, the atmofphere is generally full of a great number of feparate clouds, motionlefs, and of odd and whimfical fhapes. All thefe, upon the appearance of the thunder cloud, draw towards it, and become more uniform in their fhapes as they approach; till, coming very near the thunder cloud, their limbs mutually ftretch towards one another; they immediately coalefce, and together make one uniform mafs. Thefe he calls *adfcititious* clouds, from their coming in, to enlarge the fize of the

* Lettere dell' elettricifmo, p. 107.

thunder

thunder cloud. But, fometimes the thunder
cloud will fwell, and increafe very faft without the conjunction of any adfcititious clouds,
the vapours in the atmofphere forming themfelves into clouds wherever it paffes. Some
of the adfcititious clouds appear like white
fringes, at the fkirts of the thunder cloud, or
under the body of it, but they keep continually growing darker and darker, as they approach to unite with it.

WHEN the thunder cloud is grown to a
great fize, its lower furface is often ragged,
particular parts being detached towards the
earth, but ftill connected with the reft. Sometimes the lower furface fwells into various large
protuberances bending uniformly towards the
earth. And fometimes one whole fide of the
cloud will have an inclination to the earth,
and the extremity of it will nearly touch the
earth *. When the eye is under the thunder
cloud, after it is grown larger, and well formed, it is feen to fink lower, and to darken
prodigioufly; at the fame time that a number
of fmall adfcititious clouds (the origin of which
can never be perceived) are feen in a rapid
motion, driving about in very uncertain directions under it. While thefe clouds are
agitated with the moft rapid motions, the rain
generally falls in the greateft plenty, and if
the agitation be exceedingly great, it commonly hails †.

* Lettere dell' elettricifmo, p. 151.
† Ibid, p. 155.

WHILE

WHILE the thunder cloud is fwelling, and extending its branches over a large tract of country, the lightning is feen to dart from one part of it to another, and often to illuminate its whole mafs. When the cloud has acquired a fufficient extent, the lightning ftrikes between the cloud and the earth, in two oppofite places, the path of the lightning lying through the whole body of the cloud and its branches. The longer this lightning continues, the rarer does the cloud grow, and the lefs dark is its appearance; till, at length, it breaks in different places, and fhows a clear fky. When the thunder cloud is thus difperfed, thofe parts which occupy the upper regions of the atmofphere are equally fpread, and very thin; and thofe that are underneath are black, but thin too: and they vanifh gradually, without being driven away by any wind *.

HAVING feen what this philofopher obferved abroad, and in the air, let us fee what he took notice of at his apparatus within doors. This never failed to be electrified upon every approach of a thunder cloud, or any of its branches; and the ftream of fire from it was generally perpetual, while it was directly over the apparatus †.

THAT thunder clouds were fometimes in a pofitive as well as negative ftate of electricity, Signior Beccaria had difcovered, before he heard of its having been obferved by Dr.

* Lettere dell' elettricifmo, p. 146. 176.
† Ibid. p 167.

Franklin,

Franklin, or any other perfon *. The fame cloud, in paffing over his obfervatory, electrified his apparatus, fometimes pofitively, and fometimes negatively †. The electricity continued longer of the fame kind, in proportion as the thunder cloud was fimple, and uniform in its direction; but when the lightning changed its place, there commonly happened a change in the electricity of his apparatus. It would change fuddenly after a very violent flafh of lightning, but the change would be gradual when the lightning was moderate, and the progrefs of the thunder cloud flow.

IT was an immediate inference from his obfervations of the lightning abroad, and his apparatus within, that the quantity of electric matter, in an ufual ftorm of thunder, is almoft inconceivably great, confidering how many pointed bodies, as trees, fpires, &c. are perpetually drawing it off, and what a prodigious quantity is repeatedly difcharged to, or from the earth ‡.

AFTER this fummary view of appearances, I fhall, in the fame fuccinct manner explain the hypothefis by which this excellent philofopher accounts for them, and fome other principal and well known phenomena of thunder ftorms.

CONSIDERING the vaft quantity of electric fire that appears in the moft fimple thunder ftorms, he thinks it impoffible that any cloud, or number of clouds fhould ever contain it

* Lettere dell' elletricifmo, p. 138.   † Ibid. p. 172.
‡ Ibid. p. 180.

all

all, fo as either to difcharge or receive it. Befides, during the progrefs and increafe of the
ftorm, though the lightning frequently ftruck
to the earth, the fame clouds were the next
moment ready to make a ftill greater difcharge, and his apparatus continued to be as
much affected as ever. The clouds muft,
confequently, have received at one place, the
moment that a difcharge was made from them
in another *. In many cafes, the electricity
of his apparatus, and confequently of the
clouds, would inftantly change from one kind
to another feveral times ; an effect which cannot be accounted for by any fimple difcharge,
or recruit. Both muft have taken place in a
very quick fucceffion †.

THE extent of the clouds doth not leffen
this difficulty : for, be it ever fo great, ftill
the quantity ought to be leffened by every difcharge ; and, befides, the points, by which
the filent difcharges are made, are in proportion to the extent of the clouds ‡. Nor is the
difficulty leffened by fuppofing that frefh
clouds bring recruits ; for befides that the
clouds are not ripe for the principal ftorm, till
all the clouds, to a great diftance, have actually coalefced, and formed one uniform mafs,
thofe recruits bear no fort of proportion to the
difcharge, and whatever it was, it would foon
be exhaufted.

THE fact, therefore, muft be, that the
electric matter is continually darting from the

* Lettere dell' elettricifmo, p. 183. 188.
† Ibid. p. 220.   ‡ Ibid. p. 185.

D d   clouds

clouds in one place, at the same time that it is discharged from the earth in another. And it is a necessary consequence from the whole, that the clouds serve as conductors to convey the electric fluid from those places of the earth which are overloaded with it, to those which are exhausted of it .

To ascertain this fact in the most complete manner, he proposes that two observatories be fixed, about two leagues asunder, in the usual path of the thunder clouds ; and that observations be made, whether the apparatus be not often positive at one place, when it is negative at the other †.

THAT great quantities of electric matter do sometimes rush out of particular parts of the earth, and rise through the air, into the higher regions of the atmosphere, he thinks is evident from the great quantities of sand, ashes, and other light substances, which have often been carried up into the air, and scattered uniformly over a large tract of country ‡. No other known efficient cause of this phenomenon can be assigned, except the wind ; and it has been observed when there was no wind stirring ; and the light bodies have even been carried against the wind §. He supposes, therefore, that these light bodies are raised by a large quantity of electric matter issuing out of the earth, where it was overcharged with it, and (by that property of it which he had demonstrated) attracting, and

---

* Lettere dell' elettricismo, p. 193.   † Ibid. p 194.
‡ Ibid. p. 199.   § Ibid. p. 225.

carry-

carrying with it every fubftance that could ferve as a conductor in its paffage. All thefe bodies, being poffeffed of an equal quantity of the electric fluid, will be difperfed equally in the air, and confequently over that part of the earth where the fluid was wanting, and whither they ferve to convey it *. Had thefe bodies been raifed by the wind, they would have been difperfed at random, and in heaps.

THIS comparatively rare phenomenon (but of which he had been more than once a fpectator) he thinks exhibits both a perfect image, and a demonftration, of the manner in which the vapours of the atmofphere are raifed to form thunder clouds. The fame electric matter, wherever it iffues, attracts to it, and carries up into the higher regions of the air, the watery particles that are difperfed in the atmofphere. The electric matter afcends to the higher regions of the atmofphere, being folicited by the lefs refiftance it finds there than in the common mafs of the earth; which, at thofe times, is generally very dry, and confequently highly electric. The uniformity with which thunder clouds fpreads themfelves, and fwell into arches, muft be owing to their being affected by fome caufe which, like the electric matter, diffufes itfelf uniformly whereever it acts, and to the refiftance they meet with in afcending through the air †. As a proof of this, fteam, rifing from an electrified eolipile, diffufes itfelf with the fame uni-

* Lettere dell' elettricifmo, p. 202.   † Ibid. p. 205.

formity, and in similar arches, extending itself towards any conducting substance *.

THE same cause which first raised a cloud,
from vapours dispersed in the atmosphere,
draws to it those that are already formed, and
continues to form new ones, till the whole
collected mass extends so far as to reach a part
of the earth where there is a deficiency of the
electric fluid †. Thither too, will those
clouds, replete with electricity, be strongly
attracted, and there will the electric matter
discharge itself upon the earth. A channel
of communication being, in this manner,
found, a fresh supply of electric matter will
be raised from the overloaded part, and will
continue to be conveyed by the medium of
the clouds, till the equilibrium of the fluid
between the two places of the earth be restored. When the clouds are attracted in their
passage by those parts of the earth where there
is a deficiency of the fluid, those detached
fragments are formed, and also those uniform
depending protuberances, which will be shown
to be, in some cases, the cause of water-spouts
and hurricanes ‡.

THAT the electric matter, which forms
and animates the thunder clouds, issues from
places far below the surface of the earth, and
that it buries itself there, is probable from the
deep holes that have, in many places, been
made by lightning §. Flashes of lightning
have, also, been seen to arise from subterrane-

* Lettere dell' elettricismo, p. 206. † Ibid. p. 212.
‡ Ibid. p. 214. § Ibid. p. 227.

ous cavities, and from wells *. Violent in-
undations have accompanied thunder ftorms,
not occafioned by rain, but by water burfting
from the bowels of the earth, from which it
muft have been diflodged by fome internal
concuffion. Deep wells have been known to
fill fafter in thunder ftorms †, and others have
conftantly grown turbid at the approach of
thunder ‡.

THIS very rife, as well as the whole progrefs of thunder clouds, has fometimes been,
in a manner, vifible. Exhalations have been
frequently feen to rife from particular caverns,
attended with a rumbling noife, and to afcend
into the higher regions of the air, with all
the phenomena of thunder ftorms defcribed
above, according to the defcription of perfons
who lived long before the connection between electricity and lightning was fufpected §.

THE greateft difficulty attending this theory
of the origin of thunder ftorms relates to the
collection, and infulation of electric matter
within the body of the earth. With refpect
to the former, he has nothing particular to
fay. Some operations in nature are certainly
attended with a lofs of the equilibrium in the
electric fluid, but no perfon has yet affigned a
more probable caufe of the redundancy of the
electric matter which, in fact, often abounds
in the clouds, than what we may fuppofe

---

* Lettere dell' elettricifmo,-p. 228. † Ibid. p. 233.
‡ Ibid. p. 360. § Ibid. p. 231.

poffible

poffible to take place in the bowels of the earth. And fuppofing the lofs of the equili- brium poffible, the fame caufe that produced the effect would prevent the reftoring of it; fo that not being able to force a way, at leaft one fufficiently ready, through the body of the earth, it would iffue at the moft convenient vent into the higher regions of the air, as the better paffage. His electrical apparatus, though communicating with the earth, has frequently, in violent thunder ftorms, given evident fparks to his finger*.

In the enumeration of the effects of thun- der ftorms, he obferves that a wind always blows from the place from which the thunder cloud proceeds; that this is agreeable to the obfervations of all mariners, and that the wind is more or lefs violent in proportion to the fuddenefs of the appearance of the thun- der cloud, the rapidity of its expanfion, and the velocity with which the adfcititious clouds join it. The fudden condenfation of fuch a prodigious quantity of vapours muft difplace the air, and repel it on all fides †.

He, in fome meafure, imitated even this effect of thunder, at leaft produced a circula- tion of all the air in his room, by the continu- ed electrification of his chain ‡.

Among other effects of lightning, he men- tions the cafe of a man rendered exceedingly ftiff, prefently after he was ftruck dead in a ftorm of thunder. But the moft remarkable

* Lettere dell' elettricifmo, p. 236.   † Ibid. p. 339, 340.
‡ Ibid. p. 343.

circum-

circumftance, in this cafe, was the lightning (chufing the beft conductor) having ftruck one particular vein, near his neck, and followed it through its minuteft ramifications ; fo that the figure of it appeared through the fkin, finer than any pencil could have drawn it *.

HE cautions perfons not to depend upon the neighbourhood of a higher, or, in all cafes, a better conductor than their own body; fince, according to his repeated obfervations, the lightning by no means defcends in one undivided track ; but bodies of various kinds conduct their fhare of it, at the fame time, in proportion to their quantity and conducting power †.

A GREAT number of obfervations, relating to the defcent of lightning, confirm his theory of the manner of its afcent: for, in many cafes, it throws before it the parts of conducting bodies, and diftributes them along the refifting medium through which it muft force its paffage ‡.

UPON this principle it is, that the longeft flafhes of lightning feem to be made, by its forcing into its way part of the vapours in the air §. One of the principal reafons why thofe flafhes make fo long a rumbling, is their being occafioned by the vaft length of a vacuum, made by the paffage of the electric matter. For though the air collapfes the mo-

---

* Lettere dell' elettricifmo, p. 242. † Ibid. p. 246.
‡ Ibid. p. 247. § Ibid. p. 851.

ment

ment after it has paffed, and the vibration (on which the found depends) commences at the fame moment, through the whole length of the track ; yet, if the flafh was directed towards the perfon who hears the report, the vibrations excited at the nearer end of the track will reach his ear much fooner than thofe excited at the more remote end ; and the found will, without any repercuffion or echo, continue till all the vibrations have fuccessively reached him *.

I must introduce in this place a very curious experiment and obfervation of Mr. Lullin, concerning the production of electricity in the clouds. He made a long infulated pole project from the fide of one of the Alps ; and, on the 29th of June 1766, obferved, that when fmall clouds of vapour, raifed by the heat of the fun, rofe near, the foot of the mountain, and afcended along the fide of it ; if they touched the extremity of the pole only, it was electrified ; but if the whole pole, and confequently part of the hill on which it ftood, was likewife involved, it was not electrified. From this he concludes, that the electricity of the clouds is produced by their paffing through the air while the fun fhines upon them. But to which of thefe two circumftances, namely the motion through the air, or the action of the fun's rays, this was owing, he could not determine, though he made feveral experiments for that purpofe †.

* Letttre dell' elettricifmo, p. 252.
† Differtatio phyfica, p. 42.

ONE of the moſt remarkable effects of lightning is that it gives polarity to the magnetic
needle, and to all bodies that have any thing
of iron in them, as bricks, &c. and by obferving which way the poles of thefe bodies
lye, it may be known, with,the utmoſt certainty, in what direction the ſtroke paſſed *.
In one cafe S. Beccaria actually afcertained the
direction of the lightning in this manner †.

SINCE a fudden ſtroke of lightning gives
polarity to magnets, he conjectures that a regular and conſtant circulation of the whole
mafs of the fluid, from North to South, may
be the original caufe of magnetifm in general ‡. This is a truly great thought; and, if
juſt, will introduce greater fimplicity into our
conceptions of the laws of nature.

THAT this etherial current is infenfible to
us, is no proof of its non-exiſtence, fince we
ourfelves are involved in it. He had feen birds
fly fo near a thunder cloud, as he was fure
they would not have done, if they had been
affected by its atmofphere §.

THIS current he would not fuppofe to arife
from one fource, but from feveral, in the
northern hemifphere of the earth. The aber-
ration of the common center of all thefe currents from the North point may be the caufe of
the variation of the needle, the period of this
declination of the center of the currents may
be the period of the variation, and the obli-
quity with which the currents ſtrike into the

* Lettere dell' elettricifmo, p. 262.   † Ibid. p. 263.
‡ Ibid. p. 268.   § Ibid.

earth

earth may be the caufe of the dipping of the needle, and alfo why bàrs of iron more eafily receive the magnetic virtue in one particular direction *.

HE thinks that the *Aurora Borealis* may be this electric matter performing its circulation, in fuch a ftate of the atmofphere as renders it vifible, or approaching nearer to the earth than ufual. Accordingly very vivid appearances of this kind have been obferved to occafion a fluctuation in the magnetic needle †.

STONES and bricks ftruck by lightning are often vitrified. He fuppofes that fome ftones in the earth, having been ftruck in this manner, firft gave occafion to the vulgar opinion of the thunder bolt ‡.

SIGNIOR BECCARIA was very fenfible that heat contributes much to the phenomena of thunder, lightning, and rain; but he could not find, by any experiment, that it tended to promote electricity. He, therefore, rather thought that heat operated, in this cafe, by exhaling the moifture of the air, and thereby cutting off the communication of the electric fluid between one place and another, particularly between the earth and the higher regions of the air, whereby its effects were more vifible §.

HAVING entertained my reader with the obfervations of this great Italian genius, I muft once more conduct him to France, where he will fee feveral experiments well worth his

---

* Lettere dell' elettricifmo, p. 269.　　† Ibid. p. 272.
‡ Ibid. p. 263.　　　§ Ibid. p. 359.

notice.

notice. In this country we have feen that Dr. Franklin's theory of the identity of electricity and the matter of lightning was firft verified, and we fhall now fee it verified in the grandeft and moft confpicuous manner.

THE greateft quantity of electricity that was ever brought from the clouds, by any apparatus prepared for that purpofe, was by Mr. De Romas, affeffor to the prefideal of Nerac. This gentleman was the firft who made ufe of a wire interwoven in the hempen cord of an electrical kite, which he made feven feet and a half high, and three feet wide, fo as to have eighteen fquare feet of furface. This cord was found to conduct the electricity of the clouds more powerfully than a hempen cord would do, even though it was wetted; and, being terminated by a cord of dry filk it enabled the obferver (by a proper management of his apparatus) to make whatever experiments he thought proper, without danger to himfelf.

BY the help of this kite, on the 7th of June 1753, about one in the afternoon, when it was raifed 550 feet from the ground, and had taken 780 feet of ftring, making an angle of near forty-five degrees with the horizon; he drew fparks from his conductor three inches long and a quarter of an inch thick, the fnapping of which was heard about 200 paces. Whilft he was taking thefe fparks, he felt, as it were, a cobweb on his face, though he was above three feet from the ftring of the kite; after which he did not think it fafe to ftand

fo

fo near, and called aloud to all the company to retire, as he did himfelf about two feet.

THINKING himfelf now fecure enough, and not being incommoded by any body very near him, he took notice of what paffed among the clouds which were immediately over the kite; but could perceive no lightning either there or any where elfe, nor fcarce the leaft noife of thunder, and there was no rain at all. The wind was Weft, and pretty ftrong, which raifed the kite 100 feet higher, at leaft, than in the other experiments.

AFTERWARDS, cafting his eyes on the tin tube, which was faftened to the ftring of the kite, and about three feet from the ground, he faw three ftraws, one of which was about one foot long, a fecond four or five inches, and the third three or four inches, all ftanding erect, and performing a circular dance, like puppets, under the tin tube, without touching one another.

THIS little fpectacle, which much delighted feveral of the company, lafted about a quarter of an hour; after which, fome drops of rain falling, he again perceived the fenfation of the cobweb on his face, and at the fame time heard a continual ruftling noife, like that of a fmall forge bellows. This was a farther warning of the increafe of electricity; and from the firft inftant that Mr. De Romas perceived the dancing ftraws, he thought it not advifeable to take any more fparks even with all his precautions; and he

again

again intreated the company to fpread themfelves to a ftill greater diftance.

IMMEDIATELY after this came on the laft
act of the entertainment, which Mr. De Romas acknowledged' made him tremble. The
longeft ftraw was attracted by the tin tube,
upon which followed three explofions, the
noife of which greatly refembled that of thunder. Some of the company compared it to
the explofion of rockets, and others to the
violent crafhing of large earthen jars againft a
pavement. It is certain that it was heard into
the heart of the city, notwithftanding the various noifes there.

THE fire that was feen at the inftant of the
explofion had the fhape of a fpindle eight
inches long and five lines in diameter. But
the moft aftonifhing and diverting circumftance was produced by the ftraw, which had
occafioned the explofion, following the ftring
of the kite. Some of the company faw it at
forty-five or fifty fathoms diftance, attracted
and repelled alternately, with this remarkable
circumftance, that every time it was attracted
by the ftring, flafhes of fire were feen, and
cracks were heard, though not fo loud as at
the time of the former explofion.

IT is remarkable, that, from the time of
the explofion to the end of the experiments,
no lightning at all was feen, nor fcarce any
thunder heard. A fmell of fulphur was perceived, much like that of the luminous electric effluvia iffuing out of the end of an electrified bar of metal. Round the ftring appeared

peared a luminous cylinder of light, three or four inches in diameter; and this being in the day-time Mr. De Romas did not queftion but that, if it had been in the night, that electric atmofphere would have appeared to be four or five feet in diameter. Laftly, after the experiments were over, a hole was difcovered in the ground, perpendicularly under the tin tube, an inch deep, and half an inch wide, which was probably made by the large flafhes that accompanied the explofions.

An end was put to thefe remarkable experiments by the falling of the kite, the wind being fhifted into the Eaft, and rain mixed with hail coming on in great plenty. Whilft the kite was falling, the ftring came foul of a penthoufe; and it was no fooner difengaged, than the perfon who held it felt fuch a ftroke in his hands, and fuch a commotion through his whole body, as obliged him inftantly to let it go; and the ftring, falling on the feet of fome other perfons, gave them a fhock alfo, though much more tolerable *.

The quantity of electric matter brought by this kite from the clouds at another time is really aftonifhing. On the 26th of Auguft 1756, the ftreams of fire iffuing from it were obferved to be an inch thick, and ten feet long. This amazing flafh of lightning, the effect of which on buildings or animal bodies, would perhaps have been equally deftructive with any that are mentioned in hiftory, was

* Gent. Magaz. for Auguft 1756, p. 378.

fafely

fafely conducted by the cord of the kite to a non-electric body placed near it, and the report was equal to that of a piftol.

MR. ROMAS had the curiofity to place a pigeon in a cage of glafs, in a little edifice, which he had purpofely placed, fo as that it fhould be demolifhed by the lightning brought down by his kite. The edifice was, accordingly, fhattered to pieces, but the cage and the pigeon were not ftruck *.

THE Abbé Nollet, who gives this account, adds, that if a ftroke of this kind had gone through the body of Mr. De Romas, the unfortunate profeffor Richman had not probably been the only martyr to electricity, and advifes, that great caution be ufed in conducting fuch dangerous experiments †.

WHEN we confider how many fevere fhocks the moft cautious and judicious electricians often receive through inadvertence, we fhall not be furprifed, that when philofophers firft began to collect and make experiments upon real lightning, it fhould fometimes have proved a little untractable in their hands, and that they were obliged to give one another frequent cautions how to proceed with it.

THE Abbé Nollet, as early as the year 1752, advifes that thefe experiments be made with circumfpection; as he had been informed, by letters from Florence and Bologna, that thofe who had made them there had had

* Nollet's Letters, Vol. ii. p 239
† Phil. Tranf. Vol. lii pt. i p. 342.

their

8

their curiofity more than fatisfied by the violent fhocks they had fuftained in drawing fparks from an iron bar electrified by thunder. One of his correfpondents informed him, that once, as he was endeavouring to faften a fmall chain, with a copper ball at one of its extremities, to a great chain, which communicated with the bar at the top of the building (in order to draw off the electric fparks by means of the ofcillations of this ball) there came a flafh of lightning, which he did not fee, but which affected the chain with a noife like that of wild fire. At that inftant, the electricity communicated itfelf to the chain of the copper ball, and gave the obferver fo violent a commotion, that the ball fell out of his hands, and he was ftruck backwards four or five paces. He had never been fo much fhocked by the experiment of Leyden *.

MR. ROMAS received a fevere ftroke when he firft raifed his kite : and Mr. Dalibard fays, that Mr. Monnier, a phyfician of St. Germain en Laye, member of the Academy of Sciences at Paris, and Mr. Bertier of the Oratory at Montmorency, a correfpondent of the Academy, were both ftruck down by ftrokes of lightning, as they were taking fparks from their apparatus †.

BUT the greateft fufferer by experiments with lightning, fince mankind have introduced fo dangerous a fubject of their inquiries, was profeffor Richman of Peterfburgh

* Phil. Tranf. Vol. xlviii. pt. i. p. 205.
† Dalibard's Franklin, Vol. ii. p. 129.

before mentioned. He was ftruck dead, on the 6th of Auguft 1753, by a flafh of lightning drawn by his apparatus into his own room, as he was attending to an experiment he was making with it. There were two accounts of this fatal accident communicated to the Royal Society, one by Dr. Watfon who had it from the beft authority*; and the other tranflated from the High Dutch †. From both thefe the following is extracted.

THE profeffor had provided himfelf with an inftrument which he called an *electrical gnomon*, the ufe of which was to meafure the ftrength of electricity. It confifted of a rod of metal terminating in a fmall glafs veffel, into which (for what reafon I do not know) he put fome brafs filings. At the top of this rod, a thread was faftened, which hung down by the fide of the rod when it was not electrified; but when it was, it avoided the rod, and ftood at a diftance from it, making an angle at the place where it was faftened. To meafure this angle, he had the arch of a quadrant faftened to the bottom of the iron rod.

HE was obferving the effect of the electricity of the clouds, at the approach of a thunder ftorm, upon this gnomon; and, of courfe, ftanding with his head inclined towards it, accompanied by Mr. Solokow (an engraver, whom he frequently took with him, to be a

* Phil. Tranf. Vol. xlviii. pt. ii. p. 765.
† Ibid. Vol. xlix. pt. i. p. 61.

joint

joint obferver of his electrical experiments, in order to reprefent them the better in cuts) when this gentleman, who was ftanding clofe to his elbow, obferved a globe of blue fire, as he called it, as big as his fift, jump from the rod of the gnomon towards the head of the profeffor, which was, at that inftant, at about a foot diftance from the rod.   This flafh killed Mr. Richman, but Mr. Solokow could give no account of the particular manner in which he was immediately affected by it: for, at the fame time that the profeffor was ftruck, there arofe a fort of fteam, or vapour, which intirely benumbed him, and made him fink down upon the ground; fo that he could not remember even to have heard the clap of thunder, which was very loud.

THE globe of fire was attended with a report as loud as that of a piftol: a wire, which brought the electricity to his metal rod, was broken to pieces, and its fragments thrown upon Mr. Solokow's cloaths. Half of the glafs veffel in which the rod of the gnomon ftood was broken off, and the filings of metal that were in it were thrown about the room.

UPON examining the effects of the lightning in the profeffor's chamber, they found the door-cafe half fplit through, and the door torn off, and thrown into the room *. They opened a vein of the breathlefs body twice, but no blood followed, and endeavoured to re-

---

* Phil. Tranf. Vol. xlviii. pt. ii. p. 763.

cover fenfation by violent chafing, but in vain. Upon turning the corpfe with the face downwards, during the rubbing, an inconfiderable quantity of blood ran out of the mouth. There appeared a red fpot on the forehead, from which fpirted fome drops of blood through the pores, without wounding the fkin. The fhoe belonging to the left foot was burft open, and, uncovering the foot at that place, they found a blue mark; from which it was concluded, that the electrical force of the thunder, having entered the head, made its way out again at that foot.

Upon the body, particularly on the left fide, were feveral red and blue fpots, refembling leather fhrunk by being burnt. Many more blue fpots were afterwards vifible over the whole body, and in particular over the back. That upon the forehead changed to a brownifh red, but the hair of the head was not finged, notwithftanding the fpot touched fome of it. In the place where the fhoe was unripped, the ftocking was intire; as was the coat every where, the waiftcoat only being finged on the foreflap, where it joined the hinder; but there appeared on the back of Mr. Solokow's coat long narrow ftreaks, as if red hot wires had burned off the nap, and which could not be well accounted for.

When the body was opened the next day, twenty-four hours after he was ftruck, the cranium was very intire, having no fiffure, nor crofs opening ; the brain as found as it poffibly could be, but the tranfparent pellicles of the windpipe were exceffively tender, gave way, and eafily rent. There was fome extravafated blood in it, as like-wife in the cavities below the lungs; thofe of the breaft being quite found, but thofe towards the back of a brownifh black co-lour, and filled with more of the above mentioned blood : otherwife, none of the entrails were touched ; but the throat, the glands, and the thin inteftines were all in-flamed. The finged leather-coloured fpots penetrated the fkin only. Twice twenty-four hours being elapfed, the body was fo far corrupted that it was with difficulty they got it into a coffin *.

* Phil. Tranf. Vol. xlix. pt. i. p. 67.

SECTION

SECTION XI.

OBSERVATIONS ON THE GENERAL STATE OF
ELECTRICITY IN THE ATMOSPHERE, AND
ITS MORE USUAL EFFECTS.

ELECTRICIANS, after obferving the
great quantity of electric matter with
which the clouds are charged during a thunder ftorm, began to attend to the leffer quantities of it which might be contained in the
common ftate of the atmofphere, and the
more ufual effects of this great and general
agent in nature. Mr. Monnier, whofe obfervations of the electricity of the air during a
thunder ftorm have been already mentioned,
was the firft who found that there was very
often, and perhaps always, a quantity of electric matter in the atmofphere, when there
was no appearance of thunder. This he confirmed by decifive experiments, made at St.
Germain en Laye, and publifhed in a memoir
read at the Royal Academy of Sciences at Paris
November the 15th, 1752 *.

BUT more accurate experiments upon the
electricity of the air were made by the Abbé
Mazeas, at Chateau de Maintenon, during
the months of June, July, and October 1753,
and communicated to the Royal Society, in a
letter to Dr. Stephen Hales.

* Phil. Tranf. Vol. xlviii. pt. i. p. 203.

THE

THE Abbé's apparatus confifted of an iron rod 370 feet long, raifed ninety feet above the horizon. It came down from a very high room in the caftle, where it was faftened to a filken cord fix feet long; and it was carried from thence to the fteeple of the town, where it was likewife faftened to another filken cord of eight feet long, and fheltered from rain. And a large key was fufpended, by the end of this wire, in order to receive the electric fluid.

ON the 17th of June, when he began his experiments, the electricity of the air was fenfibly felt every day, from fun rife till feven or eight in the evening, except in moift weather, when he could perceive no figns of electricity. In dry weather, the wire attracted minute bodies at no greater diftance than three or four lines. He repeated the experiment carefully every day, and conftantly obferved, that, in weather void of ftorms, the electricity of a piece of fealing-wax of two inches long was above twice as ftrong as that of the air. This obfervation inclined him to conclude, that in weather of equal drinefs the electricity of the air was always equal.

IT did not appear to him that hurricanes and tempefts increafed the electricity of the air, when they were not accompanied with thunder; for that, during three days of a very violent continual wind, in the month of July, he was obliged to put fome duft within four or five lines of the conductor, before any fenfible attraction could be perceived.

THE

Plate II.

His of Electricity

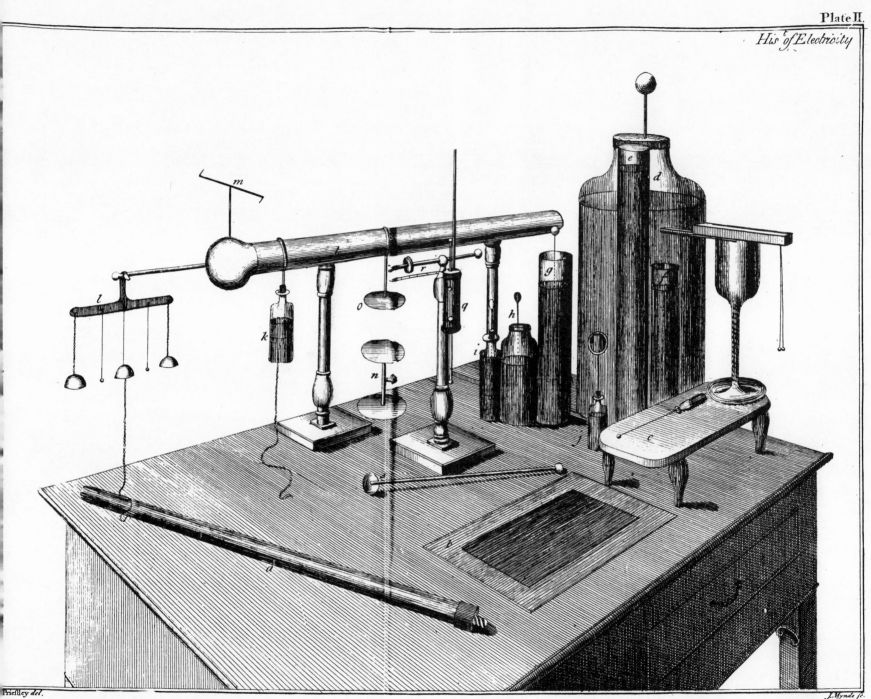

THE direction of the winds, whether Eaft, Weft, North, or South, made no fenfible alteration in the electricity of the air, except when they were moift.

IN the drieft nights of that fummer, he could difcover no figns of electricity in the air; but it returned in the morning when the fun began to appear above the horizon, and vanifhed again in the evening, about half an hour after fun-fet.

THE ftrongeft common electricity of the atmofphere, during that fummer, was perceived in the month of July, on a very dry day, the heavens being very clear, and the fun extremely hot. The diftance of ten or twelve lines was then fufficient for the approach of the duft to the conductor, in order to fee the particles rife in a vertical direction, like the filings of iron on the approach of a magnet.

ON the 27th of June, at two in the afternoon, he perceived fome ftormy clouds rifing above the horizon, and immediately went up to his apparatus; and, having applied the duft to the key, it was attracted with a force which increafed in proportion as the clouds reached the zenith. When they had come nearly over the wire, the duft was fo impetuoufly repelled, as to be entirely fcattered from the paper. He drew confiderable fparks from it, though there was neither thunder nor lightning. When the ftormy clouds were in the zenith of his wire, he obferved that the electricity was increafed to fuch a degree, that

E e 4　　　　even

even the filken thread attracted light bodies at the diftance of feven or eight inches.

THESE ftormy clouds remained about two hours above the horizon, without either thunder or lightning; nor did a very heavy rain diminifh the electricity, except about the end, when the clouds began to be diffipated *.

MR. KINNERSLEY obferved, that when the air was in its drieft ftate, there was always a confiderable quantity of electricity in it, and which might be eafily drawn from it. Let a perfon, he fays, in a negative ftate, ftanding out of doors, in the dark, when the air is dry, hold, with his arm extended, a long fharp needle, pointing upwards, and he will foon be convinced that electricity may be drawn out of the air; not indeed very plentifully, for, being a bad conductor, it feems loth to part with it, yet fome will evidently be collected. The air near the perfon's body, having lefs than the natural quantity, will have none to fpare; but his arm being extended, as above, fome will be collected from the remoter air, and will appear luminous as it converges to the point of the needle.

LET a perfon electrified negatively, he fays, prefent the point of a needle horizontally, to a cork ball fufpended by filk, and the ball will be attracted towards the point, till it has parted with fo much of its natural quantity of electricity, as to be in a negative ftate, in the

* Phil. Tranf. Vol. xlviii. pt. i. p. 377, &c.

fame

fame degree with the perfon who holds the needle; then it will recede from the point, being, as he fuppofes, attracted the contrary way by the electricity of greater denfity in the air behind it. But as this opinion, he plea- fantly fays, feems to deviate from *electrical orthodoxy*, he would be glad to fee thefe phe- nomena better accounted for by the fuperior and more penetrating genius of his friend Dr. Franklin, to whom he is writing.

WHETHER the electricity in the air, in clear dry weather, be of the fame denfity at the height of 200 or 300 yards, as near the fur- face of the earth, he thought might be fatif- factorily determined by Dr. Franklin's old ex- periment of the kite.

THE twine, he fays, fhould have through- out a very fmall wire in it, and the ends of the wire, where the feveral lengths are unit- ed, ought to be tied down with a waxed thread, to prevent their acting in the man- ner of points.

WHEN he wrote this letter, he had tried the experiment twice, when the air was as dry as it ever is in that country, and fo clear, that not a cloud had been feen, and found the twine each time in a fmall degree electrified pofitively *.

THE preceding obfervations of Mr. Mon- nier, Mr. Mazeas, and Mr. Kinnerfley, fall far fhort of the extent and accuracy of thofe of Signior Beccaria; whofe obfervations on

* Phil. Tranf. Vol. liii. pt. i. p. 87.

the

the general ſtate of electricity in the atmoſphere I have reſerved for the laſt place of the
ſection, becauſe they are the moſt conſiderable
though they were all made independent of,
and, many of them, prior to thoſe mentioned
before.

He obſerved that, during very high winds,
his apparatus gave no ſigns of being electrified *. Indeed he found that in three different
ſtates of the atmoſphere, he could find no
electricity in the air. 1. In windy and clear
weather. 2. When the ſky was covered with
diſtinct and black clouds, that had a ſlow motion. 3. In moiſt weather, not actually rain-
ing †. In a clear ſky, when the weather was
calm, he always perceived ſigns of a moderate
electricity, but interrupted. In rainy weather,
without lightning, his apparatus was always
electrified a little time before the rain fell,
and during the time of the rain, but it ceaſed to be affected a little before the rain was
over.

The higher his rods reached, or his kites
flew, the ſtronger ſigns they gave of their being electrified ‡. Alſo longer ſtrings or cords,
extended and inſulated in the open air, acquired electricity ſooner than thoſe which
were ſhorter. A cord 1500 Paris feet long,
ſtretched over the river Po, was as ſtrongly
electrified during a ſhower, without thunder, as a metallic rod, to bring lightning

* Lettere dell' elettriciſmo, p. 106.
† Ibid. p. 166.   ‡ Ibid. p. 114.

into

into his houfe, had been in any thunder ftorm *.

Having two rods for bringing the lightning into his houfe, 140 feet afunder, he obferved, that if he took a fpark from the higher of them, the fpark from the other, which was thirty feet lower, was at that inftant leffened; but, what is remarkable, is that its power revived again, though he kept his hand upon the former †.

He imagined that the electricity communicated to the air might fometimes furnifh fmall fparks to his apparatus; fince the air parts with the electricity it has received very flowly, and therefore the equilibrium of the electric matter in the air will not be reftored fo foon as in the earth and clouds ‡.

Among the effects of a moderate electricity in the atmofphere, Signior Beccaria reckons *rain, hail*, and *fnow*.

Clouds that bring rain, he thought, were produced in the fame manner as thunder clouds, only by a more moderate electricity. He defcribes them at large, and the refemblance which all their phenomena bear to thofe of thunder clouds is indeed very ftriking §.

He notes feveral circumftances attending rain without lightning, which make it very probable, that it is produced by the fame caufe as when it is accompanied with lightning. Light has been feen among the clouds by

---

* Lettere dell' elettricifmo, p. 165.   † Ibid. p. 175.
‡ Ibid. p. 347.   § Ibid. p. 284.

night

night in rainy weather ; and even by day rainy clouds are fometimes feen to have a brightnefs evidently independent of the fun *. The uniformity with which the clouds are fpread, and with which the rain falls, he thought were evidences of an uniform caufe like that of electricity †. The intenfity of electricity in his apparatus generally corre- fponded very nearly, to the quantity of rain that fell in the fame time ‡. Nor is any thing to be inferred to the contrary of this fuppofition from the apparatus not being al- ways electrified during rain. It has fome- times failed during thunder. Indeed it fol- lows from his general theory, that the elec- tricity of his apparatus could not always cor- refpond to the electricity of the clouds; fince it muft in fome meafure depend upon the fi- tuation of the obfervatory, with refpect to thofe parts of the earth or clouds which are giving or taking electric fire. This was con- firmed by an obfervation which he made up- on one thunder cloud, which paffed over his obfervatory. At its approach his apparatus was electrified pofitively, when it was direct- ly over him all figns of electricity ceafed, and when it was paffed, his apparatus was elec- trified negatively §. This obfervation very much favours his general theory of thunder clouds.

SOMETIMES all the phenomena of thunder, lightning, hail. rain, fnow, and wind, have

* Lettere deli' elettricifmo, p. 288.   † Ibid. p. 299.
‡ Ibid. p. 307.   § Ibid. p. 310.

been

been obferved at one time; which fhows the
connection they all have with fome common
caufe *.

SIGNIOR BECCARIA, therefore, fuppofes
that, previous to rain, a quantity of electric
matter efcapes out of the earth, in fome place
where there was a redundancy of it; and, in
its afcent to the higher regions of the air,
collects and conducts into its path a great
quantity of vapours. The fame caufe that
collects, will condenfe them more and more :
till, in the places of the neareft intervals, they
come almoft into contact, fo as to form fmall
drops; which uniting with others as they
fall, come down, in rain. The rain will be
heavier in proportion as the electricity is more
vigorous, and the cloud approaches more
nearly to a thunder cloud †.

HE imitated the appearance of clouds that
bring rain by infulating himfelf between the
rubber and conductor of his electrical machine,
and with one hand dropping *colophonia* into a
fpoon faftened to the conductor, and holding
a burning coal, while his other hand communicated with the rubber. In thefe circumftances the fmoke fpread along his arm, and,
by degrees, all over his body, till it came to
the other hand that communicated with the
rubber. The lower furface of this fmoke was
every where parallel to his cloaths, and the
upper furface was fwelled and arched like
clouds replete with thunder and rain ‡. In

* Lettere dell' elettricifmo, p. 290. 345.   † Ibid. p. 305.
‡ Ibid. p. 294.

this

this manner, he fuppofes, the clouds that bring rain diffufe themfelves from over thofe parts of the earth which abound with electric fire, to thofe parts that are exhaufted of it; and, by letting fall their rain, reftore the equilibrium between them.

SIGNIOR BECCARIA thought that the electricity communicated to the air, which both receives and parts with it flowly, would account for the retention of vapours in a clear fky; for fmall disjoined clouds, not difperfed into rain; for the fmaller and lighter clouds in the higher regions of the air, which are but little affected by electricity; and alfo for the darker, heavy, and fluggifh clouds in the lower regions, which retain more of it *. The degree of electricity which he could communicate to the air of his room, notwithftanding its being in contact with the floor, the walls, &c. made this appear to him both poffible and probable †.

HE even imagined, that fome alteration in the weight of the air might be made by this electricity of it ‡. He obferved his barometer to fall a little immediately upon a flafh of lightning; but he acknowledges that this circumftance is no fufficient foundation to fuppofe that electricity will account for *much* variation of the height of the barometer §. But he thought that the phenomena of rain favoured the fuppofition, that the electric matter in the air did, in fome meafure, leffen its pref-

---

* Lettere dell' elettricifmo, p. 348, 349.
† Ibid. p. 350.   ‡ Ibid.   § Ibid. p. 353.

fure.

fure. For when the electric matter is actually in the air, collecting and condensing the vapours, the barometer is lowest. When the communication is made between the earth and the clouds by the rain, the quickfilver begins to rife; the electric matter, which fupported part of the preffure, being difcharged. And this, he fhows, will be the cafe whether the electricity in the air be pofitive or negative *.

HAIL, this ingenious philofopher fuppofes to be formed in the higher regions of the air, where the cold is intenfe, and where the electric matter is very copious. In thefe circumftances, a great number of particles of water are brought near together, where they are frozen, and in their defcent collect other particles : fo that the denfity of the fubftance of the hail-ftone grows lefs and lefs from the center; this being formed firft, in the higher regions, and the furface being collected in the lower. Agreeable to this, it is obferved, that, in mountains, hail-ftones, as well as drops of rain, are very fmall; there being but fmall fpace through which they can fall, and thereby increafe their bulk. Drops of rain and hail agree alfo in this circumftance, that the more intenfe is the electricity that forms them, the larger they are †. Motion is known to promote freezing, and fo the rapid motion of the electrified clouds may promote that effect in the air ‡.

* Lettere dell' ellettricifmo, p. 354. † Ibid. p. 314.
‡ Ibid. p. 318,

CLOUDS

CLOUDS of fnow differ in nothing from clouds of rain, but in the circumftance of cold, which freezes them. Both the regular diffufion of fnow, and the regularity in the ftructure of the parts of which it confifts (particularly fome figures of fnow or hail, which he calls *rofette*, and which fall about Turin) fhow the clouds of fnow to be actuated by fome uniform caufe, like electricity *. He even endeavours, very particularly, to fhow in what manner certain configurations of fnow are made, by the uniform action of electricity †. All thefe conjectures about the caufe of hail and fnow were confirmed by obferving, that his apparatus never failed to be electrified by fnow, as well as by rain.

A MORE intenfe electricity unites the particles of hail more clofely than the more moderate electricity does thofe of fnow. In like manner, we fee thunder clouds more denfe than thofe which merely bring rain, and the drops of rain are larger in proportion, though they often fall not from fo great a height ‡.

I SHALL conclude this fection with obferving, that profeffor Winthrop found his apparatus to be ftrongly electrified for feveral hours, while the fnow, which fell the day before (and which had not electrified his apparatus while it was falling) was driven about by a high wind the fame he had obferved twice before. Franklin's Letters, new edition, p. 494.

* Lettere dell' ellettricifmo, p. 320. 322. 325.
† Ibid. p. 325. 331. 333.   ‡ Ibid. p. 328.

SECTION

SECTION XII.

THE ATTEMPTS THAT HAVE BEEN MADE
TO EXPLAIN SOME OF THE MORE UN-
USUAL APPEARANCES IN THE EARTH
AND. HEAVENS BY ELECTRICITY.

IN the two preceding sections of this period, relating to the electricity of the atmosphere, the experiments and observations
of Signior Beccaria have made a principal
figure; and the materials I have collected
from him make a no less considerable part of
this. They who may have thought he in-
dulged too much to imagination before, will
think him absolutely extravagant here; but
his extravagancies, if they be such, are those
of a great genius; and had he a thousand
more such extravagancies, I should, with
pleasure, have followed him through them
all.

THE meteor, usually called a *falling star*,
has hitherto puzzled all philosophers. Signior
Beccaria makes it pretty evident, that it is an
electrical appearance; and the fact which he
relates as a proof of it, is exceedingly curious
and remarkable.

As he was one time sitting with a friend
in the open air, an hour after sun-set, they
saw what is called a falling star directing its
course towards them, and apparently growing
larger and larger, till it disappeared not far

F f   from

from them; when it left their faces, hands, and cloaths, with the earth, and all the neighbouring objects, suddenly illuminated, with a diffused and lambent light, attended with no noise at all. While they were starting up, standing, and looking at one another, surprised at the appearance, a servant came running to them out of a neighbouring garden, and asked them if they had seen nothing; for that he had seen a light shine suddenly in the garden, and especially upon the streams which he was throwing to water it *.

ALL these appearances were evidently electrical; and Signior Beccaria was confirmed in his conjecture, that electricity was the cause of them, by the quantity of electric matter which, as was mentioned before, he had seen gradually advancing towards his kite; for that, he says, had very much the appearance of a falling star. Sometimes also he saw a kind of *glory* round the kite, which followed it when it changed its place, but left some light, for a small space of time, in the place which it had quitted †.

THAT appearances, which bear evident marks of electricity, have a very sensible progressive motion, is demonstrated from a variety of meteorological observations. I shall relate one made by Mr. Chalmers, when he was on board the Montague under the command of Admiral Chambers. The account of it

* Lettere dell' elettricifmo, p. 111.
† Ibid. p. 130.

was

was read at the Royal Society, March the 22d, 1749.

ON the 4th of November 1749, in lat. 42° 48′ long. 9° 3′ he was taking an obfervation on the quarter-deck, about ten minutes before twelve, when one of the quartermafters defired he would look to the windward; upon which he obferved a large ball of blue fire rolling on the furface of the water, at about three miles diftance from them. They immediately lowered their top-fails, &c. but it came down upon them fo faft, that before they could raife the main-tack, they obferved the ball to raife almoft perpendicular, and not above forty or fifty yards from the main-chains; when it went off with an explofion as if hundreds of cannon had been fired at one time, and left fo great a fmell of brimftone, that the fhip feemed to be nothing but fulphur. After the noife was over, which, he believed, did not laft longer than half a fecond, they found their main top-maft fhattered into above a hundred pieces, and the main maft rent quite down to the heel. There were fome of the fpikes which nail the fifh of the main-maft drawn with fuch force out of the maft, and they ftuck fo faft in the main-deck, that the carpenter was obliged to take an iron crow to get them out. There were five men knocked down, and one of them greatly burnt by the explofion. They believed, that when the ball, which appeared to them to be of the bignefs of a large mill-ftone, rofe, it took the middle of the main top-maft, as the

head

head of the maſt above the hounds was not
ſplintered. They had a hard gale of wind
from the N. by W. to the N. N. E. for two
days before the accident, with a great deal of
rain and hail, and a large ſea. From the
northward they had no thunder or lightning,
neither before nor after the exploſion. The
ball came down from the North-Eaſt, and
went to the South-Weſt.

THAT the *Aurora Borealis* is an electrical
phenomenon was, I believe never diſputed,
from the time that lightning was proved to be
one. To the circumſtances of reſemblance
which had before been taken notice of between this phenomenon and electricity;
Signior Beccaria adds, that when the *Aurora
Borealis* has extended lower than uſual into
the atmoſphere, various ſounds, as of rumbling, and hiſſing, have been heard *.

MR. BERGMAN ſays, he has often obſerved
the magnetic needle to be diſturbed by a high
aurora borealis, but that he could never procure any electricity from them, either with
pointed metallic rods, or by means of a
kite †.

MR. CANTON (beſides his conjecture, mentioned before, p. 380, that the aurora borealis may be the flaſhing of electric fire from
poſitive towards negative clouds at a great
diſtance, through the upper part of the atmoſphere, where the reſiſtance is leaſt) ſuppoſes that the aurora borealis, which happens

* Elettriciſmo artificiale e naturale, p. 221.
† Phil. Tranſ, Vol. lii. pt. ii. p. 485.

at

at the time that the needle is difturbed by the heat of the earth, is the electricity of the heated air above it; and this, he fays, will appear chiefly in the northern regions, as the alteration in the heat of the air in thofe parts will be the greateft. This hypothefis, he adds, will not feem improbable, if it be confidered, that electricity is now known to be the caufe of thunder and lightning, that it has been extracted from the air at the time of an aurora borealis; that the inhabitants of the northern countries obferve the aurora to be remarkably ftrong, when a fudden thaw happens after fevere cold weather; and that the curious in thefe matters are now acquainted with a fubftance that will, without friction, both emit and abforb the electric fluid, only by the increafe or diminution of its heat; meaning the tourmalin, in which he had difcovered that property *.

In a paper, dated November the 11th, 1754, he fays he has fometimes known the air to be electrical in clear weather, but never at night, except when there has appeared an aurora borealis, and then but to a fmall degree, which he had feveral opportunities of obferving that year. How far pofitive and negative electricity in the air, with a proper quantity of moifture between, to ferve as a conductor, will account for this, and other meteors, fometimes feen in a ferene fky, he leaves to be inquired into †.

* Phil. Tranf. Vol. li. pt. i. p. 403.
† Ibid. Vol. xlviii. pt. ii. p. 784.

F f 3   SIGNIOR

SIGNIOR BECCARIA takes some pains to show that *water spouts* have an electrical origin. To make this more evident, he first describes the circumstances attending their appearance, which are the following.

THEY generally appear in calm weather. The sea seems to boil, and send up a smoke under them, rising in a hill towards the spout. At the same time, persons who have been near them have heard a rumbling noise. The form of a water spout is that of a speaking-trumpet, the wider end being in the clouds, and the narrower end towards the sea. The size is various, even in the same spout. The colour is sometimes inclining to white, and sometimes to black. Their position is sometimes perpendicular to the sea, sometimes oblique ; and sometimes the spout itself is in the form of a curve. Their continuance is very various, some disappearing as soon as formed, and some continuing a considerable time. One that he had heard of continued a whole hour. But they often vanish, and presently appear again in the same place *.

THE very same things that water spouts are at sea are some kinds of *whirlwinds* and *hurricanes* by land. They have been known to tear up trees, to throw down buildings, make caverns in the earth ; and, in all these cases, to scatter earth, bricks, stones, timber, &c. to a great distance in every direction †. Great

* Elettricismo artificiale e naturale, p. 206, &c.
† Ibid. p. 210.

quantities

quantities of water have been left, or raifed
by them, fo as to make a kind of deluge;
and they have always been attended with a
prodigious rumbling noife.

THAT thefe phenomena depend upon electricity cannot but appear very probable from
the nature of feveral of them ; but the conjecture is made more probable from the following additional circumftances. They generally appear in months peculiarly fubject to
thunder ftorms, and are commonly preceded,
accompanied, or followed by lightning, rain,
or hail; the previous ftate of the air being
fimilar. Whitifh or yellowifh flafhes of light
have fometimes been feen moving with prodigious fwiftnefs about them. And, laftly, the
manner in which they terminate exactly refembles what might be expected from the pro-
longation of one of the uniform protuberances
of electrified clouds, mentioned before, towards the fea ; the water and the cloud mutually attracting one another : for they fuddenly contract themfelves, and difperfe almoft
at once; the cloud rifing, and the water of
the fea under it falling to its level. But the
moft remarkable circumftance, and the moft
favourable to the fuppofition of their depending upon electricity is, that they have been
difperfed by prefenting to them fharp pointed
knives or fwords. This, at leaft, is the conftant practice of mariners, in many parts
of the world where thefe water fpouts abound;
and he was affured by feveral of them, that

the

the method has often been undoubtedly effectual *.

THE analogy between the phenomena of water fpouts and electricity, he fays, may be made vifible, by hanging a drop of water to a wire communicating with the prime conductor, and placing a veffel of water under it. In thefe circumftances, the drop affumes all the various appearances of a water fpout, both in its rife, form, and manner of difappearing. Nothing is wanting but the fmoke, which may require a great force of electricity to become vifible.

MR. WILCKE alfo confiders the water fpout as a kind of great electrical cone, raifed between the cloud ftrongly electrified, and the fea or the earth †, and he relates a very remarkable appearance which occurred to himfelf, and which ftrongly confirms his fuppofition. On the 20th of July 1758, at three o'clock in the afternoon, he obferved a great quantity of duft rifing from the ground, and covering a field, and part of the town in which he then was. There was no wind, and the duft moved gently towards the Eaft, where there appeared a great black cloud, which, when it was near his zenith, electrified his apparatus pofitively, and to as great a degree as ever he had obferved it to be done by natural electricity. This cloud paffed his zenith, and went gradually towards the Weft, the duft then following it, and continuing to

---

* Elettricifmo artificiale e naturale, p. 213.
† Wilcke, p. 142.

rife

rife higher and higher till it compofed a thick pillar, in the form of a fugar-loaf, and at length feemed to be in contact with the cloud. At fome diftance from this, there came, in the fame path, another great cloud, together with a long ftream of fmaller clouds, moving fafter than the preceding. Thefe clouds electrified his apparatus negatively, and when they came near the pofitive cloud, a flafh of lightning was feen to dart through the cloud of duft, the pofitive cloud, the large negative cloud, and as far as the eye could diftinguifh, the whole train of fmaller negative clouds which followed it. Upon this, the negative clouds fpread very much, and diffolved in rain, and the air was prefently clear of all the duft. The whole appearance lafted not above half an hour *.

To Signior Beccaria's theory of water fpouts and hurricanes, I fhall add a defcription of a hurricane in the Weft Indies, from the *Account of the European Settlements in America*, part of which is tranfcribed from the Philofophical Tranfactions. Both were evidently written without the moft diftant view to any philofophical theory, and leaft of all that of electricity; and yet thofe who are difpofed to favour this hypothefis may perceive feveral circumftances, which tend to ftrengthen it. I need not point them out.

" It is in the rainy feafon, principally in the month of Auguft, more rarely in July

* Remarks on Dr. Franklin's Letters, p. 348.

and

" and September, that they are affaulted by
" *hurricanes,* the moft terrible calamity to
" which they are fubject from the climate.
" This deftroys, at one ftroke, the labour of
" many years, and fruftrates the moft exalt-
" ed hopes of the planter; and often juft at
" the moment when he thinks himfelf out of
" the reach of fortune. It is a fudden and
" violent ftorm of wind, rain, thunder, and
" lightning; attended with a furious fwelling
" of the fea, and fometimes with an earth-
" quake; in fhort, with every circumftance
" which the elements can affemble that is ter-
" rible and deftructive.

" First they fee, as a prelude to the en-
" fuing havock, whole fields of fugar canes
" whirled into the air, and fcattered over the
" face of the country. The ftrongeft trees of
" the foreft are torn up by the roots, and
" driven about like ftubble. Their wind-
" mills are fwept away in a moment. Their
" works, their fixtures, the ponderous copper
" bóilers and ftills, of feveral hundred weight,
" are wrenched from the ground, and batter-
" ed to pieces. Their houfes are no protec-
" tion : the roofs are torn off at one blaft,
" whilft the rain, which in an hour rifes five
" feet, rufhes in upon them with an irrefiftible
" violence.

" There are figns, which the Indians of
" thefe iflands taught our planters, by which
" they can prognofticate the approach of a
" hurricane. It comes on either in the quar-
" ters, or at the full or change of the moon.

If

" If it will come on at the full moon, you be-
" ing at the change, obferve thefe figns.
" That day you will fee the fky very turbu-
" lent. You will obferve the fun more red
" than at other times. You will perceive a
" dead calm, and the hills clear of all thofe
" clouds and mifts which ufually hover about
" them. In the clefts of the earth, and in
" the wells, you will hear a hollow rumbling
" found, like the rufhing of a great wind. At
" night the ftars feem much larger than ufual,
" and furrounded with a fort of burs. The
" North-weft fky has a black and menacing
" look, and the fea emits a ftrong fmell, and
" rifes into vaft waves, often without any
" wind. The wind itfelf now forfakes its
" ufual fteady Eafterly ftream, and fhifts
" about to the Weft; from whence it fome-
" times blows, with intermiffions, violent-
" ly and irregularly, for about two hours
" at a time. You have the fame figns at the
" full of the moon. The moon itfelf is fur-
" rounded with a great bur, and fometimes
" the fun has the fame appearance *."

THE firft perfon who advanced that *earthquakes* were probably caufed by electricity,
was Dr. STUKELEY, upon occafion of the
earthquakes at London, on February the 8th,
and on March the 8th, 1749; and another
which affected various other parts of England,
the center being about Daventry in Northamp-

---

* Account of the European Settlements in America, Vol. ii.
p. 96, &c.   Phil. Tranf. abridged, Vol. ii. p. 106.

tonſhire, on the 30th of September 1750.
The papers which the Doctor delivered to the
Royal Society on theſe occaſions, and which
were read, March the 22d, 1749, and December the 6th, 1750, well deſerve the attention
of all philoſophers and electricians. I ſhall
here give the ſubſtance of both; only abridg-
ing, and differently arranging the materials
of them.

THAT earthquakes are not owing to ſubterraneous winds, fires, vapours, or any thing
that occaſions an exploſion, and heaves up
the ground, he thought might eaſily be concluded from a variety of circumſtances. In the
firſt place, he thought there was no evidence
of any remarkable cavernous ſtructure of the
earth; but that, on the contrary, there is
rather reaſon to preſume, that it is, in a great
meaſure, ſolid; ſo as to leave little room for
internal changes and fermentations within its
ſubſtance; nor do coal-pits, he ſays, when on
fire, ever produce any thing reſembling an
earthquake.

IN the ſecond earthquake at London, there
was no ſuch thing as fire, vapour, ſmoke,
ſmell, or an eruption of any kind obſerved,
though the ſhock affected a circuit of thirty
miles in diameter. This conſideration alone,
of the extent of ſurface ſhaken by an earthquake, he thought was ſufficient to overthrow
the ſuppoſition of its being owing to the ex-
panſion of any ſubterraneous vapours. For it
could not poſſibly be imagined, that ſo im-
menſe a force, as could act upon that compaſs
of

of ground inftantaneoufly fhould never break
the furface of it, fo as to be difcoverable to the
fight or fmell ; when fmall fire balls, burfting
in the air, have inftantly propagated a fulphureous fmell all around them, to the diftance of feveral miles.

BESIDES, the operation of this great fermentation, and production of elaftic vapours,
&c. ought to be many days in continuance,
and not inftantaneous ; and the evaporation of
fuch a quantity of inflammable matter would
require a long fpace of time.

HE thought that if vapours and fubterraneous fermentations, explofions, and eruptions
were the caufe of earthquakes, they would
abfolutely ruin the whole fyftem of fprings
and fountains wherever they had once been :
which is quite contrary to fact, even where
they have been frequently repeated. Mentioning the great earthquake which happened
A. D. 17, when no lefs than thirteen great
cities of Afia Minor were deftroyed in one
night, and which may be reckoned to have
fhaken a mafs of earth 300 miles in diameter,
he afks, How can we poffibly conceive the action of any fubterraneous vapours to produce
fuch an effect fo inftanteoufly? How came it
to pafs, that the whole country of Afia Minor
was not at the fame time deftroyed, its mountains reverfed, its fountains and fprings broken up, and ruined for ever, and the courfe
of its rivers quite changed? Whereas, nothing
fuffered but the cities. There was no kind of
altera-

alteration in the furface of the country, which, indeed, remains the fame to this day.

To make the hypothefis of fubterraneous vapours, &c. being the caufe of earthquakes the more improbable, he obferves, that any fubterraneous power, fufficient to move a furface of earth thirty miles in diameter, as in the earthquakes which happened at London, muft be lodged at leaft fifteen or twenty miles below the furface of the earth, and therefore muft move an inverted cone of folid earth, whofe bafis is thirty miles in diameter, and axis fifteen or twenty miles; an effect which, he fays, no natural power could produce.

Upon the fame principle, the fubterraneous caufe of the earthquake in Afia Minor muft have moved a cone of earth of 300 miles in bafe, and 200 in the axis; which, he fays, all the gun-powder which has ever been made fince the invention of it would not have been able to ftir, much lefs any vapours, which could be fuppofed to be generated fo far below the furface.

It is not upon the principles of any fubterraneous explofion that we can, in the leaft, account for the manner in which fhips, far from any land, are affected during an earthquake; which feem as if they ftruck upon a rock, or as if fomething thumped againft their bottoms. Even the fifhes are affected by an earthquake. The ftroke, therefore, muft be occafioned by fomething that could communicate motion with unfpeakably greater velocity
than

than any heaving of the earth under the fea,
by the elafticity of generated vapours. This
could only produce a gradual fwell, and could
never give fuch an impulfe to the water, as
would make it feel like a ftone.

COMPARING all thefe circumftances, Dr.
Stukeley fays, he had always thought, that
an earthquake was an electrical fhock, of the
fame nature with thofe which are now become
familiar in electrical experiments. And this
hypothefis he thought was confirmed by the
phenomena preceding and attending earthquakes, particularly thofe which occafioned
this publication.

THE weather, for five or fix months before
the firft of thefe earthquakes, had been dry
and warm to an extraordinary degree, the
wind generally South and South-Weft, and
that without rain; fo that the earth muft have
been in a ftate of electricity ready for that particular vibration in which electrification confifts. On this account, he obferves, that the
Northern regions of the world are but little
fubject to earthquakes in comparifon with the
Southern, where the warmth and drynefs of
the air, fo neceffary to electricity, are common. All the flat country of Lincolnfhire
before the earthquake in September, though,
underneath it is a watery bog, yet, through
the whole preceding fummer and autumn (as
they can have no natural fprings in fuch a
level), the drought had been fo great on the
furface of the earth, that the inhabitants were
obliged to drive their cattle feveral miles to
water.

water. This, he fays, fhows how fit the dry
furface was for an electrical vibration; and alfo, which is of great importance, that earthquakes reach but very little below the furface
of the earth.

BEFORE the earthquake at London, all vegetables had been uncommonly forward. At
the end of February, in that year, all forts of
garden ftuff, fruits, flowers, and trees were
obferved to be as forward as, in other years,
about the middle of April; and electricity is
well known to quicken vegetation.

THE aurora borealis had been very frequent about the fame time, and had been
twice repeated juft before the earthquake, of
fuch colours as had never been feen before. It
had alfo removed to the South, contrary to
what is common in England; fo that fome
Italians, and people from other places where
earthquakes are frequent, obferving thefe
lights, and the peculiar temperature of the
air, did actually foretell the earthquake. For
a fortnight before the earthquake in September, the weather was ferene, mild, and calm;
and, one evening, there was a deep red Aurora Borealis, covering the cope of heaven,
very terrible to behold.

THE whole year had been exceedingly remarkable for fire-balls, thunder, lightning,
and corufcations, almoft throughout all England. Fire balls were more than once feen in
Ireland and Lincolnfhire, and particularly obferved. And all thefe kinds of meteors, the
Doctor fays, are rightly judged to proceed

teed from the electrical state of the atmosphere.

IN these previous circumstances of the state
of the earth and air, nothing, he says, is
wanting to produce the wonderful effect of an
earthquake, but the touch of some non-electric body, which must necessarily be had *ab
extra*, from the region of the air, or atmosphere. Hence, he infers that, if a non-electric cloud discharge its contents upon any
part of the earth in that highly electrical state,
an earthquake must necessarily ensue. As the
discharge from an excited tube produces a
commotion in the human body, so the discharge of electric matter from the compass of
many miles of solid earth must needs be an
earthquake, and the snap from the contact be
the horrid uncouth noise attending it.

THE Doctor had been informed, by those
who were up and abroad the night preceding
the earthquake, and early in the morning,
that coruscations in the air were extremely
frequent ; and that, a little before the earthquake, a large and black cloud suddenly covered the atmosphere, which probably occasioned the shock, by the discharge of a shower.
Dr. Childrey, he says, observes, that earthquakes are always preceded by rain, and
sudden tempests of rain in times of great
drought.

A SOUND was observed to roll from the
river Thames towards Temple Bar, before
the houses ceased to nod, just as the electrical
snap precedes the shock. This noise, an ob-

G g   server

ferver faid, was much greater than any he had ever heard. Others, who write upon earthquakes, commonly obferve, that the noife precedes the fhock: whereas it muft have been quite the contrary, if the concuffion had depended upon a fubterraneous eruption. This noife attending earthquakes, the Doctor thought, could not be accounted for, but upon the principles of electricity. The earthquake in September was attended with a rufhing noife, as if houfes were falling, and people, in fome places, were fo univerfally frighted, as to run out of their houfes, imagining that their own, and thofe of their neighbours were tumbling on their heads. In fome villages, the people, being at divine fervice, were much alarmed with the noife; which they faid, beyond all comparifon, exceeded all the thunder they had ever heard.

THE flames and fulphureous fmells, which are fometimes obferved during earthquakes, the Doctor thought were more eafily accounted for, from the fuppofition of their being electrical phenomena, than from their being occafioned by the eruption of any thing from the bowels of the earth.

THE impreffion made by an earthquake upon land and water, to the greateft diftances is, as was obferved before, inftantaneous, which could only be effected by electricity. In the earthquake in September, the concuffion was felt through a fpace of 100 miles in length, and forty in breadth; and, as far as could be judged, at the fame inftant of time.

That

That this tract of ground, which amounted
to 4000 fquare miles in furface, fhould be
thrown into fuch agitation in a moment, is
fuch a prodigy, the Doctor fays, as we could
never believe, or conceive, did we not know
it to be fact from our fenfes. But if we feek
the folution of it, we cannot think any natural power equal to it but that of electricity,
which acknowledges no fenfible tranfition of
time, no bounds.

THE little damage generally done by earthquakes, the Doctor thought to be an argument
of their being occafioned by a fimple vibration, or tremulous motion of the furface of
the earth, by an electrical fnap. This vibration, he fays, impreffed on the water, meeting with the folid bottoms of fhips and light-
ers, occafions that thump which is faid to be
felt by them : yet, of the millions of ordinary
houfes, over which it paffed, not one fell. A
confideration which fufficiently points out
what fort of a motion this was not; alfo what
fort of a motion it was, and whence derived ;
not a convulfion in the bowels of the earth,
but an uniform vibration along its furface,
like that of a mufical ftring, or what we put
a drinking-glafs into, by rubbing one's finger
on the edge; which yet, being brought to a
certain pitch, breaks the glafs; undoubtedly,
he adds, an electrical repulfion of its parts.

THAT earthquakes are electrical phenomena, is farther evident, he fays, from their
chiefly affecting the fea-coaft, places along
rivers, and, I may add, eminences. The

earth-

earthquake in September fpread moftly to the
North and South, which the Doctor fays is
the direction of the Spalding river, whereby
it was conveyed to the fea fhore, where it was
particularly fenfible; thence up Bofton channel, and fo up Bofton river to Lincoln. The
greateft part of this earthquake difplayed its
effects along, and between the two rivers
Welland and Avon, and that from their
fources down to their mouths. It likewife
reached the river Witham, which directed the
electrical ftream that way alfo to Lincoln;
for which reafon, meeting the fame coming
from Bofton, it was moft fenfibly felt there.
It reached, likewife, to the Trent at Notting-
ham, which conveyed it to Newark.

THE firft electrical ftroke in this earthquake feemed to the Doctor to have been
made on the high ground about Daventry, in
Northamptonfhire. From thence it defcended chiefly Eaftward, and along the river Welland, from Harborough to Stamford, Spalding, and the fea; and along the rivers Avon
and Nen to Northampton, Peterborough,
Wifbich, and the fea. It fpread itfelf all over
the vaft level of the ifle of Ely, promoted by
a great number of canals, natural and artificial, made for draining that country. It was
ftill conducted Eaftward, by Mildenhall river
in Suffolk, to Bury, and the parts adjacent.
All thefe circumftances duly confidered were
to him a confirmation of the doctrine he advanced on this fubject.

LASTLY,

LASTLY, the Doctor adds, as a farther argument in favour of his hypothesis, that pains in the back, rheumatic, hysteric, and nervous cafes; head-aches, cholics, &c. were felt by many people of weak constitutions, for a day or two after the earthquake; just as they would after electrification; and, to some, these diforders proved fatal.

IN what manner the earth and atmosphere are put into that electrical and vibratory state, which prepares them to give or receive that snap and shock, which we call an earthquake, and whence it is that this electric matter comes, the Doctor does not pretend to say, but thinks it as difficult to account for as magnetism, gravitation, muscular motion, and many other secrets in nature *.

To these obfervations of Dr. Stukeley, I shall add some circumstances which were obferved by Dr. Hales, in the earthquake at London, on March the 8th, 1749, as tending to strengthen the hypothesis of its being caused by electricity; though the Doctor, who relates them, thought that the electric appearances were only occafioned by the great agitation which the electric fluid was put into, by the shock of so great a mass of the earth.

AT the time of the earthquake, about twenty minutes before six in the morning, the Doctor, being awake in bed, on a ground floor, at a houfe near the church of St. Mar-

* Phil. Tranf. abridged, Vol. x. p. 526. 535. and p. 541. 551.

tin's

tin's in the Fields, very fenfibly felt his bed heave, and heard an obfcure rufhing noife in the houfe, which ended in a loud explofion up in the air, like that of a fmall cannon, The whole duration, from the beginning to the end, feeming to be about four feconds.

THIS great noife, the Doctor conjectured, was owing to the rufhing, or fudden expan-fion of the electric fluid at the top of St. Mar-tin's fpire, where all the electric effluvia, which afcended along the large body of the tower, being ftrongly condenfed, and acce-lerated at the point of the weathercock, as they rufhed off, made fo much the louder ex-panfive explofion.

THE Doctor farther fays, that the foldiers, who were upon duty in St. James's park, and other perfons who were then up, faw a blackifh cloud, and a confiderable lightning, juft before the earthquake began *.

MR. HARTMAN is of opinion that elec-tricity is the caufe of earthquakes, and gives a fuccinct enumeration of all the circumftances which favour this hypothefis †.

MY reader, who has feen to how great an extent Signior Beccaria has already carried the principles of electricity, will have no doubt but that he fuppofes *earthquakes* to be derived from that caufe. And indeed, without any knowledge of what Dr. Stukeley had done, he did fuppofe them to be electrical phenomena ; but, contrary to the Doctor, imagined the

* Phil. Tranf. abridged, Vol. x. p. 540, 541.
† Abhandlung, p. 148.

electric

PLATE III.

His.t of Electricity

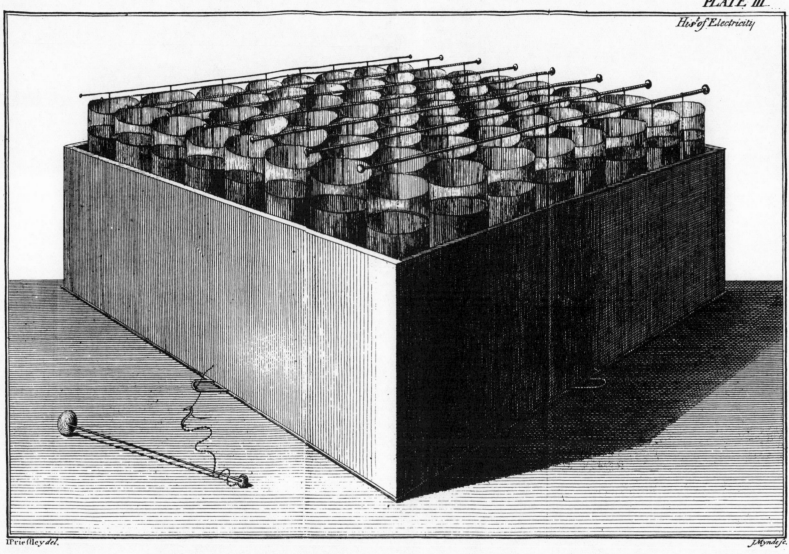

I. Priestley del.

J. Mynde sc.

electric matter which occafioned them to be lodged deep in the bowels of the earth, agreeable to his hypothefis concerning the origin of lightning.

IT is certain that if Signior Beccaria's account of the origin of thunder clouds be admitted, there will be little difficulty in admitting farther, that *earthquakes* are to be reckoned among the effects of electricity. For if the equilibrium of the electric matter can, by any means, be loft in the bowels of the earth; fo that the beft method of reftoring it fhall be by the fluid burfting its way into the air, and traverfing feveral miles of the atmofphere to come to the place where it is wanted; it may eafily be imagined, that violent concuffions may be given to the earth, by the fudden paffage of this powerful agent. And feveral circumftances attending earthquakes he thought rendered this hypothefis by no means improbable.

VOLCANOS are known to have a near connection with earthquakes; and flafhes of light, exactly refembling lightning, have frequently been feen to rufh from the top of Mount Vefuvius, at the time that afhes and other light matter have been carried out of it into the air, and been difperfed uniformly over a large tract of country. Of thefe he produces a great number of inftances, from the beft authority *.

* Lettere dell' elettricifmo, p. 226. 362, &c.

A RUM-

A RUMBLING noise, like thunder, is generally heard during an earthquake. At such times, also, flashes of light have been seen rising out of the ground, and darting up into the air. Real lightning hath sometimes occasioned small shakings of the earth, at least has been attended by them. But the strongest circumstance of resemblance which he observed is the same that Dr. Stukeley lays so much stress on, viz. the amazing swiftness with which the earth is shaken in earthquakes. An earthquake, says he, is by no means a gradual heaving, as we might have expected from other causes, but an instantaneous concussion, so that the fluidity of the water is no security against the blow. The very ships, many leagues off the coast, feel as if they struck against a rock.

THIS admirable philosopher, having imitated all the great phenomena of natural electricity in his own room, doth not let the earthquake escape him. He says, that if two pieces of glass, inclosing a thin piece of metal, be held in the hand, while a large shock is sent through them, a strong vibration, or concussion will be felt; which sometimes, as in Dr. Franklin's experiments, breaks them to pieces.

SIGNIOR BECCARIA thinks, that there are traces of electrical operations in the earthquake, that happened at Julian's attempt to rebuild the temple of Jerusalem *.

* Lettere dell' elettricismo, p. 363.

THAT

THAT the electric fluid is fometimes collected in the bowels of the earth, he thought
was probable from the appearance of *ignes
fatui* in mines, which fometimes happens,
and is very probably an electrical phenomenon *.

WHICH of thefe two philofophers have advanced the more probable opinion concerning
the feat of the electric matter which occafions
earthquakes, I fhall not pretend to decide. I
fhall only obferve that, perhaps, a more probable general hypothefis than either of them
may be formed out of them both. Suppofe
the electric matter to be, fome way or other,
accumulated on one part of the furface of the
earth, and, on account of the drynefs of the
feafon, not eafily to diffufe itfelf; it may, as
Signior Beccaria fuppofes, force itfelf a way
into the higher regions of the air, forming
clouds in its paffage out of the vapours which
float in the atmofphere, and occafion a fudden fhower, which may farther promote the
paffage of the fluid. The whole furface, thus
unloaded, will receive a concuffion, like any
other conducting fubftance on parting with, or
receiving a quantity of the electric fluid. The
rufhing noife will, likewife, fweep over the
whole extent of the country. And, upon
this fuppofition, alfo, the fluid, in its difcharge from the country, will naturally follow the courfe of the rivers, and alfo take the

---

* Dell' elettricifmo artificiale e naturale, p. 223.

advantage

advantage of any eminences, to facilitate its afcent into the higher regions of the air.

I SHALL clofe this account of the theory of lightning and other phenomena of the atmofphere, with an enumeration of the principal appearances of natural electricity obferved by the ancients, and which were never underftood before the difcovery of Dr. Franklin. It will be very eafy for me to do this, as I find them already collected to my hands by Dr. Watfon *.

A LUMINOUS appearance, which muft have been of an electrical nature, is mentioned by Plutarch in his life of Lyfander. He confidered it as a meteor.

PLINY, in his fecond book of Natural Hiftory, calls thofe appearances *ftars*, and tells us, that they fettled not only upon the mafts, and other parts of fhips, but alfo upon men's heads. *Exfiftunt*, fays that hiftorian, *ftellæ et in mari terrifque. Vidi nocturnis militum vigiliis inhærere pilis pro vallo fulgorem effigie ea: et antennis navigantium aliifque navium partibus, ceu vocali quodam fono infiftunt, ut volucres, fedem ex fede mutantes ——Geminæ autem falutares et profperi curfus prænunciæ; quarum adventu, fugari diram illam ac minacem appellatamque Helenam ferunt. Et ob id Polluci et Caftori id numen affignant, eofque in mari deos invocant. Hominum quoque capiti vefpertinis horis, magno præfagio circumfulgent.*

* Phil. Tranf. Vol. xlviii. pt. i. p. 210.

But,

But, adds he, thefe things are *incerta ratione et in naturæ majeftate abdita.*

" STARS make their appearance both at
" land and fea. I have feen a light in that
" form on the fpears of foldiers, keeping
" watch by night upon the ramparts. They
" are feen alfo on the fail-yards, and other
" parts of fhips, making an audible found,
" and frequently changing their places. Two
" of thefe lights forebode good weather, and
" a profperous voyage; and drive away *one*
" that appears fingle, and wears a threatening
" afpect. This the failors call Helen, but
" the *two* they call Caftor and Pollux, and
" invoke them as Gods. Thefe lights do
" fometimes, about the evening, reft on
" men's heads, and are a great and good
" omen. But thefe are among the awful
" myfteries of nature."

SENECA in his Natural Queftions, chap. i. takes notice of the fame phenomenon. *Gylippo, Syracufas petenti vifa eft ftella fupra ipfam lancem conftitiffe. In Romanorum caftris vifa funt ardere pila, ignibus fcilicet in illis delapfis.*

" A STAR fettled on the lance of Gylip-
" pus, as he was failing to Syracufe: and
" fpears have feemed to be on fire in the Ro-
" man camp."

IN Cæfar, de Bello Africano, cap. vi. edit. Amftel. 1686, we find them attending a violent ftorm. *Per id tempus fere Cæfaris exercitui res accidit incredibilis auditu; nempe*

Vir-

Virgiliarum figno confeĉto, circiter vigilia fe-
cunda noĉtis, nimbus cum faxea grandine fubito
eſt coortus ingens. Eadem noĉte legionis V. pi-
lorum cacumina fua ſponte arferunt.

" About that time, there was a very extra-
" ordinary appearance in the army of Cæfar.
" In the month of February, about the fecond
" watch of the night, there fuddenly arofe a
" thick cloud, followed by a fhower of ftones;
" and the fame night, the points of the
" fpears belonging to the fifth legion feemed
" to take fire."

LIVY, cap. xxxii. mentions two fimilar
faĉts. *In Sicilia militibus aliquot ſpicula, in*
Sardinia muro circumeunti vigilias equiti, fci-
pionem, quem in manu tenuerat, arſiſſe ; et litora
crebris ignibus fulfiſſe.

" THE fpears of fome foldiers in Sicily,
" and a walking-ftick, which a horfeman in
" Sardinia was holding in his hand, feemed to
" be on fire. The fhores were alfo luminous
" with frequent fires."

THESE appearances are called, both by the
French and Spaniards, inhabiting the coafts
of the Mediterranean, St. Helme's, or St.
Telme's fires ; by the Italians the fires of St.
Peter, and St. Nicholas ; and are frequently taken notice of by the writers of
voyages.

IF fome late accounts from France, adds
the Doĉtor, are to be depended upon, this
phenomenon has been obferved at Plauzet
for time immemorial, and Mr. Binon, the
Curé

Curé of the place fays, that for twenty-feven years, which he has refided there, in great ftorms accompanied with black clouds, and frequent lightning, the three pointed extremities of the of the crofs of the fteeple of that place appeared furrounded with a body of flame; and that when this phenomenon has been feen, the ftorm was no longer to be dreaded, and calm weather returned foon after.

MODERN hiftory furnifhes a great number of examples of flames appearing at the extremities of pointed metallic bodies projecting into the air. Little notice was taken of thefe, while the caufe of them was unknown; but fince their near affinity with lightning has been difcovered, they have been more attended to, and collected.

SECTION

S E C T I O N   XIII.

OBSERVATIONS ON THE USE OF METALLIC
CONDUCTORS TO SECURE BUILDINGS,
&c. FROM THE EFFECTS OF LIGHTNING.

THE former fections of this period relate
chiefly to the theory of electricity. In
the two next I fhall confider what has been
done towards reducing this fcience into practice. And, in the firft place, I fhall recite
the obfervations that have been made refpecting the ufe of metallic conductors, to fecure
buildings from lightning, as having the neareft
connection with the fubject of the fections immediately preceding.

DR. FRANKLIN's propofal to preferve buildings from the dreadful effects of lightning
was by no means a matter of mere theory.
Several ftriking facts, which occurred within
the period of which I am treating, demonftrate
its utility.

INNUMERABLE obfervations fhow how
readily metallic rods actually conduct lightning, and how fmall a fubftance of metal is
fufficient to difcharge great quantities of it.
Mr. Calendrini, who afterwards applied to
Dr. Watfon, to be informed of the beft methods of fecuring powder magazines, fays that
he himfelf was an eye-witnefs of the effect of
a flafh of lightning, where he obferved it had
ftruck the wire of a bell, and had been completely

pletely conducted by it, from one room of a
house to another, through a very small hole in
the partition. This observation was prior to
the discoveries of Dr. Franklin, but was recollected and recorded afterwards *.

DR. FRANKLIN himself, in a letter to Mr.
Dalibard, dated Philadelphia, June the 29th,
1755, relating what had been shown him of
the effects of lightning on the church of
Newbury in New England, observes, that a
wire not bigger than a common knitting
needle, did in fact conduct a flash of lightning, without injuring any part of the building as far as it went, though the force of it
was so great, that from the termination of the
wire down to the ground, the steeple was exceedingly rent and damaged, some of the
stones, even in the foundation, being torn
out, and thrown to the distance of twenty or
thirty feet. No part of the wire, however,
could be found, except about two inches at
each extremity, the rest being exploded, and
its particles dissipated in smoke and air, as the
Doctor says, like gunpowder by a common
fire. It had only left a black smutty track
upon the plaister of the wall along which it
ran, three or four inches broad, darkest in
the middle, and fainter towards the edges.
From the circumstances of this fact it was very
evident, that, had the wire been continued
to the foot of the building, the whole shock
would have been conducted without the least

* Phil. Tranf. Vol. liv. pt. i. p. 203.

injury

injury to it, though the wire would have been deſtroyed *.

BUT the moſt complete demonſtration of the real uſe of Dr. Franklin's method of ſecuring buildings from the effects of lightning, is Mr. Kinnerſley's account of what happened to the houſe of Mr. Weſt, a merchant of Philadelphia in Penſilvania, which was guarded by an apparatus conſtructed according to the directions of Dr. Franklin. It conſiſted of an iron rod, which extended about nine feet and an half above a ſtack of chimnies, to which it was fixed. It was more than half an inch in diameter in the thickeſt part, and went tapering to the upper end, in which there was a hole that received a braſs wire about three lines thick and ten inches long, terminating in a very acute point : the lower part of the apparatus joined to an iron ſtake, driven four or five feet into the ground.

MR. WEST judging, by the dreadful flaſh of lightning and inſtant crack of thunder, that the conductor had been ſtruck, got it examined; when it appeared, that the top of the pointed rod was melted, and the ſmall braſs wire reduced to ſeven inches and a half in length, with its top very blunt. The ſlendereſt part of the wire he ſuſpected, had been diſſipated in ſmoke; but ſome of it, where the wire was a little thicker, being only melted by the lightning, ſunk down (while in a fluid ſtate) and formed a rough irregular cap, lower

* Phil. Tranſ. Vol. xlix. pt. i. p. 309.

on

on one fide than on the other, round the upper end of what remained, and became intimately united with it. It is remarkable, that, notwithftanding the iron ftake, in which the apparatus terminated, was driven three or four feet into the ground, yet the earth did not conduct the lightning fo faft, but that, in thunder ftorms the lightning would be feen diffufed near the ftake two or three yards over the pavement, though at that time very wet with rain *.

In order to fecure fhips from fuftaining damage by lightning, Dr. Watfon, in a letter to Lord Anfon, read at the Royal Society, December the 16th, 1762, advifes, that a rod of copper, about the thicknefs of a goofe quill, be connected with the fpindles and iron work of the maft; and, being continued down to the deck, be from thence, in any convenient direction, fo difpofed, as always to touch the fea water †.

With refpect to powder magazines, Dr. Watfon advifed Mr. Calandrini above mentioned, that the apparatus to conduct the lightning from them be detached from the buildings themfelves, and conveyed to the next water.

What lately happened to St. Bride's church in London is a fufficient proof of the utility of metallic conductors for lightning. Dr. Watfon, who publifhed an account of this fact in the Philofophical Tranfactions, ob-

* Phil. Tranf. Vol. liii. pt. i. p. 96.
† Ibid. Vol. lii. pt. i. p. 633.

H h

ferves, that the lightning firft took a weathercock, which was fixed at the top of the
fteeple; and was conducted without injuring
the metal, or any thing elfe, as low as where
the large iron bar or fpindle which fupported
it (and which came down feveral feet into the
top of the fteeple) terminated. There, the
metallic communication ceafing, part of the
lightning exploded, cracked, and fhattered
the obelifk, which terminated the fpire of the
fteeple, in its whole diameter, and threw off
at that place feveral large pieces of Portland
ftone, of which the fteeple was built. Here
it likewife removed a ftone from its place, but
not far enough to be thrown down. From
thence the lightning feemed to have rufhed
upon two horizontal iron bars, which were
placed within the building crofs each other, to
give additional ftrength to the obelifk, almoft
at the bafe of it, and not much above the upper
ftory. At the end of one of thefe iron bars,
on the Eaft and North-Eaft fide, it exploded
again, and threw off a confiderable quantity
of ftone. Almoft all the damage done to the
fteeple, except near the top, was confined
to the Eaft and North-Eaft fide, and generally, where the ends of the iron bars had been
inferted into the ftone, or placed under it; and,
in fome places, by its violence in the ftone,
its paffage might be traced from one iron bar
to another.

It is very remarkable, that, to leffen the
quantity of ftone in this beautiful fteeple,
cramps of iron had been employed in feveral
parts

parts of it; and upon thefe, ftones of no great thicknefs had been placed, both by way of ornament, and to cover the cramped joint. In feveral places thefe ftones had, on account of their covering the iron, been quite blown off, and thrown away. A great number of ftones, fome of them large ones, were thrown from the fteeple, three of which fell upon the roof of the church, and did great damage to it; and one of them broke through the large timbers which formed the roof, and lodged in the gallery.

Upon the whole, the fteeple was found, on a furvey, to be fo much damaged in feveral of its parts, that eighty-five feet were taken down, in order to reftore it fubftantially; and the manner in which this fteeple was damaged completely indicated, as Dr. Watfon obferves, the great danger of infulated maffes of metal from lightning; and, on the contrary, evinced the utility and importance of maffes of metal continued, and properly conducted, in defending them from its direful effects. The iron and lead employed in this fteeple, in order to ftrengthen and preferve it, did almoft occafion its deftruction; though, after it was ftruck by the lightning, had it not been for thefe materials keeping the remaining parts together, a great part of the fteeple muft have fallen.

This building fuffered the more, on account of the thunder ftorm having been preceded by feveral very warm days. The nights had fcarce furnifhed any dew, the air

was

was quite dry, and in a ftate perfectly unfit
to part with its highly accumulated electricity,
without violent efforts. This great drynefs
had made the ftones of St. Bride's fteeple,
and all other buildings under the like circumftances, far lefs fit, than if they had been in
a moift ftate, to conduct the lightning, and
prevent the mifchief. For, though the thunder
ftorm ended in a heavy fhower of rain, none,
except a few very large drops, fell till after
the church was ftruck And Dr. Watfon had
no doubt, but that the fucceeding rain prevented many accidents of a fimilar kind, by
bringing down, with every drop of it, part of
the electric matter, and thereby reftoring the
equilibrium between the earth and clouds.

It is frequently obferved, he fays, that, in
attending to the apparatus for collecting the
electricity of the clouds, though the fky is
much darkened, and there have been feveral
claps of thunder, at no great diftance, yet
the apparatus will fcarcely be affected by it;
but that, as foon as the rain begins and falls
upon fo much of the apparatus as is placed in
the open air, the bells belonging to it will
ring, and the electrical fnaps fucceed each
other in a very extraordinary manner. This,
as he obferves, demonftrates, that every drop
of rain brings down part of the electric matter of a thunder cloud and diffipates it in the
earth and water, thereby preventing the mif-
chiefs of its violent and fudden explofion.
Hence when the heavens have a menacing appearance, a fhower of rain is much to be
wifhed for.

FROM

FROM all these considerations, Dr. Watson had no doubt, but that the mischief done to St. Bride's steeple was owing to the efforts of the lightning, after it had possessed the apparatus of the weathercock, endeavouring to force itself a passage from thence to the iron work employed in the steeple. As this must be done *per saltum*, as he expresses it, there being no regular metallic communication, it was no wonder, when its force was vehement, that it rent every thing which was not metallic that obstructed its easy passage; and that, in this particular instance, the ravages increased, as the lightning, to a certain distance, came down the steeple.

THE Doctor advises that, in order to have ocular demonstration when these metallic conductors do really discharge the lightning, they be discontinued for an inch or two, in some place convenient for observation; in which case the fire will be seen to jump from one extremity of the wire to the other. If any danger be apprehended from this discontinuance of the metallic conductor, he says that a loose chain may be ready to hang on, and complete the communication *.

MR. DELAVAL, who also gives an account of the same accident, observed, that, in every part of the building that was damaged, the lightning had acted as an elastic fluid, endeavouring to expand itself where it was accumulated in the metal; and that the effects

* Phil. Transf. Vol. liv. p. 201, &c.

were

were exactly fimilar to thofe which would
have been produced by gunpowder pent up in
the fame places, and exploded.

IN the fame paper Mr. Delaval gives it as
his opinion, that a wire, or very fmall rod of
metal, did not feem to have been a canal fufficiently large to conduct fo great a quantity
of lightning as ftruck this fteeple; efpecially
if any part of it, or of the metal communicating with it, was inclofed in the ftone work,
in which cafe, he thought, the application of
it would tend to increafe its bad effects, by
conducting it to parts of the building which it
might otherwife not have reached.

UPON the whole, he thought that a conductor of metal, lefs than 'fix or eight inches
in breadth, and a quarter of an inch in thicknefs (or an equal quantity of metal in any
other form that might be found more convenient) cannot with fafety be depended on,
where buildings are expofed to the reception
of a great quantity of lightning *.

MR. WILSON, in a paper written upon the
fame occafion, advifes, that pointed bars or
rods of metal be avoided in all conductors of
lightning.

As the lightning, he fays, muft vifit us
fome way or other, from neceffity, there can
be no reafon to invite it at all; but, on the
contrary, when it happens to attack our
buildings, we ought only fo to contrive our
apparatus, as to be able to carry the lightning

---

* Phil. Tranf. Vol. liv. p. 234.

away

away again, by fuch fuitable conductors, as will very little, if at all, promote any increafe of its quantity.

To attain this defirable end, in fome degree at leaft, he propofes, that the feveral buildings remain as they are at the top; that is, without having any metal above them, either pointed or not, by way of conductor; but that on the infide of the higheft part of the building, within a foot or two of the top, a rounded bar of metal be fixed, and continued down along the fide of the wall, to any kind of moifture in the ground *.

SIGNIOR BECCARIA whofe obfervations and experience with refpect to lightning give a weight to his opinion fuperior to that of any other man whatever, feems to think very differently from Mr. Wilfon on this fubject. He fays that no metallic apparatus can attract more lightning than it can conduct. And fo far is he from thinking one conductor, rounded at the top, and a foot or two under the roof fufficient; that if the building be of any extent, he advifes to have feveral of the ufual form; that is, pointed, and higher than the building. One conductor he thought fufficient for one tower, fteeple, or fhip; but he thought, two neceffary for the wing of a building 200 feet long, one at each extremity; three for two fuch wings, the third being fixed in the middle; and four for a fquare palace of the fame front, one at each corner †.

* Phil. Tranf. Vol. liv. p. 249.
† Lettere dell' elettricifmo, p. 278.

My readers at a diſtance from London will hardly believe me, when I inform them, that the elegant ſpire which has been the ſubject of a great part of this ſection, and which has been twice damaged by lightning (for it is now very probable, that a damage it received in the year 1750, was owing to the ſame cauſe) is now repaired, without any metallic conductor, to guard it in caſe of a third ſtroke.

S E C T I O N XIV.

Of MEDICAL ELECTRICITY

THE ſubject of medical electricity falls almoſt wholly within the period of which I am now treating. For, though ſome effects of electricity upon animal bodies had been noted by the Abbé Nollet, and a few diſeaſed perſons had ſaid they had received benefit from being electrified; yet very little had been done this way, and phyſicians had ſcarcely attended to 'it, till within this period; whereas electricity is now become a conſiderable article in the *materia medica*.

THE firſt account I have met with of the application of electricity to medical purpoſes is of Mr. C. Kratzenſtein, profeſſor of medicine at Halle; who, in the year 1744, cured a woman of a contracted little finger in a quarter of an hour. He alſo ſo far relieved a perſon who had two lame fingers, by once electrifying them, that he could play upon
the

the harpficord, which he had before been dif-
abled from doing. He alfo obferved, that a
man's pulfe, which had beat eighty in a fecond before he was electrified, immediately
after beat eighty-eight, and was prefently increafed to ninety-fix *.

THERE is, another celebrated inftance of
the cure of a palfy before this period; which
is that performed by Mr. Jallabert, profeffor
of philofophy and mathematics at Geneva, on
a lock-fmith of the age of fifty-two †, whofe
right arm had been paralytic fifteen years, occafioned by a blow of a hammer. He was
brought to Mr. Jallabert on the 26th of December 1747, and was almoft completely
cured by the 28th of February 1748. In this
interval he was frequently electrified, fparks
being taken from the arm, and fometimes the
electric fhock fent through it ‡. Mr. Jallabert's own account of this cure is very circumftantial. But it appears from the Abbé Nollet's account of his fecond journey to Italy,
that this perfon relapfed to the condition in
which Mr. Jallabert found him. See the
French tranflation of this book, vol. ii.
p. 396.

THE report of this cure performed at Geneva engaged Mr. Sauvages of the Academy
in Montpelier to attempt the cure of paralytics, in which he had confiderable fuccefs.
In one cafe it occafioned a falivation, and in

* Dantzick Memoirs, Vol. i. p. 294.
† Jallabert's Experiences, 143.
‡ Hiftoire, pt. iii. p. 36.

another

another a profuse fweat. Many paralytics, however, were electrified without any fuccefs. Indeed the prodigious concourfe of patients of all kinds, which the report of thefe cures brought together, was fo great, that few of them could be electrified, except very imperfectly. For two or three months together, twenty different patients were electrified every day. It is not furprifing to find, that the neighbouring populace confidered thefe cures as an affair of witchcraft, and that the operators were obliged to have recourfe to their priefts to undeceive them *. In the courfe of thefe experiments it was found, by very accurate obfervations made with a pendulum, that electrification increafes the circulation of the blood about one fixth.

ONE of the firft who attended to electricity in a medical way was Dr. Bohadtch a Bohemian ; who, in a treatife upon medical electricity, communicated to the Royal Society, gave it as his opinion, after the refult of much experience, that of all diftempers the *hemiplegia* feemed to be the moft proper object of electricity. He alfo thought it might be of ufe in intermitting fevers †.

THE palfy having happened to be the firft diforder in which electricity gave relief, there was a confiderable number of cafes publifhed pretty early, in which paralytics were faid to have found benefit from this new method of treatment. In the year 1757, Mr. Patric

---

* Hiftoire, p. 97.   † Phil. Tranf. Vol. xlvii. p. 351.

PLATE IV.

His'of Electricity.

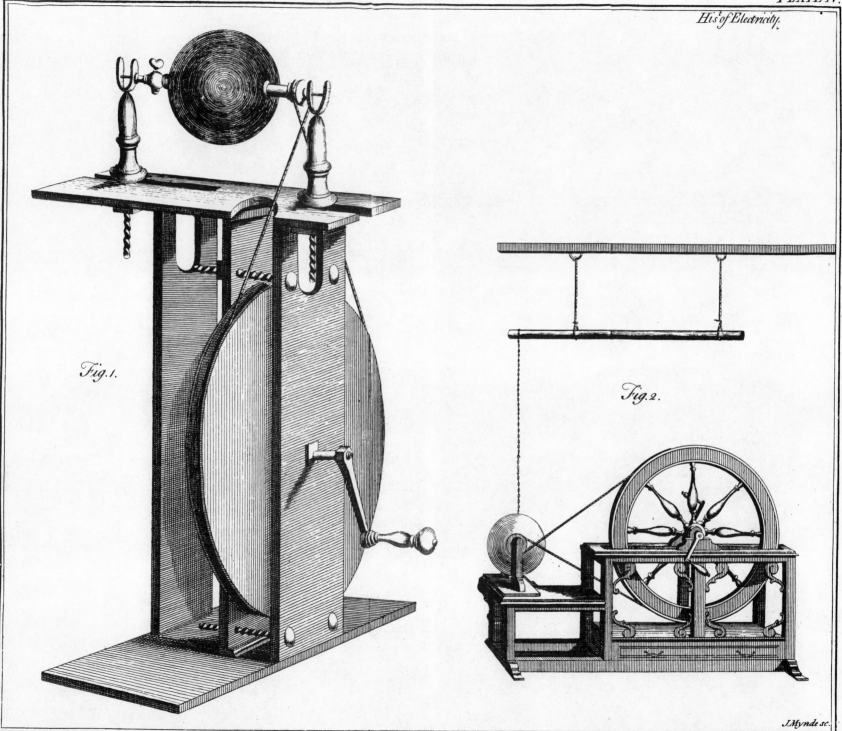

Fig. 1.

Fig. 2.

J. Mynde sc.

Brydone performed a complete cure of a hemi-plegia, and, indeed, an almoſt univerſal pa-ralytic affection, in about three days. The patient was a woman, aged thirty-three, and the palſy was of about two years continu-ance *. And John Godfrey Teſke, very near-ly cured a young man, of the age of twenty, of a paralytic arm, of which he had not had the leaſt uſe from the age of five years †.

THE Abbé Nollet's experiments upon pa-ralytics had no permanent good effect ‡. He obſerves, however, that, during fifteen or ſixteen years that he had electrified all ſorts of perſons, he had known no one bad effect to have ariſen from it to any of them §.

DR. HART, in a letter to Dr. Watſon, dat-ed Salop, March the 20th, 1756, mentions a cure performed by electricity upon a woman of twenty-three years of age, whoſe hand and wriſt had for ſome time been rendered uſeleſs by a violent contraction of the muſcles. She was not ſenſible of the firſt ſhock that was given her; but, as the ſhocks were repeated, the ſenſation increaſed, till ſhe was perfectly well. She was alſo cured a ſecond time, after a relapſe occaſioned by a cold ‖.

BUT perhaps the moſt remarkable caſe that has yet occurred of the uſe of electricity in curing a diſorder of this kind, and indeed of any that is incident to the human body was

* Phil. Tranſ. Vol. l. pt i. p. 392.
† Ibid. Vol. li. pt. i. p. 179.
‡ Recherches, p. 412.   § Ibid. p. 416.
‖ Phil. Tranſ. Vol. xlix. pt. ii. p 558.

of that dreadful diforder, an univerfal *tetanus*. It is related by Dr. Watfon in the Philofophical Tranfactions; and the account was read at the Royal Society the 10th of February 1763. The patient was a girl belonging to the Foundling hofpital, about feven years of age, who was firft feized with a diforder occafioned by the worms, and at length by an univerfal rigidity of her mufcles; fo that her whole body felt more like that of a dead animal than a living one. She had continued in this difmal condition above a month, and about the middle of November 1762, after all the ufual medicines had failed, Dr. Watfon began to electrify her; and continued to do it by intervals, till the end of January following; when every mufcle of her body was perfectly flexible, and fubfervient to her will, fo that fhe could not only ftand upright, but could walk, and even run like other children of her age *.

Dr. Edward Spry relates a complete cure which he made of a locked jaw and paralyfis, in the cafe of a girl of eighteen years of age. Small fhocks were given to the mufcles particularly affected †.

That electricity may he hurtful, and even in fome cafes in which analogy would lead us to promife ourfelves it might be of ufe, is evident from many cafes, and particularly from one related by Dr. Hart of Shrewfbury, in a letter to Dr. Watfon, which was read at the Royal Society, November the 14th, 1754.

* Phil. Tranf. Vol. liii. p. 10.   † Ibid. Vol. lvii. p. 88.

A YOUNG

A YOUNG girl about sixteen, whose right arm was paralytic, and greatly wasted in comparison of the other, on being electrified twice, became universally paralytic, and remained so above a fortnight ; when the new palsy was removed by proper medicines, though the first diseased arm remained as before.

However Dr. Hart, notwithstanding this bad accident, had a mind to try electricity again. The girl submitted to it, but after having been electrified about three or four days, she became a second time universally paralytic, and even lost her voice, and the use of her tongue, so that it was with great difficulty she could swallow. She was relieved of this additional palsy a second time by a proper course of medicines, continued about four months; but was discharged out of the hospital as incurable of her first palsy. It is said that the Doctor would have tried electricity a third time; but the girl, being more nearly concerned in the experiment than her physician, thought proper to decline it *.

DR. FRANKLIN's account of the effects of electricity, in the manner in which he applied it, is by no means favourable to its use in such cases. He says, in a letter to Sir John Pringle, read at the Royal Society, January the 12th, 1758, that some years before, when the news-papers made mention of great cures performed in Italy and Germany by electri-

* Phil. Transf. Vol. xlviii. pt. ii. p 785.

ciy,

city, a number of paralytics were brought to him, from different parts of Penſilvania and the neighbouring provinces, to be electrified, and that he performed the operation at their requeſt. His method was, firſt to place the patient in a chair, or upon an electrical ſtool, and draw a number of large ſtrong ſparks from all parts of the affected limb or ſide. He then fully charged two ſix-gallon glaſs jars, and ſent the united ſhock of them through the affected limb or limbs, repeating the ſtroke commonly three times each day.

THE firſt thing he obſerved was an immediate greater ſenſible warmth in the affected limbs, which had received the ſtroke, than in the others; and the next morning the patients uſually ſaid, that, in the night, they had felt a prickling ſenſation in the fleſh of the paralytic limbs; and would ſometimes ſhow a number of ſmall red ſpots, which they ſuppoſed were occaſioned by thoſe prickings. The limbs too were found more capable of voluntary motion, and ſeemed to receive ſtrength. A man, for inſtance, who could not, the firſt day, lift his lame hand from off his knee, would the next day raiſe it four or five inches; the third day higher; and on the fifth was able, but with a feeble languid motion, to take off his hat. Theſe appearances, the Doctor ſays, gave great ſpirits to the patients, and made them hope for a perfect cure; but he did not remember that he ever ſaw any amendment after the fifth day; which

the

the patients perceiving, and finding the ſhocks pretty ſevere, became diſcouraged, went home, and in a ſhort time relapſed; ſo that he never knew any permanent advantage from electricity in palſies.

PERHAPS, ſays he, ſome permanent advantage might be obtained, if the electric ſhocks had been accompanied with proper medicine and regimen, under the direction of a ſkilful phyſician. He thought too, that many ſmall ſhocks might have been more proper than the few great ones which he gave; ſince, in an account from Scotland, a caſe was mentioned in which 200 ſhocks from a phial were given daily, and a perfect cure had been made *.

THAT there is an intimate connection between the ſtate of electricity in the air and the human body, is evident from ſeveral facts, particularly a very remarkable one related by the Abbé Mazeas, in a letter to Dr. Hales. He was electrifying a perſon who was ſubject to epileptic fits, by his apparatus to make obſervations upon the electricity of the common atmoſphere. At firſt this perſon bore the ſparks very well, but in two or three minutes the Abbé, perceiving his countenance to change, begged he would retire, leſt any accident ſhould happen; and he was no ſooner returned home, than his ſenſes failed him, and he was ſeized with a moſt violent fit. His convulſions were taken off with ſpirits of

* Phil. Tranſ. Vol. l. pt. ii, p. 481.

hartſhorn,

hartſhorn, but his reaſon did not return in an hour and an half. He went up and down the ſtairs like one who walks in his ſleep, without ſpeaking to, or knowing any perſon, ſettling his papers, taking ſnuff, and offering chairs to all who came in. When he was ſpoken to, he pronounced inarticulate words, which had no connection.

WHEN this poor man recovered his reaſon, he fell into another fit; and his friends told the Abbé, he was more affected with that diſtemper when it thundered than at any other time; and if it ever happened, which it rarely did, that he then eſcaped, his eyes, his countenance, and the confuſion of his expreſſions, ſufficiently demonſtrated the weakneſs of his reaſon.

THE next day, the Abbé learned from the perſon himſelf, that the fear of thunder was not the cauſe of his diſeaſe; but that, however, he found a fatal connection between that phenomenon and his diſtemper. He added, that when the fit ſeized him, he perceived a vapour riſing in his breaſt, with ſo much rapidity, that he loſt all his ſenſes before he could call for help *.

MR. WILSON cured a woman of a deafneſs of ſeventeen years ſtanding. He alſo obſerves, that ſhe had a very great cold when ſhe began to be electrified; but that the inflammation ceaſed the firſt time, and the cold was quite gone when the operation had been

* Phil. Tranſ. Vol. xlviii. pt. i. p. 383.

performed

performed again the fecond day. But he acknowledges, that he had tried the fame experiment upon fix other deaf perfons with out
any fuccefs *.

THE fame perfon obferves, that one gentleman, near feventy years old, could never be
made to receive a fhock except in his wrifts.
He fays that he himfelf could once have borne
very great fhocks without inconvenience, but
that he could not bear them at the time that
he wrote.

MEDICAL electricity is very much obliged
to the labours and obfervations of Mr. Lovet,
lay-clerk of the cathedral church at Wor-
cefter, who has for many years been indefatigable in the application of electricity to a
great variety of difeafes. His fuccefs has been
very confiderable, and all the cafes he has
publifhed feem to be well authenticated.

ACCORDING to Mr. Lovet, electricity is almoft a fpecific in all cafes of violent pains,
of however long continuance, in every part
of the body; as in obftinate head-achs, the
fciatica, the cramp, and diforders refembling
the gout. He had no trials of the proper
gout, but only on thofe who were flightly
attacked, and who received immediate relief.

THE tooth-ach, he fays, is generally cured
inftantly, and he fcarce ever remembered any
one who complained of its raging a minute
after the operation †.

* Wilfon's Effay, p. 207.　　† Lovet's Effay, p. 112.

IT has feldom failed, he fays, to cure ri-
gidities, or a wafting of the mufcles, and
hyfterical diforders, particularly if they be attended with coldnefs in the feet. According
to him, it cures inflammations, it has ftopped
a mortification, cured a fiftula lachrymalis,
and difperfed extravafated blood *. He alfo
fays it has been of excellent ufe in bringing
to a fuppuration, or in difperfing without fuppuration, obftinate fwellings of various kinds,
even thofe that were fcrophulous. In his
hands it cured the falling ficknefs, and feveral kinds of fits, though the patients had been
fubject to them for many years ; and one cure
he mentions of a hemiplegia†. Laftly, he
relates a well attefted cafe, from Mr. Floyer,
furgeon at Dorchefter, of a complete cure of
what feemed to be a *gutta ferena*. The fame
Mr. Floyer, he alfo fays, cured with it two
young women of obftructions, one of whom
had taken medicines a year to no purpofe‡.

IN the rheumatifm, Mr. Lovet candidly
confeffes, it has failed ; but he fays it was feldom in the cafe of young perfons, if they
were taken in time.

THE manner in which electricity operated
in thefe cures, Mr. Lovet imagined to be, by
removing fecret obftructions, which are probably the caufe of thofe diforders. In all his
practice he never knew an inftance of harm
being done by it, and thinks that, in all the
cafes in which it has done harm, the manner

---

* Lovet's Effay, p. 76.　　† Ibid. p. 101.
‡ Ibid. p. 119.

of adminiftering it has been injudicious. In general, he thinks the fhocks have been made too great. This he imagined to have been the cafe of the patient before mentioned of Dr. Hart, who was made more paralytic by electric fhocks. Mr. Lovet advifes to begin, in general, with fimple electrification, efpecially in hyfterical cafes; then to proceed to taking fparks, and laftly to giving moderate fhocks, but hardly ever any that are violent, or painful.

THE account of the application of electricity by Dr. Zetzel of Upfal, which may be feen in Mr. Lovet's treatife, agrees in the main with the refult of his own practice; and where there is any difference between them, Mr. Lovet thinks there are evident marks of unfairnefs in the Swedifh account. And a fubfequent account from Sweden mentions feveral cures being made in thofe very cafes, in which Dr. Zetzel fays that no relief was to be had from electricity.

THE Rev. Mr. J. Wefley has followed Mr. Lovet in the fame ufeful courfe of medical electricity, and recommends the ufe of it to his numerous followers, and to all people. Happy it is when an afcendency over the minds of men is employed to purpofes favourable to the increafe of knowledge, and to the beft interefts of mankind. Mr. Wefley's account of cures performed by electricity agrees very well with that of Mr. Lovet, whom he often quotes. He adds, that he has fcarce ever known an inftance in which fhocks all

over the body have failed to cure a quotidian
or tertian ague *. He mentions cases of
blindness cured or relieved by it; and says
that he has known hearing given by it to a
man that was born deaf †. He mentions
cures in cases of bruises, running sores, the
dropsy, gravel in the kidnies (causing the patient to part with it) a palsy in the tongue, and
lastly in the genuine consumption. But Mr.
Boisier says it is of disservice in phthisical
complaints ‡.

Mr. Wesley candidly says, he has not
known any instance of the cure of an hemi-
plegia; and though many paralytics have been
helped by electricity, he scarcely thinks that
any palsy of a year's standing has been
thoroughly cured by it. He asserts, however, that he has never yet known any person, man, woman, or child, sick or well, who
has found (what Mr. Wilson says, that some
persons complained of) an unusual pain some
days after the shock. Mr. Wesley had only
known that the rheumatic pains, which were
afterwards perfectly cured, had increased on
the first or second application §.

Mr. Wesley directs the same method of
administration with Mr. Lovet. In deep
hysterical cases, he advises that the patients
be simply electrified, sitting on cakes of rosin,
at least half an hour morning and evening;

* Wesley's Desideratum, p. 3.　　† Ibid. p. 48.
‡ Carmichael Tentamen inaugurale medicum de Paralysi,
p. 34. ex Act. Upf.
§ Wesley's Desideratum, p. 50.

when,

when, after fome time, fmall fparks may be taken from them, and afterwards fhocks given to them, more or lefs ftrong, as their diforder requires ;‘ which, he fays, has feldom failed of the defired effect *.

THIS account of the medical ufe of electricity by Mr. Lovet and Mr. Wefley is certainly liable to an objection, which will always lie againft the accounts of thofe perfons who, not being of the faculty, cannot be fuppofed capable of diftinguifhing with accuracy either the nature of the diforders, or the confequences of a feeming cure. But, on the other hand, this very circumftance of their ignorance of the nature of diforders, and confequently of the beft method of applying electricity to them, fupplies the ftrongeft argument in favour of its innocence at leaft. If in fuch unfkilful hands it has produced fo much good, and fo little harm ; how much more good, and how much lefs harm would it probably have produced in more fkilful hands.

BUT whatever weight there be in this objection againft the laft mentioned writers, it certainly cannot be urged againft Antonius de Haen, one of the moft eminent phyficians of the prefent age; who, after fix years uninterrupted ufe of it, reckons it among the moft valuable affiftances of the medical art; and exprefsly fays, that though it has often been applied in vain, it has often afforded relief

* Wefley's Defideratum, p. 56.

where no other application would have been effectual. But I shall recite in a summary manner, from his *Ratio Medendi*, the result of all his observations on this subject.

WITH respect to partial palsies, in particular, he says, it never did the least harm; that one or two persons who had received no benefit from it in six intire months, were yet much relieved by persevering in the use of it. That some persons discontinuing it, after having received some benefit, relapsed again; but afterwards, by recurring to the use of electricity, recovered, though more slowly than before. Some persons, he says, were relieved who had been paralytic one, three, six, nine, and twelve years, and some longer; but that in one or two of these cases, the patients had received less relief, and more slowly than was usual in recent cases. In some cases, he says, a most unexpected benefit had been found by those who had been paralytic in their tongues, eyes, fingers, and other particular limbs. A paralysis and trembling of the limbs, from whatever cause it arose, he says, never failed to be relieved by it; and he relates one instance of a perfect cure being performed in a remarkable case of this nature, after receiving ten shocks *.

DE HAEN's custom was to apply the operation for half an hour together at least. He seems to have used gentle shocks, and he joined to electricity, the use of other remedies,

---

* Ratio Medendi, Vol. i. p. 234, 199.

which,

which, however, would not have been effectual without it *.

St. Vitus's dance, he says, never failed to be cured by electricity †. He always observed it to promote a more copious discharge of the menses, and to relieve in cases of obstruction; but, for this reason, he advises that it be not administered to women with child. He found it of use in some cases of deafness, but it entirely failed in its application to a gutta serena, and to a strumous neck ‡.

Lastly, he relates a remarkable case, communicated to him by Mr. Velse at the Hague, of the cure of a mucous apoplexy §.

To the cases which have been mentioned occasionally, in which harm may be apprehended from electrification, may perhaps be added the venereal disease in which Mr. Veratti advises, that electrification be by all means avoided ||.

I shall conclude this account of medical electricity with observing, that there are two general effects of electricity on the human body, of which, it should seem, that physicians might greatly avail themselves. These are, that it promotes insensible perspiration, and glandular secretion. The former is effected by simple electrification, and the latter

---

* Ratio Medendi, Vol. i. p. 233.　　† Ibid. p. 389.
‡ Ibid. Vol. ii. p. 200.　　§ Ibid.
|| Carmichael Tentamen, p. 34.

　　　　by

by taking fparks from the glands, or the parts contiguous to them; on which it acts like a ftimulus. Of the former, inftances have been produced in the experiments of the Abbe Nollet, and a few have been given occafionally of the latter.

To thefe I fhall now add, that Linnæus obferved, that when electric fparks have been drawn from the ear, it has inftantly promoted a more copious fecretion of ear-wax; and that it has alfo been obferved, that, when the eye, or the parts about the eye, have been electrified, the tears have flowed copioufly. But the moft remarkable cafe that I have met with, is, of its promoting the fecretion of that matter which forms the hair; whereby hair has been actually reftored to a part that had long been bald *.

HITHERTO electricity has been generally applied to the human body either in the method of drawing fparks, as it is called, or of giving fhocks. But thefe operations are both violent, and though the ftrong concuffion may fuit fome cafes, it may be of differvice in others, where a moderate fimple electrification might have been of fervice.

THE great objection to this method is the tedioufnefs and expence of the application. But an electrical machine might be contrived to go by wind or water, and a

* Carmichael Tentamen, p. 33.

convenient

convenient room might be annexed to it; in which a floor might be raifed upon electrics, and a perfon might fit down, read, fleep, or even walk about during the electrification. It were to be wifhed, that fome phyfician of underftanding and fpirit would provide himfelf with fuch a machine and room No harm could poffibly be apprehended from electricity, applied in this gentle and infenfible manner, and good effects are, at leaft, poffible, if not highly probable. It would certainly be more for the honour of the faculty, that the practice fhould be introduced in this manner, than that it be left to fome rich Valetudinarian, who may take it into his head, that fuch an operation may be of fervice to him.

SECTION

SECTION XV.

MISCELLANEOUS EXPERIMENTS AND DIS
COVERIES MADE WITHIN THIS PERIOD.

HAVING diftributed into diftinct fections all the fubjects, under which I had collected materials enow to form a feparate account; I have referved for the laft place, thofe fmaller articles, which could neither with propriety be introduced under the former heads, nor were large enough to make a fection themfelves.

IT has been a great controverfy among electricians, whether glafs be permeable to the electric fluid. Mr. Wilfon appeared in favour of the permeability, and, in a paper read at the Royal Society, December the 6th, 1759, produced the following experiments to fupport his opinion; notwithftanding he, even afterwards, acknowledged, in a paper read at the Royal Society, November the 13th, 1760; that, in the Leyden experiment, Dr. Franklin had proved that the fluid did not go through the glafs *.

HE took a very large pane of glafs, a little warmed; and holding it upright by one edge, while the oppofite edge refted upon wax, he rubbed the middle part of the furface

* Phil. Tranf. Vol. li. pt. ii. p. 896.

with

with his finger, and found both fides electrified *plus* *.

UPON this I cannot help obferving that it
ought to be fo on Dr. Franklin's principles.
If one fide be rubbed by the finger, it acquires from the finger fome of the electric
fluid. This, being fpread on the glafs as far
as the rubbing extended, repels an equal quantity of that contained in the other fide of the
glafs, and drives it out on that fide, where it
ftands as an atmofphere, fo that both fides are
found *plus*. If the unrubbed fide were in
contact with a conductor communicating with
the earth, the electric fluid would be carried
away, and then that fide would be left *apparently* in the natural ftate. If the electric fluid
found on the unrubbed fide was really part of
that which had been communicated by and
from the finger, and fo had actually *permeated*
the glafs, it might, when conducted away,
be continually replaced by frefh permeating
fluid communicated in the fame manner : But
if the effect is continually diminifhing, while
the fuppofed caufe, repeated, continues the
fame, there feems reafon to doubt the fuppofed relation between that caufe and the
effect. For it appears difficult to conceive
how fome electric fluid, having paffed through
a permeable body, fhould make it more difficult for other particles of the fame electric
fluid to follow, till, at length, none could pafs
at all.

* Phil. Tranf. Vol. li. pt. i. p. 314.

MR.

MR. WILSON alſo ſays, that, holding 'the ſame pane of glaſs within two feet of the prime condućtor, which was elećtrified *plus*, that part of the glaſs which was oppoſite to the condućtor became elećtrified *minus* on both ſides ; but, in a few minutes, the *minus* electricity diſappeared, and the *plus* continuing, diffuſed itſelf into the place of the other, ſo that now the whole was elećtrified *plus*.

THE experiment ſo far ſucceeding, induced him to make uſe of a leſs piece of glaſs, that the whole might be elećtrified *minus*. Theſe advances, he ſays, led him to obſerve the power of elećtrifying that ſmall piece of glaſs at different diſtances.

HE expoſed the ſame ſmall piece of glaſs to the prime condućtor, at the diſtance of two feet, and obſerved a *minus* elećtricity at both ſurfaces.

As he moved the glaſs nearer, to a certain diſtance, it was more ſenſibly elećtrified *minus*; and after that, on moving it ſtill nearer, the *minus* appearance was leſs and leſs ſenſible; till it came within 'the diſtance of about one inch, and then it was elećtrified *plus* on both ſides.

THIS *plus* elećtricity in the glaſs, he found, might be changed to a *minus* again, by removing the glaſs, and holding it for a time at a greater diſtance; which he thought to be a proof of the repulſive power of that fluid *.

HAVING by him a pane of glaſs, one ſide of which was rough and the other ſmooth, he

* Phil. Tranſ. Vol. li. pt. i. p. 528.

rubbed

rubbed it flightly on one fide; upon doing which, both fides were electrified *minus.*

On this I muft alfo take the liberty to obferve that, as the electric fluid contained in glafs in its natural ftate, is kept equal in both fides by the common repulfion; if the quantity in one fide is diminifhed, the fluid in the other fide, being lefs repelled, retires inward, and leaves that furface alfo *minus.*

Slight changes, *plus* or *minus,* may be made in either furface, that have not ftrength to act on the other fide, by repulfion, or by abating repulfion, through the glafs; and fo *plus* electricity may be given to one furface, and *minus* to the other in fome degree. Both fides may alfo be made *plus,* and both *minus,* by rubbing, or by communication, without any neceffity of fuppofing the glafs *permeable.*

And yet it is probable that fome glafs, from having a greater mixture of non-electric matters in its compofition, may be permeable, when cold, in fome fmall degree, as all glafs is found to be when warmed.

Mr. Wilson treated the other fide of this pane of glafs in the fame manner, after which the *minus* electricity was changed into a *plus* on both fides.

Though Dr. Franklin was of opinion, that glafs when cold is not permeable to electricity, he had made no experiments upon it when hot; but Mr. Kinnerfley, a friend of his, made one, which feemed to prove, that it was very differently affected in this refpect, in the different ftates of hot and cold. He found,

that

that a coated Florence flafk (made of very
thin glafs, and full of air bubbles) containing
boiling water, could not be electrified. The
electricity, he fays, paffed as readily through
it as through metal. The charge of a three
pint bottle went freely through it, without injuring the flafk in the leaft. When it became cold, he could charge it as before. This
effect he attributed to the dilatation of the
pores of glafs by heat *.

ALL Mr. Wilfon's experiments to prove
the permeability of glafs were repeated by
Mr. Bergman of Upfal; and, as he fays, with
fuccefs †.

MR. ÆPINUS, however, was by no means
fatisfied with Mr. Wilfon's experiments concerning the permeability of glafs; and yet he
brings no other fact in anfwer to his arguments, but a very common one, which fhows
that a glafs tube both receives and lofes its
electricity very flowly; fo that he only afferts
a *difficulty*, and a *flownefs* in the electric fluid
paffing through electric fubftances, as was
mentioned before; and confequently Mr.
Wilfon feems to have an advantage in the
controverfy : for, as he fays, paffing through,
though ever fo flowly, is a real paffing
through ‡.

MR. ÆPINUS has fhown, by a curious experiment, that though a metallic conductor
and a cork ball be both electrified pofitively,

* Phil. Tranf. Vol. liii. pt. i. p. 85.
† Ibid. Vol. lii. pt. ii. p. 485.
‡ Ibid. Vol. liii. p. 443.

fo as to repel one another; yet, that, if the ball be forcibly brought within two, three, or four lines of the conductor, it will be attracted by it; and that it will be repelled again, if it be forcibly pushed beyond that limit of attraction. If the ball be confined to move within the fame fmall diftance, a moderate electrification of the conductor will repel the ball to its utmoft limit; but a ftronger electrification of the conductor will caufe it to be attracted. He, therefore, limits the general maxim, that bodies poffeffing the fame kind of electricity repel one another; and afferts, that this will be the cafe, only when the quantity of electric fluid belonging to them both, as one body is greater, or lefs than that which is natural to them *. This experiment deferves particular attention.

SIGNIOR BECCARIA, who has contributed fo largely to feveral former fections in this period, furnifhes a few articles which well deferve a place in this.

HE thought it was evident, that the electric fluid tended to move in a right line, becaufe a longer fpark may be taken in a direct line, from the end of a long conductor, than can be taken from the fame place in any other direction. But he thought it was ftill more evident, from obferving, both in the air, and in vacuo; that, prefenting the finger, or a brafs ball, at a proper diftance, and in a certain angle with the conductor (which experi-

* Æpini Tentamen, p. 146.

ence

ence will foon find) the electric fpark will make an exact curve, to which the conductor produced will be a tangent: as if the electric matter was acted upon by two different forces, one its own acquired velocity, urging it forward in a right line; the other the attraction of the body prefented to it, which throws it out of the right line *.

In his obfervations on pointed bodies, he fays, that two pointed bodies, equally fharp, in their approach to an electrified conductor, will appear luminous only at half the diftance at which one of them would have done †.

The fame ingenious philofopher reports a curious, but cruel experiment which he made on a live cock. He detached the belly of one of the mufcles from the thigh of the animal, leaving the extremities in their proper infertions, and then difcharging a fhock through it. At the inftant of the ftroke, the leg was violently diftended, and the mufcle greatly inflated; the motion beginning at the tendon, and the extenfion of it refembling the opening of a lady's fan. No pricking with a pin could make it act fo ftrongly ‡.

I must not omit to mention, in this chapter of mifcellaneous experiments, what the Dutch writers have reported concerning the gymnotus, a fifh peculiar to Surinam, which very much refembles what naturalifts relate concerning the torpedo. Mr. Mufchenbroeck

---

* Elettricifmo artificiale, p. 56. † Ibid. p. 67.
‡ Lettere dell' elettricifmo, p. 129.

fays,

fays, the gymnotus is poffeffed of a kind of
natural electricity, but different from the common electricity, in that perfons who touch it
in water are fhocked, and ftunned by it, fo
as to be in danger of· drowning. The fifh
has been taken, and put into a veffel; when
experiments were made upon it at leifure;
and it was found, that it might be touched
with all fafety with a ftick of fealing-wax;
but if it was touched with the naked finger,
or with a piece of metal, and efpecially a gold
ring, held in the fingers, the arm was fhocked as high as the elbow. If it was touched with the foot, the fenfation reached as high
as the knee, and the pain was as great as
if the part had been ftruck with fomething
hard. This kind of electricity is the fame by
night or by day, when the wind is in every
direction, when the fifh was put in veffels
of any materials, and whether it was in water or out of water. Every part of the body
of the fifh is capable of giving this fhock,
but more efpecially the tail. The fenfation
is the ftrongeft when the fifh is in motion,
and it is tranfmitted to a great diftance; fo
that if perfons in a fhip happen-to dip their
fingers or feet in the fea, when the fifh is
fwimming at the diftance of fifteen feet
from them they are affected by it. Other
fifhes, put into the fame veffel with it, prefently died; but it is itfelf killed by the
lobfter. The gymnotus is found in the upper
part of the river of Surinam, particularly the

K k   rocky

rocky part of it. It feeds upon all kinds of fish, and will even eat bread. This author proposes as a query whether the sensation communicated by the torpedo does not depend upon a similar electricity; since Monsieur Reaumur says, that when it is touched, the hand, arm, and shoulder are seized with a sudden stupor, which lasts for some time; and is unlike any other sensation *.

This gymnotus, I suppose, is a different fish from the *Anguille tremblante, the trembling eel*, which is also a native of Surinam, and lives in marshy places, from whence it cannot be drawn, except when it is intoxicated. It cannot be touched with the hand, or with a stick, without feeling a terrible stun, which reaches as high as the shoulder. If it be trod upon with shoes, the legs and thighs are affected in a similar manner. Fourteen persons joining hands, and the first of them touching it with a stick, they were all shocked violently. It is conjectured that this power of giving a shock resides in two muscles, which are particularly prominent and conspicuous †.

It is to be regretted, that none of the persons who have made experiments on these fishes should have endeavoured to ascertain whether they were capable of exhibiting the phenomena of attraction and repulsion, or

* Muschenbroeck's Introd. ad philosoph. naturalem, No. 901—909.
† P. Fermin's Nat. Hist. of Surinam, p. 59.

the

the appearance of electric light, as experiments of this kind are of principal consequence, and must have been very easy to make.

MR. HAMILTON, professor of Philosophy at the university of Dublin, made a curious experiment with a wire, five or six inches long, finely pointed at each end. To the middle of this wire he fitted a brass cap, which rested on the point of a needle communicating with the conductor. Half an' inch at each extremity of this wire he bent, in opposite directions, perpendicular to the rest of the wire, and in the plane of the horizon. The consequence of electrifying this apparatus was, that the wire would turn round with very great velocity; moving, as he says, always in a direction contrary to that in which the electric fluid issues from its point, without having any conducting substance near it, except the air. He also observes, that if this wire were made to turn the contrary way, it would stop, and turn as before *.

THE same experiment was also made by Mr. Kinnersley of Boston, with this addition, that he electrified the wire negatively; and observed, to his great surprize, that it still turned the same way. This he endeavoured to account for by supposing that, in the former case, the points, having more electricity than

* Phil. Tranf. Vol. li. pt. ii. p. 905.

the

the air, were attracted by it; in the latter cafe, the air, having more than the points, was attracted by them *.

It may, by fome, be thought that this pointed wire turning the fame way, whether it be electrified negatively or pofitively, is a proof that the electric fluid iffues out at the points in both cafes alike, and by the reaction of the air is, together with the points, driven backwards; contrary to what ought to have been the cafe if the electric fluid had really iffued out of the point in one cafe, and entered it in the other. But it will be found by experiment, that an eolipile, with its ftem bent like the wire above mentioned, and fufpended on its center of gravity by a fine thread, will move in the fame direction, whether it be throwing fteam out at the orifice; or, after it is exhaufted, and cooling, it be drawing the air or water in.

With refpect to the power of points, it has been obferved by Mr. Villette of Liege, that a needle, concealed in a glafs tube, which projected an inch beyond it, takes a ftronger fpark from a prime conductor than a man's finger; alfo that when the points of needles are covered with tallow, bees-wax, fulphur, &c. they take peculiarly ftrong fparks. He adds, that, when fulphur is ufed, and the fparks are taken obliquely, they are fometimes of a beautiful citron colour †.

---

* Phil Tranf. Vol. liii. pt. i. p. 86.
† Nollet's Letters. Vol. iii. p. 212.

MR.

MR. LULLIN has made an additional obferva.'on to Monfieur du Fay's, concerning the diffei.nt manner in which conducting and non-conducting fubftances are affected, when they are expofed to the dew. He fays, that if a plate of glafs be extended upon filken threads, and expofed to the open air all night, and a plate of metal, lefs than the glafs, be laid upon it, in the morning, the metal will be dry, and likewife the glafs, on both fides, exactly under the metal; but that the edges of the glafs, where the metal did not reach, will be wet on both fides *.

I SHALL clofe this fection of mifcellaneous articles, and the whole hiftory of electricity, with a fuccinct account of fome of the chief particulars in which the analogy between electricity and magnetifm confifts; very nearly as it was drawn up, in an abridgment of Mr. Æpinus, and communicated to me for this purpofe by Dr. Price.

1. As a rod of iron held near a magnet will have feveral fucceffive poles; fo will a glafs tube touched by an excited tube have a fucceffion of pofitive and negative parts.

2. BODIES pofitively and negatively electrical, when in contact, will unite to one another; as will magnets, when they are laid with their oppofite poles to one another.

---

* Nollet's Letters, Vol. iii. p. 54.

3. GLASS

3. GLASS is a fubftance of a nature fimilar to hardened fteel. The pofitive and negative fides of the former anfwer to the attracting and repelling ends of the latter, when magnetical.

4. As it is difficult to move the electric fluid in the pores of the former; fo, likewife, it is difficult to move the magnetic fluid in the pores of the latter.

5. As there can be no condenfation of the electric fluid in the former, without a rarefaction; fo, in the latter, if there be a condenfation, or pofitive magnetifm in one end of a bar, there muft be an evacuation, or negative magnetifm in the other end.

6. STEEL correfponds to electrics per fe, and iron in fome meafure, to conductors of electricity.

7. STEEL is lefs fufceptible of the magnetic virtue, but when it has acquired it, it retains it more ftrongly than iron; juft as electrics per fe will not fo eafily receive the electric fluid, but, when it is forced into them, will retain it more ftrongly than conductors.

8. MR. ÆPINUS adds, and reckons it one of his difcoveries, that an electrified body does not act on other bodies, except they are themfelves electrified; juft as a magnet will not act on any other fubftances, except they are themfelves poffeffed of the magnetic virtue. So that an electrified body attracts and repels another body, only in confequence of rendering it firft of all electrical; as a magnet attracts
iron,

iron, only in confequence of, firft of all making it a magnet.

9. Mʀ. Canton has alfo found, that if the tourmalin be cut into feveral pieces, each piece will have a pofitive and negative fide, juft as the pieces of a broken magnet would have.

Thus far, fays Dr. Price, there is an analogy, and, in fome inftances, a ftriking one, between magnetifm and electricity, upon the fuppofition that the caufe of magnetifm is a fluid. But there is no magnetic fubftance which anfwers perfectly to the conductors of electricity. There is no afflux or efflux of the magnetical fluid ever vifible. The equilibrium in a magnet cannot be inftantaneoufly reftored, by forming a communication between the oppofite ends with iron, as it may in charged glafs. Nor are there any fubftances pofitively or negatively magnetical only, as there are bodies which are pofitively or negatively electrical only.

END OF THE FIRST VOLUME.